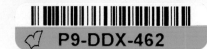

P9-DDX-462

FOUNDATIONS OF MATHEMATICS

Online Lessons

- Contain highly engaging and interactive videos that use cutting-edge Cloud Learning™ technologies.
- Break-down math concepts into logical and intuitive steps that enhance the learning process.
- Prepare you for upcoming classes, labs, and quizzes through self-study lessons.
- Contain lessons that proceed at your own pace and are excellent for visual learners.

Online Labs

- Contain a comprehensive test-bank of real-world problems, which may be used as an assessment tool.
- Break-down every answer into dynamic, step-by-step solutions that include calculator methods for solving problems.
- Provide unlimited amount of practice through algorithmically generated problems.
- Contain numerous statistical tools to analyze your strengths and weaknesses.

Vretta™

FOUNDATIONS OF MATHEMATICS

First Edition

T. Kugathasan, Seneca College
B.W. Pratt, Seneca College

Vretta

Copyright © 2013 by Vretta Inc.
ISBN 978-0-9877351-3-3

Foundations of Mathematics, First Edition

Textbook printed in Canada.

Authors: Thambyrajah Kugathasan and Betty L. Pratt
Textbook editor: Lakshmi Kugathasan
Solution manuals and online labs: Phoebe Wu
Typesetting: Steven Demelo and Dylan Hamada
Instructional design: Charles Anifowose and Ali Alavi
Online lessons' voice talent: Scott Fox and Ashley Grecco
Copyrights researcher: Venessa Edwards

Expert advice: TK Academic Consulting Inc.
Pre-programmed financial calculator: Texas Instruments BAII Plus
Online resources use Vretta's proprietary Cloud Learning ™ technologies.

All rights reserved.
Photocopying, recreating, reproducing, storing in any retrieval system, translating, or transmitting in any form or by any means, electronic, digital, graphic, mechanical, physical, audio-video recording, or otherwise of any part of the Mathematics of Business and Finance resources beyond that permitted by the Copyright Act of Canada without the permission of Vretta Inc., the copyright owner, is unlawful. Request for permission or further information should be addressed to the Permissions Department, Vretta Inc. via email at copyright@vretta.com.

Disclaimer

Vretta Inc. has taken complete care to trace the ownership of copyright material contained in these resources. However, if you have any information which would enable us to rectify any reference or credit for subsequent editions and/or identify any errors or omissions which require correction, please email us at copyright@vretta.com.

The examples and exercises in the Foundations of Mathematics resources are fictitious, unless otherwise stated. Any resemblance to real life people, businesses, organizations, institutions, facts or circumstances is purely coincidental.

Preface

Mathematics is for everyone.

Why is it important to have a strong foundation in mathematics? - A common question that most students in business, marketing, human resources, hospitality, tourism, or even fire-fighting may ask repeatedly.

You may be surprised to know that you will come across many of the concepts that are taught in this textbook throughout your personal and professional lives. As a marketing or business professional, you may be responsible for devising product pricing strategies; as a human resource professional, you may be required to calculate the payroll for your employees; as a restaurant manager, you may be responsible for ensuring cost efficiencies to keep the restaurant profitable; as a ticketing specialist, you may be responsible for devising creative vacation packages while being mindful of the bottom-line of the company; as a firefighter, you may want to calculate the volume of a water tank or water-delivery rates. Therefore, you will need to be adept in the foundations of mathematics to succeed in almost every field that you choose.

Mastery-based learning, true to its nature, is meant to break down learning concepts to help students master them step-by-step at an individual pace.

This type of learning reduces gaps in performance levels and improves proficiency. Students receiving instruction of educational content through mastery-based learning programs have also been shown to be more receptive of the material and have in-turn, demonstrated improved understanding. Through the advancement of Cloud Learning™ technologies that have been integrated into this resource, the application of mastery-based learning for mathematics has been successfully implemented at numerous colleges to significantly improve the success rates for thousands of students.

We are aware that each of you will learn mathematics using different methods and styles. To be able to cater to most of these learning styles, we have strived to build this unique learning resource. It not only contains this comprehensive textbook but also contains highly interactive online lessons and assessment labs that break-down every concept into micro-steps to ensure that you have a thorough understanding of the practical application of these concepts. It follows a mastery-based learning application that helps you to master these concepts sequentially.

Our aim is to inspire and empower every learner in the world and we hope that you will thoroughly enjoy discovering this resource and the value it will bring to you.

Kuga, Betty, and the math team at Vretta

Brief Contents

Contents

Chapter 1
Whole Numbers

Chapter 2
Fractions and Decimal Numbers

Chapter 3
Exponents, Roots, and Order of Operations

Chapter 4
Ratios and Proportions

Chapter 5
Percents and Percent Changes

Chapter 6

Basic Business Applications

Chapter 7

Basic Algebra

Chapter 9
Systems of Linear Equations with Two Variables

Chapter 10
Units of Measurement

List of Tables, Exhibits, Diagrams, and Formulas

Tables

Exhibits

Formulas

Resources

Language The language used in this textbook is simple and straight-forward, while maintaining the levels of sophistication required to thoroughly prepare students for the next stage in their academic and professional careers.

Pedagogies and Learning Methods

Numerous pedagogies and learning methods that have been developed and proven over 30 years are incorporated into the textbook. These pedagogies have succeeded in simplifying critical mathematical concepts and significantly improving retention of concepts. The different learning methods to solve problems have also proven to cater to the varied student learning styles.

Exercises The textbook has over 2,000 exercises, review exercises, and self-test exercises, as well as over 225 solved examples. Problems are designed to test students on real-world, practical applications and are presented in increasing levels of difficulty. The problems are categorized into pairs of similar questions to provide professors with an opportunity to solve the even-numbered problems in class and assign the odd-numbered problems as home work.

Solution Manual

All problems in the end-of-section exercises, review exercises, and self-test exercises have been solved using detailed step-by-step methods as demonstrated in the solved examples. The solution manual is available online for professors and for students.

PowerPoint Presentations

The animated PowerPoint presentations are available for professors to use in class. The PowerPoint presentations are designed to work with clickers to gauge student understanding of concepts.

Test Bank

A comprehensive test bank, of over 350 problems in varying levels of difficulty, that covers all concepts in the textbook is provided for professors to use as a database for exercises, quizzes, group projects, or assignments.

Online Lessons

The online lessons are created as a pre-study component for students. They contain pedagogies that are highly interactive and engaging, and which teach concepts in a very logical and intuitive way. These lessons are not PowerPoint presentations but are interactive movies that have been created to enrich and enhance the learning experience. Every frame is locked to ensure that students go through the lessons sequentially as they are designed to build on learning concepts in succession. The system automatically records students' progress and performance. Once students complete a lesson, the frame unlocks itself, allowing students to navigate back and forth through the lesson. Professors, on the other hand, have administrative access which allows them to navigate through the online lessons without any restrictions.

Online Labs

The online lab assessment system contains a rich comprehensive test-bank of real-world problems that are algorithmically generated and that provide students with dynamic feedback on their responses. The labs can also be customized based on course requirements. A few of the customizable features include, previewing and selecting questions, setting the number of questions, setting and modifying start and due dates, opening, closing and re-opening labs, creating new labs and quizzes, and determining the weighting and number of attempts for each question.

Administrative Tools

The following administrative tools will provide professors with the ability to monitor overall class performance and individual student performance on online lessons and labs.

Performance Dashboard for Professors

The lesson performance dashboard provides professors with the average completion percentage per chapter, including a lesson-by-lesson percentage completed visualization for the entire class. The lab performance dashboard provides them with the average percentage mark on each lab for the class. Professors can also download or export individual grades for lessons and labs to a spreadsheet or to the college's course management system.

Performance Dashboard for Students

The lesson performance dashboard provides students with their chapter completion mark, including a lesson-by-lesson percentage completed visualization. The lab performance dashboard provides them with their lab percentage marks.

Lab Management System

The lab management system is provided for administrators or subject leaders to create new labs, quizzes and case studies, preview and select questions, set the number of questions, set and modify start and due dates, open, close and re-open labs, and determine the weighting and number of attempts for each question.

FOUNDATIONS OF MATHEMATICS

First Edition

T. Kugathasan, Seneca College
B.W. Pratt, Seneca College

Vretta

Chapter 1
Whole Numbers

Learning Outcomes

- Identify whole numbers.
- Read, write, and round whole numbers correctly.
- Solve problems involving arithmetic operations, whole numbers, and signed numbers.
- Perform order of operations with whole numbers.
- Determine the lowest common multiple and highest common factor.

Chapter Outline

Arithmetic is the most elementary branch of mathematics that we use in everyday life. When we count, we use arithmetic; when we perform the simple operations of addition, subtraction, multiplication, and division, we use principles of arithmetic. We use arithmetic for everyday tasks such as buying, selling, estimating expenses, and checking bank balances. Arithmetic is woven into our general interaction with the real world, and as such, it forms the basis of all science, technology, engineering, and business. In this chapter, you will learn about mathematical operations involving whole numbers, including powers and roots of perfect squares.

1.1 | Understanding Whole Numbers

Introduction

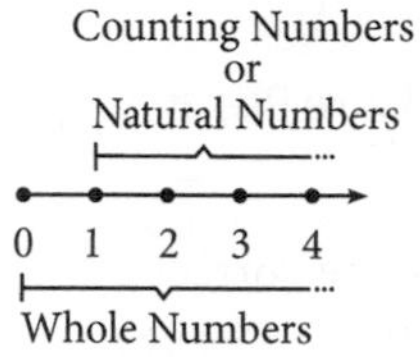

Whole numbers are simply the numbers 0, 1, 2, 3, 4.... They include all counting numbers, also known as natural numbers or positive integers (1, 2, 3, 4...), and zero (0).

The representation of 3 dots (1, 2, 3, 4...) to the right of the number 4 is read as "and so on". This means that the numbers that follow occur in the same pattern as the previous numbers; in this case, 1 must be added to the last number to determine the next number.

All whole numbers are integers. However, whole numbers and integers are not the same because integers include counting numbers (positive integers) and the opposite of counting numbers (negative integers).

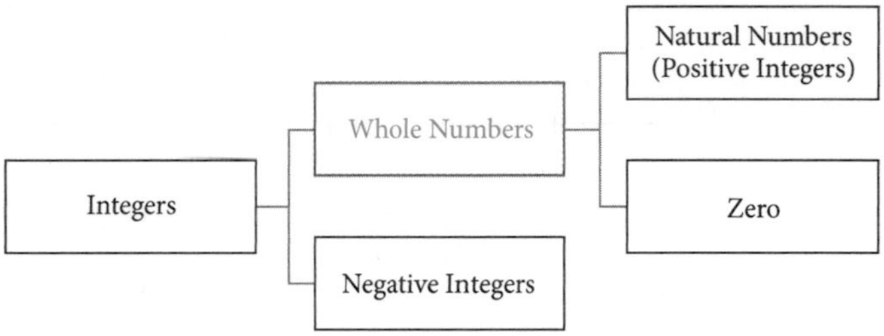

Number Line

Whole numbers can be represented graphically as a point on a horizontal line, called the number line, as shown below.

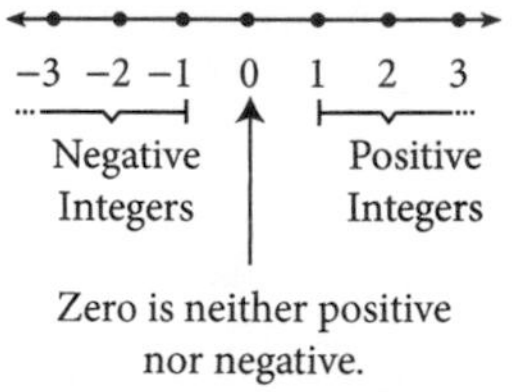

The arrowhead at the end shows that the line continues indifinitely in that direction.

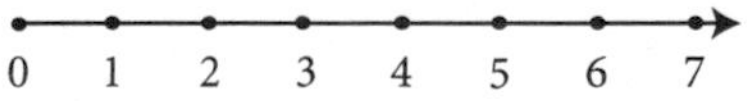

The smallest whole number is zero (0). It is not possible to find the largest whole number because for any given number, there will always be another number greater than that number.

Writing numbers on a number line helps in comparing and identifying numbers that are smaller or larger than other numbers. Numbers that lie to the left of a number on the number line are smaller than the numbers that lie to the right of that number, and vice versa.

For example, 6 is greater than 2 and 5 is smaller than 7.

The signs used to show the relative position of two numbers (or quantities) are:

(i) '$>$' read as "**is greater than**", meaning that the number on the left of the sign has a value greater than that on the right.

For example, "6 is greater than 2" is written as $6 > 2$.

(ii) '$<$' read as "**is less than**", meaning that the number on the left of the sign has a value less than that on the right.

For example, "5 is less than 7" is written as $5 < 7$.

Example 1.1-a

Graphing Numbers on a Number Line and Using Signs to Show the Relative Positions of the Numbers

Graph the numbers 12, 5, 7, 11, and 3 on a number line and place the correct sign, $\boxed{<}$ or $\boxed{>}$, in the spaces between the following sets of numbers:

(i) $7 \square 11 \square 5$ (ii) $11 \square 12 \square 5$

(iii) $3 \square 5 \square 12$ (iv) $12 \square 7 \square 3$

Solution

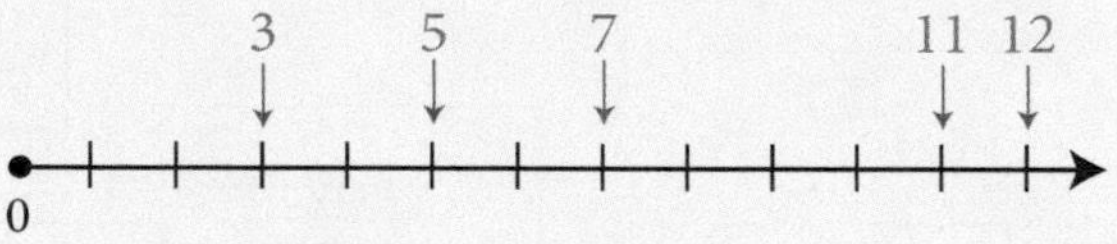

(i) $7 < 11 > 5$ (ii) $11 < 12 > 5$

(iii) $3 < 5 < 12$ (iv) $12 > 7 > 3$

Example 1.1-b

Writing a Statement to Represent "$>$" or "$<$"

Write statements using the words "is greater than" or "is less than" for the following expressions:

(i) $24 > 22$ (ii) $36 < 39$

(iii) $9 > 0$ (iv) $0 < 5$

Solution

(i) 24 is greater than 22 ***or*** 22 is less then 24.

(ii) 36 is less than 39 ***or*** 39 is greater than 36.

(iii) 9 is greater than 0 ***or*** 0 is less than 9.

(iv) 0 is less than 5 ***or*** 5 is greater than 0.

Whole numbers do not include fractions, decimal numbers, and negative integers.

A fraction or a decimal number may contain a whole number portion but the number itself is not a whole number.

For example, although $12\frac{3}{4}$ has a whole number portion of '12', it is not a whole number because it has a fractional portion of '$\frac{3}{4}$'.

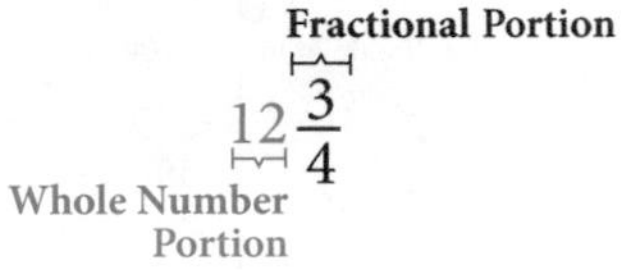

Similarily, although the number 45.32 has a whole number portion of '45', it is not a whole number because it has a decimal portion of '0.32'.

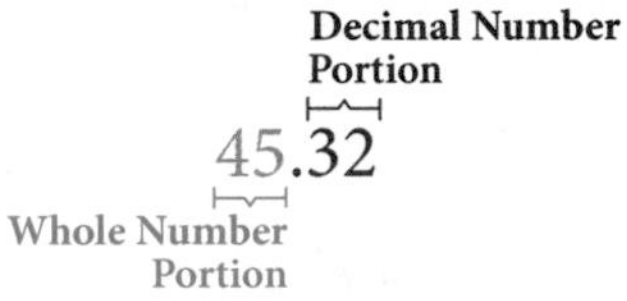

A number with a decimal point followed by zeros is considered as a whole number.

For example, 12.0 and 23.00 are considered as whole numbers because the decimal portion is zero. Furthermore, these numbers can be represented on the number line as a whole number.

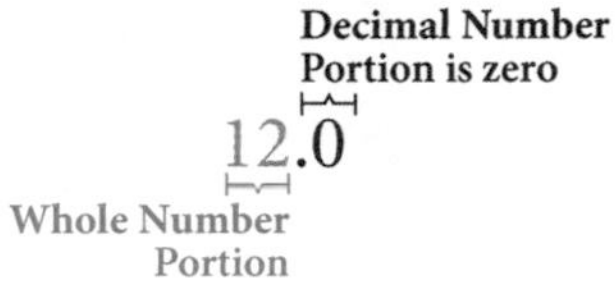

When the numerator of a fraction is divisible by its denominator, the fraction is considered as a whole number.

For example, $\frac{6}{3}$ and $\frac{15}{5}$ are considered as whole numbers because they are divisible by their denominators:

6 is divisible by 3, resulting in 2, ($\frac{6}{3}$ = **2**), which is a whole number.

15 is divisible by 5, resulting in 3, ($\frac{15}{5}$ = **3**), which is a whole number.

Place Value of Whole Numbers

The **position** of each digit in a whole number determines the **place value** for the digit. Exhibit 1.1 illustrates the place value of the ten digits in the whole number, 3,867,254,129. In this example, 4 occupies the 'thousands' place value and represents 4000, whereas 7 occupies the 'millions' place value and represents 7,000,000.

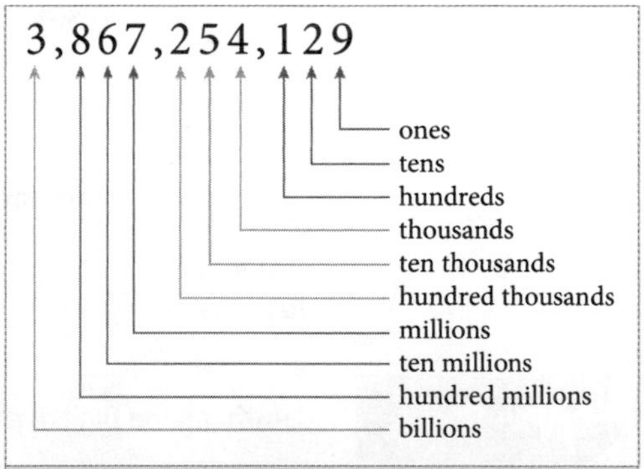

Exhibit 1.1 Place Value of a Ten-Digit Whole Number

We read and write numbers from the left to the right. A comma (or alternatively, a space) separates every three digits into groups, starting from the place value for 'ones', thereby making it easier to read a whole number.

The place value of 'ones' is 10^0 (= 1) and each position has a value 10 times the place value to its right, as shown in Table 1.1.

Table 1.1 **Place Value Chart of Whole Numbers**

10^9	10^8	10^7	10^6	10^5	10^4	10^3	10^2	10^1	10^0
1,000,000,000	100,000,000	10,000,000	1,000,000	100,000	10,000	1000	100	10	1
Billions	Hundred millions	Ten millions	Millions	Hundred thousands	Ten thousands	Thousands	Hundreds	Tens	Ones

The vertical red lines in Table 1.1 denote the positions of the commas that separate the groups of three numbers, starting from the place value for 'ones'. The above 10-digit number, written as 3,867,254,129, is represented in its standard form for writing numbers.

3	8	6	7	2	5	4	1	2	9

This can be written in expanded form, as follows:

3,000,000,000 + 800,000,000 + 60,000,000 + 7,000,000 + 200,000 + 50,000 + 4,000 + 100 + 20 + 9

Or

3 billion + 800 million + 60 million + 7 million + 200 thousand + 50 thousand + 4 thousand + 1 hundred + 2 tens + 9 ones

This can also be written in word form, as follows:

Three billion, eight hundred sixty-seven million, two hundred fifty-four thousand, one hundred twenty-nine.

Example 1.1-c **Identifying the Place Value of a Digit and the Amount it Represents**

What is the place value of the digit 5 in each of the following and what amount does it represent?

(i) $675,342 (ii) $35,721,890 (iii) $5,916,203,847 (iv) $2,543

Solution

	(i) $675,342	(ii) $35,721,890	(iii) $5,916,203,847	(iv) $2,543
Place Value	Thousands	Millions	Billions	Hundreds
Amount it Represents	$5,000	$5,000,000	$5,000,000,000	$500

Example 1.1-d **Identifying the Digit of a Number Given its Place Value**

In 320,948 identify the digit that occupies the following place values:

(i) Hundred thousands (ii) Ten thousands

(iii) Thousands (iv) Tens

Solution

(i) 320,948
↑
Hundred thousands

(ii) 320,948
↑
Ten thousands

(iii) 320,948
↑
Thousands

(iv) 320,948
↑
Tens

Example 1.1-e **Writing Numbers in Expanded Form**

Write the following numbers in expanded form:

(i) 9,865,323
(ii) 43,583,621
(iii) 8,213,505,235
(iv) 47,825

Solution

(i) 9,865,323

9,000,000 + 800,000 + 60,000 + 5,000 + 300 + 20 + 3

(ii) 43,583,621

40,000,000 + 3,000,000 + 500,000 + 80,000 + 3,000 + 600 + 20 + 1

(iii) 8,213,505,235

8,000,000,000 + 200,000,000 + 10,000,000 +
3,000,000 + 500,000 + 5,000 + 200 + 30 + 5

(iv) 47,825

40,000 + 7,000 + 800 + 20 + 5

Reading and Writing Whole Numbers

To make it easier to read and write numbers, any number larger than three digits is separated into smaller groups of three digits, starting from the last digit of the number. Each group of these three digits has a name.

The first group of 3 digits on the right is the "**Units**" group.

The second group from the right is the "**Thousands**" group.

The word 'and' does not appear in the word form of whole numbers.

The third group from the right is the "**Millions**" group.

The fourth group from the right is the "**Billions**" group.

The fifth group from the right is the "**Trillions**" group and so on, as shown in the following chart.

Trillions			Billions			Millions			Thousands			Units		
Hundreds	Tens	Ones	Hundreds	Tens	Ones	Hundreds	Tens	Ones	Hundreds	Tens	Ones	Hundreds	Tens	Ones

To write large numbers in word form, start from the group furthest to the left and write the number formed by the digits in that group, followed by the name of that group. Then, write the number formed by the next group, followed by the name of that group, and continue to do this for each of the groups. For the last group however (i.e., the group furthest to the right), do not write the name of this group. When a group contains all zeros, that group is not read or written.

Also, commas and hyphens are used when expressing numbers in word form.

Commas (,) are used between the groups to separate them.

Hyphens (-) are used to express the two digit numbers in each group;

i.e., 21 to 29, 31 to 39, 41 to 49,…91 to 99.

For example, 2,835,197,000,642 expressed in word form using the above rule would be as follows:

Trillions			Billions			Millions			Thousands			Units		
Hundreds	Tens	Ones	Hundreds	Tens	Ones	Hundreds	Tens	Ones	Hundreds	Tens	Ones	Hundreds	Tens	Ones
		2	8	3	5	1	9	7	0	0	0	6	4	2

Two trillion, eight hundred thirty-five billion, one hundred ninety-seven million, six hundred forty-two.

When writing the numbers in word form, the names of the groups remain in their singular form, irrespective of the number preceeding; i.e., hundred, thousand, million, billion, trillion, etc.

For Example:

Eight **hundred** thirty-five **billion.**

One **hundred** ninety-seven **million.**

Example 1.1-f

Writing Numbers in Word Form

Write the following numbers in word form:

(i)	680,743	(ii)	25,345,006	(iii)	120,015,017
(iv)	1,000,629	(v)	64,246,783,251	(vi)	2,875,000,630,042

Solution

(i) 680,743 — Six hundred eighty thousand, seven hundred forty-three.

(ii) 25,345,006 — Twenty-five million, three hundred forty-five thousand, six.

(iii) 120,015,017 — One hundred twenty million, fifteen thousand, seventeen.

Solution *continued*

(iv) 1,000,629 One million, six hundred twenty-nine.

(v) 64,246,783,251 Sixty-four billion, two hundred forty-six million, seven hundred eighty-three thousand, two hundred fifty-one.

(vi) 2,875,000,630,042 Two trillion, eight hundred seventy-five billion, six hundred-thirty thousand, forty-two.

Example 1.1-g

Writing Whole Numbers Given its Word Form

Write the following in standard form:

(i) Thirty-five thousand, eight hundred twenty-five

(ii) Two million, three hundred forty-two thousand, six hundred seventeen

(iii) Half of a million

(iv) Three-quarters of a billion

Solution

(i) 35,825

(ii) 2,342,617

(iii) Half of a million is $\frac{1}{2} \times 1{,}000{,}000 = 500{,}000$

(iv) Three-quarters of a billion is $\frac{3}{4} \times 1{,}000{,}000{,}000 = 750{,}000{,}000$

Rounding Whole Numbers

Rounding numbers make them easier to work with and easier to remember. Rounding changes some of the digits in a number but keeps its value close to the original. It is used in reporting large quantities or values that change often, such as population, income, expenses, etc.

For example, the population of Canada is approximately 33 million or Henry's car expense for this month is approximately $700.

The rounding of numbers also makes arithmetic operations faster and easier, especially when determining the exact answer is not required.

For example, if you are required to estimate the area of a rectangular plot of land that measures 114 m by 97 m, you would have to multiply 114 × 97, which would result in 11,058 m^2. However, rounding the measurements to the nearest tens can provide a quick estimate; i.e., rounding 114 m to 110 m and 97 m to 100 m. This would result in an area of $110 \times 100 = 11{,}000$ m^2.

Rounding Whole Numbers to the Nearest Ten, Hundred, Thousand, etc.

Rounding whole numbers refers to changing the value of the whole number to the nearest ten, hundred, thousand, etc. It is also referred to as rounding whole numbers to multiples of 10, 100, 1000, etc.

For example,

Rounding a whole number to the nearest ten is the same as rounding it to a multiple of 10.

Rounding a whole number to the nearest hundred is the same as rounding it to a multiple of 100.

Rounding an amount to the nearest $10 refers to rounding the amount to a multiple of $10.

Rules for Rounding Whole Numbers

Step 1: Identify the digit to be rounded (this is the place value for which the rounding is required).

Step 2: If the digit to the immediate right of the required rounding digit is less than 5 (0, 1, 2, 3, 4), do not change the value of the rounding digit.

If the digit to the immediate right of the required rounding digit is 5 or greater than 5 (5, 6, 7, 8, 9), increase the value of the rounding digit by one (round up by one number).

Step 3: After step 2, change the value of all digits that are to the right of the rounding digit to 0.

Example 1.1-h **Rounding to Indicated Place Values**

Round the following to the indicated place values:

(i) 18,568 to the nearest ten

(ii) $24,643 to the nearest $100

Solution

(i) Rounding 18,568 to the nearest ten.

Identify the rounding digit in the tens place:
18,568 (6 is the digit in the tens place).

The digit to the immediate right of the rounding digit is 8, which is greater than 5; therefore, increase the value of the rounding digit by one, from 6 to 7, and change the value of the digits that are to the right of the rounding digit to 0, which will result in 18,570.

Therefore, 18,568 rounded to the nearest ten (or multiple of 10) is 18,570.

Solution
continued

(ii) Rounding $24,643 to the nearest $100.

Identify the rounding digit in the hundreds place:
24,643 (6 is the digit in the hundreds place).

The digit to the immediate right of the rounding digit is 4, which is less than 5; therefore, do not change the value of the rounding digit, but change the value of the digits that are to the right of the rounding digit to 0, which will result in 24,600.

Therefore, $24,643 rounded to the nearest $100 (or multiple of $100) is $24,600.

Example 1.1-i **Rounding Numbers (Visual Method)**

Round the following to the indicated place value:

(i) 627 to the nearest ten (multiple of 10)

(ii) 150 to the nearest hundred

Solution

We can visualize these numbers on a number line to determine the nearest number

(i) 627 to the nearest ten (multiples of 10)

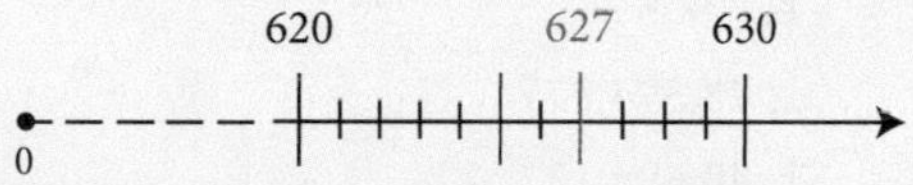

627 is closer to 630 than to 620.

Therefore, 627 rounded to the nearest ten is 630.

(ii) 150 to the nearest hundred (multiples of 100)

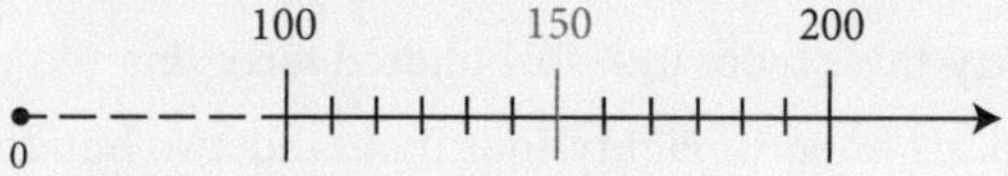

150 is exactly between 100 and 200. By convention, if a number is exactly in the middle, we round it up.

Therefore, 150 rounded to the nearest hundred is 200.

1.1 | Exercises

Answers to odd-numbered problems are available online.

For Problems 1 and 2, graph the numbers on a number line.

1. 14, 19, 15, 7

2. 12, 8, 17, 5

For Problems 3 to 6, place the correct sign, ‘ < ’ or ‘ > ’, in the space between the numbers.

3. a. 7 ☐ 15 b. 19 ☐ 14
4. a. 12 ☐ 17 b. 8 ☐ 5
5. a. 0 ☐ 5 b. 19 ☐ 0
6. a. 17 ☐ 0 b. 0 ☐ 8

For Problems 7 and 8, express the relationship between the numbers using the statement “is less than”.

7. a. 6 < 9 b. 18 > 11
8. a. 5 < 10 b. 10 > 0

For Problems 9 and 10, express the relationship between the numbers using the statement “is greater than”.

9. a. 4 < 8 b. 19 > 15
10. a. 10 < 15 b. 0 < 15
11. a. What is the largest 2 digit number?
    b. What is the smallest 3 digit number?
12. a. What is the smallest 2 digit number?
    b. What is the largest 3 digit number?

For Problems 13 to 16, express the numbers in their expanded form.

13. a. 9,407 b. 31,060
14. a. 2,056 b. 7,805
15. a. 3,229,186 b. 78,394,975
16. a. 5,464,448 b. 40,684,137

For Problems 17 to 20, express the numbers in their standard form.

17. a. Sixty-five thousand, two hundred forty-four
    b. Twelve million, four hundred fifty-two thousand, eight hundred thirty-two
18. a. Eight hundred thirty-three thousand, six hundred forty-one
    b. Thirty-two million, six hundred eighty-four thousand, two hundred fifty-six
19. a. One-eighth of a million
    b. Half of a billion
20. a. Three-quarters of a million
    b. One-tenth of a billion
21. Express the numbers in Problem 13 in their word form.
22. Express the numbers in Problem 14 in their word form.
23. Express the numbers in Problem 15 in their word form.
24. Express the numbers in Problem 16 in their word form.
25. Express the numbers in Problem 17 in their expanded form.
26. Express the numbers in Problem 18 in their expanded form.
27. Express the numbers in Problem 19 in their expanded form.
28. Express the numbers in Problem 20 in their expanded form.

For Problems 29 to 32, round the numbers to the nearest ten.

29. a. 895 b. 1,645
30. a. 9,157 b. 53,562
31. a. 9,558 b. 25,972
32. a. 1,095 b. 7,915
33. Round the numbers in Problem 29 to the nearest hundred.
34. Round the numbers in Problem 30 to the nearest hundred.
35. Round the numbers in Problem 31 to the nearest hundred.
36. Round the numbers in Problem 32 to the nearest hundred.
37. Round the numbers in Problem 29 to the nearest thousand.
38. Round the numbers in Problem 30 to the nearest thousand.
39. Round the numbers in Problem 31 to the nearest thousand.
40. Round the numbers in Problem 32 to the nearest thousand.

For Problems 41 to 44, round the numbers to the nearest ten thousand.

41. a. 875,555 b. 1,656,565
42. a. 3,254,599 b. 759,850
43. a. 3,368,850 b. 4,568,310
44. a. 7,555,450 b. 2,959,680
45. Round the numbers in Problem 41 to the nearest hundred thousand.
46. Round the numbers in Problem 42 to the nearest hundred thousand.
47. Round the numbers in Problem 43 to the nearest hundred thousand.
48. Round the numbers in Problem 44 to the nearest hundred thousand.
49. Round the numbers in Problem 41 to the nearest million.
50. Round the numbers in Problem 42 to the nearest million.
51. Round the numbers in Problem 43 to the nearest million.
52. Round the numbers in Problem 44 to the nearest million.

For Problems 53 to 56, arrange the numbers in order from smallest to largest (ascending order).

53. 794,870 ; 795,349 ; 794,687
54. 9,489 ; 9,929 ; 9,887
55. 683,360 ; 609,999 ; 690,678
56. 8,764 ; 8,467; 8,676

For Problems 57 to 60, create the smallest and largest possible numbers using all the given digits.

57. 7, 9, 1, 8
58. 9, 5, 6, 8, 7
59. 3, 5, 4, 8
60. 4, 7, 2, 6, 5

1.2 | Arithmetic Operations

Addition of Whole Numbers

Addition can be done in any order.

A + B = B + A

For example,

9 + 5 = 5 + 9 = 14

Addition of whole numbers refers to combining (finding the total or sum of) numbers. To add one number to another number, start by writing the numbers one under the other by aligning the place values (ones, tens, hundreds, etc.) of these numbers and drawing a horizontal line.

Starting with the ones place value, add all the numbers in the 'ones' column. If their total is less than 10, write the total under the horizontal line. If the total is 10 or more, write the 'ones' digit of the total under the horizontal line and write the tens digit above the tens column. This is called 'carrying'.

Next, add the numbers in the tens column followed by the hundreds column, etc., by following the same procedure for each column.

Example 1.2-a **Adding Whole Numbers**

Perform the following additions:

(i) 3,514 + 245 (ii) 8,578 + 3,982 + 564 + 92

Solution

(i) 3,514 + 245

$$\begin{array}{r} 3{,}514 \\ +\ \ 245 \\ \hline 3{,}759 \end{array}$$

The sum of the digits in the **ones column** is 9. Write 9 in the ones column below the horizontal line.

The sum of the digits in the **tens column** is 5. Write 5 in the tens column below the horizontal line.

The sum of the digits in the **hundreds column** is 7. Write 7 in the hundreds column below the horizontal line.

As only 3 is in the **thousands column**, the sum of the digits in the **thousands column** is 3. Write 3 in the thousands column below the horizontal line.

Therefore, adding 3,514 and 245 results in 3,759.

(ii) 8,578 + 3,982 + 564 + 92

$$\begin{array}{r} {}^{2}\ \ {}^{3}\,{}^{1}\ \ \\ 8{,}578 \\ 3{,}982 \\ 564 \\ +\ \ \ \ 92 \\ \hline 13{,}216 \end{array}$$

The sum of the digits in the **ones column** is 16, which is 1 ten and 6 ones. Write 6 in the ones column and carry the 1 above the tens column.

The sum of the digits in the **tens column** is 31, which is 3 hundreds and 1 ten. Write 1 in the tens column and carry the 3 above the hundreds column.

The sum of the digits in the **hundreds column** is 22, which is 2 thousands and 2 hundreds. Write 2 in the hundreds column and carry the 2 above the thousands column.

The sum of the digits in the **thousands column** is 13, which is 1 ten-thousand and 3 thousands. Write 3 in the thousands column and 1 in the ten-thousands column for the final answer.

Therefore, adding 8,578, 3,982, 564, and 92 results in 13,216.

Subtraction of Whole Numbers

Subtraction should be done in the given order.

$A - B \neq B - A$

For example,

$8 - 5 = 3$ but $5 - 8 = -3$

i.e., $(B - A)$ gives the opposite answer of $(A - B)$.

Subtraction of whole numbers refers to finding the difference between numbers.

To subtract one number from another number, start by writing the numbers one under the other by aligning the same place values (ones, tens, hundreds, etc.) of these numbers and drawing a horizontal line. Ensure that the number that is being subtracted from is in the top row and that the number that is being subtracted is below.

Starting from the ones place value, subtract the bottom number from the top number. If the top digit is greater than the bottom digit, subtract the ones column and write the number under the line. If the top digit is smaller than the bottom digit, borrow one ten from the digit to the left of this top digit for an additional 10 ones. Add this to the ones digit on the top, find the difference, and write the difference under the horizontal line. This is called "borrowing".

Next, subtract the numbers in the tens column, followed by the hundreds column, etc., by following the same procedure for each column.

Example 1.2-b

Subtracting Numbers

Perform the following subtractions:

(i) Subtract 1,314 from 3,628 (ii) Subtract 789 from 8,357

Solution

(i) Subtract 1,314 from 3,628

$$\begin{array}{r} 3,628 \\ -\ 1,314 \\ \hline 2,314 \end{array}$$

$8 - 4$ in the **ones column** is 4. Write 4 in the ones column below the horizontal line.

$2 - 1$ in the **tens column** is 1. Write 1 in the tens column below the horizontal line.

$6 - 3$ in the **hundreds column** is 3. Write 3 in the hundreds column below the horizontal line.

$3 - 1$ in the **thousands column** is 2. Write 2 in the thousands column below the horizontal line.

Therefore, subtracting 1,314 from 3,628 results in 2,314.

(ii) Subtract 789 from 8,357

$$\begin{array}{r} \scriptstyle 12\ 14\ \ \\ \scriptstyle 7\ \ \ 2\ \ 4\ 17 \\ \not{8},\not{3}\not{5}\not{7} \\ -\ \ \ 789 \\ \hline 7,568 \end{array}$$

In the **ones column**, the ones digit on the top (7) is smaller than the ones digit on the bottom (9). Borrow one ten from the tens digit on the top row to get 17 ones. $17 - 9 = 8$. Write 8 in the ones column.

In the **tens column**, the tens digit on the top (4) is smaller than the tens digit on the bottom (8). Borrow one hundred from the hundreds digit on the top row to get 14 tens. $14 - 8 = 6$. Write 6 in the tens column.

In the **hundreds column**, the hundreds digit on the top (2) is smaller than the hundreds digit on the bottom (7). Borrow one thousand from the thousands digit on the top row to get 12 hundreds. $12 - 7 = 5$. Write 5 in the hundreds column.

As only 7 is in the **thousands column**, write 7 in the thousands column below the horizontal line.

Therefore, subtracting 789 from 8,357 results in 7,568.

Multiplication of Whole Numbers

Multiplication of whole numbers can be thought of as repeated additions.

For example, 5 × 4 refers to repeatedly adding 5, four times:

$$\begin{array}{r} 5 \\ +\ 5 \\ \hline 10 \\ +\ 5 \\ \hline 15 \\ +\ 5 \\ \hline 20 \end{array}$$

5 has been added 4 times

When numbers are multiplied, the answer is called the product and each number is called a factor of the answer.

Multiplication can be done in any order.

A × B = B × A

For example,

9 × 5 = 5 × 9 = 45

Factors

5 × 4 = 20

Product

This is also written as 5·4 or (5)(4).

Example 1.2-c Multiplying Numbers

Perform the following multiplication:

(i) Multiply 38 by 6

(ii) Multiply 36 by 24

(iii) Multiply 263 by 425

Solution

(i) Multiply 38 by 6

$$\begin{array}{r} {}^{4} \\ 38 \\ \times\ \ 6 \\ \hline 228 \end{array}$$

Multiplying 8 ones by 6 results in 48 ones. This is 4 tens and 8 ones.

Write 8 in the ones column and 4 above the tens column.

Multiplying 3 tens by 6 results in 18 tens. Add the 4 tens to 18 to obtain 22 tens. Write 22 in the tens and hundreds column.

Therefore, multiplying 38 by 6 will result in 228.

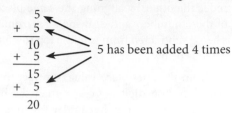

Solution
continued

(ii) Multiply 36 by 24

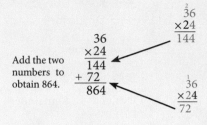

$$\begin{array}{r} \overset{2}{3}6 \\ \times 24 \\ \hline 144 \end{array}$$

Multiply 36 by 4 ones as shown to obtain 144.

$$\begin{array}{r} \overset{1}{3}6 \\ \times 24 \\ \hline 72 \end{array}$$

Multiply 36 by 2 tens. To do this, write a '0' under the ones column (you may omit the zero and leave it blank as shown) and multiply 36 by 2 to obtain 72.

$$\begin{array}{r} 36 \\ \times 24 \\ \hline 144 \\ +\ 72 \\ \hline 864 \end{array}$$

Add the two numbers to obtain 864.

Therefore, multiplying 36 by 24 results in 864.

(iii) Multiply 263 by 425

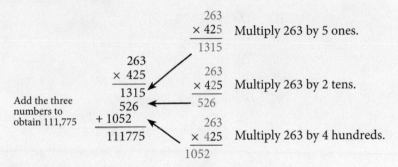

$$\begin{array}{r} 263 \\ \times\ 425 \\ \hline 1315 \end{array}$$

Multiply 263 by 5 ones.

$$\begin{array}{r} 263 \\ \times\ 425 \\ \hline 526 \end{array}$$

Multiply 263 by 2 tens.

$$\begin{array}{r} 263 \\ \times\ 425 \\ \hline 1052 \end{array}$$

Multiply 263 by 4 hundreds.

$$\begin{array}{r} 263 \\ \times\ 425 \\ \hline 1315 \\ 526 \\ +\ 1052 \\ \hline 111775 \end{array}$$

Add the three numbers to obtain 111,775

Therefore, multiplying 263 by 425 results in 111,775.

Division of Whole Numbers

Division of whole numbers can be thought of as repeated subtractions.

For example, 20 ÷ 5 refers to repeatedly subtracting 5 from 20.

$$\begin{array}{r} 20 \\ -\ 5 \\ \hline 15 \\ -\ 5 \\ \hline 10 \\ -\ 5 \\ \hline 5 \\ -\ 5 \\ \hline 0 \end{array}$$

5 has been subtracted 4 times

0 No remainder

Therfore, 20 ÷ 5 = 4.

The number that is being divided is called the **dividend**, the number that is dividing the dividend is called the **divisor**, the answer is called the **quotient**, and the number left behind is called the **remainder**.

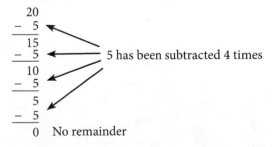

For example, 25 ÷ 7

$$\begin{array}{r l}
 & \;\;3 \longleftarrow \text{Quotient} \\
\text{Divisor} \longrightarrow 7 & \overline{\big)\,25} \longleftarrow \text{Dividend} \\
 & \;\;\underline{21} \\
 & \;\;\;4 \longleftarrow \text{Remainder}
\end{array}$$

Division should be done in the given order. $A \div B \neq B \div A$.

For example,

$6 \div 2 = 3$ but $2 \div 6 = \frac{1}{3}$

i.e., $(B \div A)$ is the reciprocal of $(A \div B)$

$$\begin{array}{ccccccc}
\text{Dividend} & = & \text{Divisor} & \times & \text{Quotient} & + & \text{Remainder} \\
25 & = & 7 & \times & 3 & + & 4
\end{array}$$

Example 1.2-d **Dividing Numbers**

Perform the following divisions and state the quotient and remainder:

(i) Divide 88 by 3

(ii) Divide 635 by 25

(iii) Divide 6543 by 12

Solution

(i) Divide 88 by 3

$$\begin{array}{r}
29 \\
3\,\overline{)\,88} \\
-6\downarrow \\
\hline
28 \\
-27 \\
\hline
1
\end{array}$$

8 can be divided by 3. Therefore, determine the number of multiples of 3 there are in 8.

There are two 3's in 8. Write 2 in the quotient area.

Multiply 2 by 3 (= 6) and subtract this from 8. Write the remainder 2.

Bring down the 8 and determine the number of multiples of 3 there are in 28.

There are nine 3's in 28. Write 9 in the quotient area.

Multiply 9 by 3 (= 27) and subtract this from 28 to get the final remainder of 1.

Therefore, the quotient is 29 and the remainder is 1.

(ii) Divide 635 by 25

$$\begin{array}{r}
25 \\
25\,\overline{)\,635} \\
-50\downarrow \\
\hline
135 \\
-125 \\
\hline
10
\end{array}$$

6 cannot be divided by 25. Therefore, determine the number of multiples of 25 there are in 63.

There are two 25's in 63. Write 2 in the quotient area.

Multiply 2 by 25 (= 50) and subtract this from 63. Write the remainder 13.

Bring down 5 and determine the number of multiples of 25 there are in 135.

There are five 25's in 135. Write 5 in the quotient area.

Multiply 5 by 25 (= 125) and subtract this from 135 to get the final remainder of 10.

Therefore, the quotient is 25 and the remainder is 10.

Solution
continued

(iii) Divide 6,543 by 12

6 cannot by divided by 12. Therefore, determine the number of multiples of 12 there are in 65.

$$\begin{array}{r} 545 \\ 12\overline{)6543} \\ -60\downarrow \\ 54 \\ -48\downarrow \\ 63 \\ -60 \\ \hline 3 \end{array}$$

There are five 12's in 65. Write 5 in the quotient area.

Multiply 5 by 12 (= 60) and subtract this from 65. Write the remainder 5. Bring down 4 and determine the number of multiples of 12 there are in 54.

There are four 12's in 54. Write 4 in the quotient area. Multiply 4 by 12 (= 48) and subtract this from 54 to get the remainder 6. Bring down 3 and determine the number of multiples of 12 there are in 63.

There are five 12's in 63. Write 5 in the quotient area. Multiply 5 by 12 (= 60) and subtract this from 63 to get the final remainder of 3.

Therefore, the quotient is 545 and the remainder is 3.

Arithmetic Operations with Zero and One

Table 1.2-a **Arithmetic Operations with Zero**

Operation	Description	Examples
Addition	When 0 is added to a number or when a number is added to 0, there will be no change to that number.	$25 + 0 = 25$ $0 + 25 = 25$
Subtraction	When 0 is subtracted from a number, there will be no change to that number.	$16 - 0 = 16$
	When a number is subtracted from 0, the answer will be the negative value of that number.	$0 - 16 = -16$
Multiplication	When 0 is multiplied by a number or when a number is multiplied by 0, the answer will be 0.	$0 \times 35 = 0$ $35 \times 0 = 0$
Division	When 0 is divided by a number, the answer will be 0.	$0 \div 25 = 0$
	When a number is divided by 0, the answer has a very large value (undefined), which is referred to as infinity (∞).	$25 \div 0$ = Undefined (∞)

Table 1.2-b **Arithmetic Operations with One**

Operation	Description	Examples
Addition	When 1 is added to a number, or a number is added to 1, the answer will be 1 greater than that number.	$14 + 1 = 15$ $1 + 14 = 15$
Subtraction	When 1 is subtracted from a number, the answer will be 1 less than that number.	$10 - 1 = 9$
	When a number is subtracted from 1, the answer will be 1 more than the negative value of that number. (Negative of 10 is −10, and 1 more than − 10 is − 9.)	$1 - 10 = -9$
Multiplication	When 1 is multiplied by a number, or when a number is multiplied by 1, there will be no change to that number.	$1 \times 12 = 12$ $12 \times 1 = 12$
Division	When 1 is divided by a number, the answer is the reciprocal of that number.	$1 \div 35 = \frac{1}{35}$
	When a number is divided by 1, there will be no change to that number.	$35 \div 1 = \frac{35}{1} = 35$

1.2 | Exercises

Answers to odd-numbered problems are available online.

For Problems 1 to 8, perform the additions.

1. a. 48 + 29 b. 38 + 95
2. a. 16 + 79 b. 69 + 47
3. a. 875 + 48 b. 574 + 79
4. a. 459 + 27 b. 356 + 65
5. a. 286 + 109 + 15 b. 839 + 645 + 27
6. a. 989 + 215 + 25 b. 798 + 237 +12
7. a. 7,105 + 459 + 8 b. 3,074 + 816 + 6
8. a. 1,879 + 642 + 9 b. 2,987 + 724 + 8

For Problems 9 to 16, perform the subtractions.

9. a. 62 – 25 b. 33 – 18
10. a. 43 – 27 b. 71 – 59
11. a. 208 – 79 b. 315 – 4
12. a. 327 – 28 b. 500 – 73
13. a. 767 – 159 b. 804 – 308

14. a. 904 – 629 b. 584 – 167
15. a. 8,302 – 7,244 b. 2,927 – 888
16. a. 9,185 – 6,728 b. 5,765 – 777

For Problems 17 to 20, first round the numbers to the nearest ten then perform the arithmetic operations.

17. a. 745 + 1,045 b. 428 + 255 c. 326 + 1,555
18. a. 357 + 245 b. 451 + 625 c. 3,255 + 2,105
19. a. 2,449 – 2,225 b. 946 – 452 c. 855 – 251
20. a. 495 – 357 b. 868 – 745 c. 1,858 – 255
21. Perform the operations in Problem 17 by first rounding the numbers to the nearest hundred.
22. Perform the operations in Problem 18 by first rounding the numbers to the nearest hundred.
23. Perform the operations in Problem 19 by first rounding the numbers to the nearest hundred.
24. Perform the operations in Problem 20 by first rounding the numbers to the nearest hundred.
25. Find the difference between the answers of Problems 17 and 21.
26. Find the difference between the answers of Problems 18 and 22.
27. Find the difference between the answers of Problems 19 and 23.
28. Find the difference between the answers of Problems 20 and 24.

For Problems 29 to 34, perform the multiplications.

29. 67 × 79
30. 46 × 78
31. 709 × 408
32. 761 × 253
33. 8,994 × 35
34. 5,905 × 37

For Problems 35 to 40, perform the divisions.

35. 6,131 ÷ 14
36. 4,130 ÷ 12
37. 777 ÷ 6
38. 654 ÷ 4
39. 4,235 ÷ 15
40. 3,281 ÷ 11

For Problems 41 to 44, first round the numbers to the nearest ten then perform the arithmetic operations.

41. a. 58 × 75 b. 472 × 48 c. 95 × 71
42. a. 63 × 59 b. 35 × 97 c. 246 × 45
43. a. 85 ÷ 9 b. 396 ÷ 24 c. 145 ÷ 26
44. a. 78 ÷ 19 b. 245 ÷ 45 c. 38 ÷ 8

For Problems 45 to 48, formulate arithmetic expressions and evaluate.

45. a. $784 is $365 more than what amount?

    b. $98 is $35 less than what amount?

46. a. $487 is $279 more than what amount?

    b. $52 is $97 less than what amount?

47. a. $515 more than what amount is $847?

    b. $745 less than what amount is $125?

48. a. $745 more than what amount is $1,274?

    b. $526 less than what amount is $346?

49. Mythili went to a bookstore and bought a dictionary. She gave the cashier a $100 note and received $47 as change. How much did the dictionary cost?

50. There were 744 students in a primary school. In May, some students left to join another school. 576 students remained in the school. How many students left for the other school?

51. There were 450 passengers on a train. Half of them were men, 125 were children, and the rest were women. How many more men than women were there on the train?

52. Out of the 3,678 visitors at an art exhibition, 1,469 were men, 1,234 were women, and the rest were children. How many more adults than children went to the exhibition?

53. Andy has $1,238 and Bill has $346 less than Andy. How much money do both of them have together?

54. A television costs $649 more than a DVD player. If the DVD player cost $235, how much will it cost to buy the TV and the DVD player?

55. Aran had some money saved up. On his birthday, Aran's grandparents gave him $125. After spending $98 on toys and $75 on clothes, he had $115 remaining. What amount did Aran have in savings before his birthday?

56. Girija had some biscuits. She ate 19 and gave 27 to her brother and 5 to her parents. She had 12 biscuits left. How many biscuits did Girija have originally?

57. Peter earns $18 per hour. If he worked 25 hours last week, calculate his earning for that week.

58. Sam's overtime rate is $37 per hour. If he worked 29 hours overtime last week, calculate his overtime pay for that week.

59. Earl wanted to save $3,150. If he saves $75 per week, how many weeks will it take for him to achieve his goal?

60. How long will it take to travel 1190 km at 85 km per hour?

61. A large group of students visited an exhibition on Friday. The first 275 students were given one free balloon each. 487 students were disappointed that they didn't receive any balloons. How many students visited the exhibition?

62. There were 2,415 boys and 1,875 girls that attended a fair. The first 2,650 visitors to the fair recieved gifts. How many visitors did not recieve gifts?

63. There are 19 girls in a class of 43 students. Fifteen of the girls and 11 of the boys are wearing eye glasses. How many boys are there in the class? How many students do not wear eye glasses?
64. There are 22 players on a soccer field. Ten players are wearing blue and 2 are wearing green. The rest of the players are wearing red. How many players are wearing red?

1.3 | Factors and Multiples

Introduction

Factors of a number are whole numbers that can divide the number with no remainder.

1 is a factor of every number and every number is a factor of itself.

For example, factors of 12 are 1, 2, 3, 4, 6, and 12. We can express factors of a number by showing how the product of two factors results in the number.

$12 = 1 \times 12$

$12 = 2 \times 6$

$12 = 2 \times 2 \times 3$

$12 = 3 \times 4$

Multiples of a number are whole numbers that can be divided by the number with no remainder. Multiples of a number can be expressed as the product of the number and a whole number.

For example, multiples of 10:

10	10+10	10+10+10	10+10+10+10	10+10+10+10+10
10×1	10×2	10×3	10×4	10×5
10	20	30	40	50

Therefore, multiples of 10 are 10, 20, 30, 40, 50, etc.

Prime Numbers and Composite Numbers

0 and 1 are neither prime numbers nor composite numbers.

A **prime number** is a whole number that has only two factors: 1 and the number itself; i.e., prime numbers can be divided only by 1 and the number itself.

For example, 7 is a prime number because it only has two factors: 1 and 7.

A **composite number** is a whole number that has at least one factor other than 1 and the number itself; i.e., all whole numbers that are not prime numbers are composite numbers.

For example, 8 is a composite number because it has more than 2 factors: 1, 2, 4, and 8.

Example 1.3-a **Identifying Prime Numbers**

Identify all the prime numbers less than 25.

Solution

All the prime numbers less than 25 are 2, 3, 5, 7, 11, 13, 17, 19, and 23.

Example 1.3-b **Identifying Composite Numbers**

Identify all the composite numbers less than 25.

Solution

All the composite numbers less than 25 are
4, 6, 8, 9, 10, 12, 14, 15, 16, 18, 20, 21, 22, and 24.

Example 1.3-c **Finding Factors of Prime Numbers**

Find all the factors of 13.

Solution

1 and 13 are the only factors of 13.

Example 1.3-d **Finding All Factors of Composite Numbers**

Find all the factors of:

(i) 16

(ii) 20

Solution

(i) The factors of 16 are 1, 2, 4, 8, and 16.

(ii) The factors of 20 are 1, 2, 4, 5, 10, and 20.

Example 1.3-e **Finding the Prime Factors of Composite Numbers**

Find all the prime factors of 24.

Solution

All the factors of 24 are 2, 3, 4, 6, 8, 12, and 24.
Of the above factors, only 2 and 3 are prime numbers.
Therefore, the prime factors of 24 are 2 and 3.

Least or Lowest Common Multiple (LCM)

LCM is the smallest integer that is a multiple of a set of numbers.

The **Lowest Common Multiple (LCM)** of two or more whole numbers is the smallest multiple that is common to those numbers. The LCM can be determined from one of the following methods:

Method 1: First, select the largest number and check to see if it is divisible by all the other numbers. If it divides, then the largest number is the LCM.

If the largest number does not divide the other numbers, then find a multiple of the largest number that is divisible by all the other numbers.

If none of the multiples of the largest number are divisible by all the other numbers (i.e., if the numbers have no common factors), then the LCM of the numbers is the product of all the numbers.

A number is divisible by 2 if the last digit of the number ends in a 0, 2, 4, 6, or 8.

A number is divisible by 3 if the sum of all the digits of a number is divisble by 3.

A number is divisible by 5 if the last digit of the number is a 0 or a 5.

Method 2: **Step 1**: Find the prime factors of each of the numbers and list the different prime numbers (using a factor tree as shown in the example that follows).

Step 2: Count the number of times each different prime number appears in each of the factorizations.

Step 3: Find the largest of these counts for each prime number.

Step 4: List that prime number as many times as you counted it in step 3. The LCM is the product of all the prime numbers listed.

Example 1.3-f

Least Common Multiple

Find the LCM of 3, 6, and 18.

Solution

Method 1: The largest number, 18, is divisible by both 6 and 3. Therefore, 18 is the LCM of 3, 6, and 18.

Method 2:

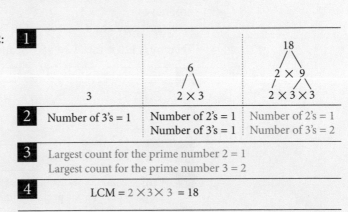

Step			
1	3	6 → 2×3	18 → 2×9 → $2 \times 3 \times 3$
2	Number of 3's = 1	Number of 2's = 1 Number of 3's = 1	Number of 2's = 1 Number of 3's = 2
3	Largest count for the prime number 2 = 1 Largest count for the prime number 3 = 2		
4	LCM = $2 \times 3 \times 3 = 18$		

Example 1.3-g

Least Common Multiple

Find the LCM of 9 and 15.

Solution

Method 1: The largest number, 15, is **not** divisible by 9.

Multiples of 15 are 15, 30, 45…

45 is divisible by 9.

Therefore, 45 is the LCM of 9 and 15.

Method 2:

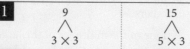

1

9	15
3×3	5×3

2

Number of 3's = 1	Number of 3's = 2 Number of 5's = 1

3

Largest count for the prime number 3 = 2
Largest count for the prime number 5 = 1

4

$\text{LCM} = 3 \times 3 \times 5 = 45$

Example 1.3-h

Least Common Multiple

Find the LCM of 3, 5, and 8.

Solution

Method 1: The largest number, 8, is ***not*** divisible by 3 and 5.

Multiples of 8 are 16, 24, 32, 40, 48, 56, 64… None of the multiples listed above are divisible by 3 and 5.

Since 3, 5, and 8 have no common factors, the LCM is the product
of all the numbers: $3 \times 5 \times 8 = 120$.

Therefore, 120 is the LCM of 3, 5, and 8.

Method 2:

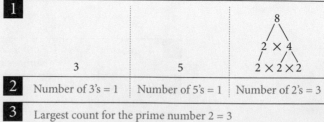

1

3	5	8
		2×4
3	5	$2 \times 2 \times 2$

2

Number of 3's = 1	Number of 5's = 1	Number of 2's = 3

3

Largest count for the prime number 2 = 3
Largest count for the prime number 3 = 1
Largest count for the prime number 5 = 1

4

$\text{LCM} = 2 \times 2 \times 2 \times 3 \times 5 = 120$

Example 1.3-i

Least Common Multiple

Two flashing lights are turned on at the same time. One light flashes every 16 seconds and the other flashes every 20 seconds. How often will they flash together?

Solution

In this example, we are required to find the least common interval for both lights to flash together. Thereafter, both lights will continue to flash together at this interval (multiple).

Method 1: The largest number, 20, is ***not*** divisible by 16.

Multiples of 16 are 16, 32, 48, 64, 80…

80 is divisble by 20. 80 is the LCM of 16 and 20.

Therefore, the two flashing lights will flash together every 80 seconds.

Method 2:

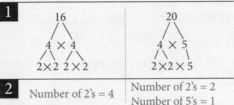

1

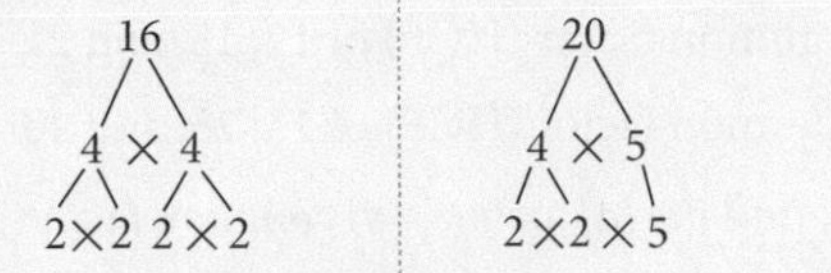

2 Number of 2's = 4 | Number of 2's = 2, Number of 5's = 1

3 Largest count for the prime number 2 = 4
Largest count for the prime number 5 = 1

4 LCM = $2 \times 2 \times 2 \times 2 \times 5 = 80$

1.3 | Exercises

Answers to odd-numbered problems are available online.

1. List all the prime numbers below 20.
2. List all the prime numbers between 20 and 40.

For Problems 3 to 6, find all the prime factors of the numbers.

3. a. 15 b. 24
4. a. 18 b. 35
5. a. 64 b. 54
6. a. 56 b. 60

For Problems 7 and 8, find the first 10 multiples of the numbers.

7. a. 6 b. 8
8. a. 15 b. 12
9. Find the common multiples of 3, 6, and 15.
10. Find the common multiples of 4, 8, and 12.

11. Find the lowest common multiple (LCM) of 3, 6, and 15.
12. Find the lowest common multiple (LCM) of 4, 8, and 12.

For Problems 13 to 16, find the lowest common multiple (LCM) of the numbers.

13. a. 18, 24 b. 35, 45
14. a. 10, 25 b. 60, 45
15. a. 24, 36, 12 b. 6, 15, 18
16. a. 5, 12, 15 b. 24, 40, 48

For Problems 17 and 18, find all the factors of the numbers.

17. a. 12 b. 18 c. 21
18. a. 15 b. 25 c. 40
19. Find all the common factors of 12, 18, and 21.
20. Find all the common factors of 15, 25, and 40.
21. Find the highest common factor (HCF) of 12, 18, and 21.
22. Find the highest common factor (HCF) of 15, 25, and 40.

For Problems 23 and 24, find the (a) factors, (b) common factors, and (c) highest common factor (HCF) of the sets of numbers.

23. a. 18, 48 b. 32, 60 c. 8, 12, 15
24. a. 16, 30 b. 36, 42 c. 6, 15, 20
25. Three wires measuring 18 m, 45 m, and 36 m are to be cut into pieces of equal lengths, without wastage. What is the maximum possible length of each piece?
26. A store has 54 green marbles, 72 yellow marbles, and 90 red marbles. The owner decides to package all the marbles into bags, such that each bag contained the same number of marbles. As well, each bag had to contain marbles of the same colour. Find the maximum possible number of marbles in each bag.
27. Three lights, red, blue, and green, flash at intervals of 15, 18, and 40 seconds, respectively if they begin flashing at the same time, how long will it take (in minutes) until all 3 flash at the same time again?
28. Three bells ring simultaneously. If they ring at intervals of 24, 36, and 40 seconds, how long will it take (in minutes) until they ring together again?

1.4 | Powers, Roots, and Order of Operations

Powers of Whole Numbers

We learned that multiplication is a shorter way to write repeated addition of a number. Similarly, when a number is multiplied by itself repeatedly, it is represented by **exponential notation.** In this section, we will learn about exponential notation and the positive powers of whole numbers.

When 2 is multiplied 5 times, in repeated multiplication, it is represented by;

$$2 \times 2 \times 2 \times 2 \times 2.$$

1 raised to any power = 1

0 raised to any power = 0

However, when 2 is multiplied 100 times, it would be tedious to represent it using repeated multiplication. The notation to represent such repeated multiplication is called exponential notation.

When 2 is multiplied 5 times, it is represented as $\mathbf{2^5}$ using exponential notation.

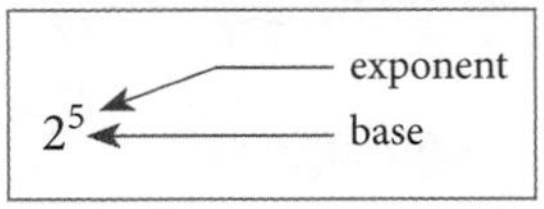

The whole representation is read as "2 raised to the power of 5" or "2 to the 5th power".

In the notation 2^5, 2 is called the **'base'** and 5 is called the **'exponent'**.

The "base" represents the number and the "exponent" represents the number of times the "base" is multiplied. The "exponent" is the number written in superscript to the right of the "base" number.

Example 1.4-a

Converting an Exponential Notation to a Standard Notation

Expand 8^2 to show the repeated multiplication and simplify.

Solution

Repeated Multiplication

$$8^2 = 8 \times 8 = 64$$

Exponential Notation (8^2) — Standard Notation (64)

Example 1.4-b

Writing in Exponential Form

Express the repeated multiplication $9 \times 9 \times 9 \times 9 \times 9 \times 9$ in exponential form.

Solution

Number 9 is multiplied repeatedly 6 times.

The **base** is **9** and the **exponent** is **6**.

Therefore, $9 \times 9 \times 9 \times 9 \times 9 \times 9 = \mathbf{9^6}$

Example 1.4-c

Simplifying Expressions in Standard Form

Express the following in standard form:

(i) 5×3^4

(ii) $2^3 \times 3^2$

(iii) $5^4 \times 2^2$

(iv) $5^2 - 4^2$

Solution

(i) $5 \times 3^4 = 5 \times [\,3 \times 3 \times 3 \times 3\,] = 5 \times 81 = 405$

(ii) $2^3 \times 3^2 = [\,2 \times 2 \times 2\,] \times [\,3 \times 3\,] = 8 \times 9 = 72$

(iii) $5^4 \times 2^2 = [\,5 \times 5 \times 5 \times 5\,] \times [\,2 \times 2\,] = 625 \times 4 = 2{,}500$

(iv) $5^2 - 4^2 = [\,5 \times 5\,] - [\,4 \times 4\,] = 25 - 16 = 9$

Example 1.4-d

Knowing One Power and Using it to Find Another of the Same Base

If $6^5 = 7{,}776$, find:

(i) 6^6 (ii) 6^4

Solution

(i) $6^6 = 6 \times 6^5$

$= 6 \times 7{,}776$

$= 46{,}656$

(ii) $6^5 = 6 \times 6^4$

$7{,}776 = 6 \times 6^4$

$6^4 = \dfrac{7{,}776}{6}$

$= 1{,}296$

Table 1.4

Examples of Powers of Exponents 2, 3, 4 and 5

$1^2 = 1$	$11^2 = 121$	$1^3 = 1$	$1^5 = 1$
$2^2 = 4$	$12^2 = 144$	$2^3 = 8$	$2^5 = 32$
$3^2 = 9$	$13^2 = 169$	$3^3 = 27$	$3^5 = 243$
$4^2 = 16$	$14^2 = 196$	$4^3 = 64$	$4^5 = 1{,}024$
$5^2 = 25$	$15^2 = 225$	$5^3 = 125$	$5^5 = 3{,}125$
$6^2 = 36$	$16^2 = 256$	$1^4 = 1$	
$7^2 = 49$	$17^2 = 289$	$2^4 = 16$	
$8^2 = 64$	$18^2 = 324$	$3^4 = 81$	
$9^2 = 81$	$19^2 = 361$	$4^4 = 256$	
$10^2 = 100$	$20^2 = 400$	$5^4 = 625$	

Roots of Perfect Squares

Square root of a number is one of the idential factors of that number.

Any whole number base with an exponent of 2 is called a perfect square. For example, 1, 4, 9, 16, 25, 36, 49, 64, 81, 100, ... are perfect squares.

$1^2 = 1$ $6^2 = 36$

$2^2 = 4$ $7^2 = 49$

$3^2 = 9$ $8^2 = 64$

$4^2 = 16$ $9^2 = 81$

$5^2 = 25$ $10^2 = 100$

Finding the root of a perfect square is the inverse of raising a number to the power of 2.

2 is a **square root** of 4 because $2^2 = 4$ or $2 \times 2 = 4$

5 is a **square root** of 25 because $5^2 = 25$ or $5 \times 5 = 25$

That is, a whole number multiplied by itself results in a perfect square. The number multiplied by itself to get that perfect square is called the square root of that perfect square.

For example,

16 is a **perfect square** because it has two identical factors of 4.

i.e., $16 = 4 \times 4$

Therefore, 4 is the square root of 16.

The square root symbol is '$\sqrt{\ }$', which is known as a radical sign. The square root of 16, using the radical sign, is represented by $\sqrt{16}$.

Example 1.4-e **Finding the Square Root of Perfect Squares**

Find the square root of the following:

(i) $\sqrt{36}$ (ii) $\sqrt{81}$ (iii) $\sqrt{144}$

Solution

(i) $\sqrt{36} = \sqrt{6 \times 6} = 6$ (Using $36 = 6 \times 6$)

(ii) $\sqrt{81} = \sqrt{9 \times 9} = 9$ (Using $81 = 9 \times 9$)

(iii) $\sqrt{144} = \sqrt{12 \times 12} = 12$ (Using $144 = 12 \times 12$)

Example 1.4-f **Evaluating by Finding the Square Root**

Evaluate the following:

(i) $\sqrt{49} + \sqrt{25}$ (ii) $\sqrt{64} - \sqrt{16}$ (iii) $\sqrt{4} \times \sqrt{9}$

Solution

(i) $\sqrt{49} + \sqrt{25} = \sqrt{7 \times 7} + \sqrt{5 \times 5} = 7 + 5 = 12$

(ii) $\sqrt{64} - \sqrt{16} = \sqrt{8 \times 8} - \sqrt{4 \times 4} = 8 - 4 = 4$

(iii) $\sqrt{4} \times \sqrt{9} = \sqrt{2 \times 2} \times \sqrt{3 \times 3} = 2 \times 3 = 6$

Example 1.4-g **Evaluating Expressions by Finding the Square Roots**

Evaluate the following expressions:

(i) $5 \times \sqrt{121}$ (ii) $\sqrt{100} \div 5$ (iii) $35 + \sqrt{49} - \sqrt{9}$

Solution

(i) $5 \times \sqrt{121} = 5 \times \sqrt{11 \times 11} = 5 \times 11 = 55$

(ii) $\sqrt{100} \div 5 = \sqrt{10 \times 10} \div 5 = 10 \div 5 = 2$

(iii) $35 + \sqrt{49} - \sqrt{9} = 35 + \sqrt{7 \times 7} - \sqrt{3 \times 3} = 35 + 7 - 3 = 39$

Order of Operations for Whole Numbers

The six arithmetic operations that you have learned are: addition, subtraction, multiplication, division, powers, and roots of whole numbers. In this section, you will learn the correct order (or sequence) for performing the combined arithmetic operations of whole numbers.

When there are no groupings (operations within brackets or a radical sign), the six arithmetic operations are performed in the following sequence:

1. Exponents (Powers) and Roots.
2. Division and Multiplication in order from left to right.
3. Addition and Subtraction in order from left to right.

Example 1.4-h

Evaluating Expressions with Mixed Arithmetic Operations

Solve the following arithmetic expressions and round your answer to two decimal places wherever required:

(i) $16 \div 2^2 + 44 - 3^3$

(ii) $\sqrt{144} \div 3 \times 2 + 5^2$

Solution

(i) $16 \div \mathbf{2^2} + 44 - \mathbf{3^3}$ — Working on the exponents,

$= \mathbf{16 \div 4} + 44 - 27$ — Dividing,

$= \mathbf{4 + 44} - 27$ — Adding,

$= \mathbf{48 - 27}$ — Subtracting,

$= 21$

(ii) $\sqrt{\mathbf{144}} \div 3 \times 2 + 5^2$ — Working on the square root,

$= 12 \div 3 \times 2 + \mathbf{5^2}$ — Working on the exponent,

$= \mathbf{12 \div 3} \times 2 + 25$ — Dividing,

$= \mathbf{4 \times 2} + 25$ — Multiplying,

$= \mathbf{8 + 25}$ — Adding,

$= 33$

Where there are groupings, the arithmetic operations within the groupings are to be done first. Common symbols used for groupings are brackets '( )', '[ ]', '{ }', and the radical sign '$\sqrt{\ }$'.

The arithmetic operations within these groupings are to be evaluated first in the order of arithmetic operations explained earlier; i.e., the expressions within the groupings are to be evaluated as one quantity.

Example 1.4-i

Evaluating Expressions with Groupings

Solve the following arithmetic expressions:

(i) $4 \times 50 \div (8 - 3)^2 - 1$

(ii) $(100 - 3 \times 24) \div 2\,(6 - 3) \div 2$

(iii) $\sqrt{3^2 + 4^2} \times (7 - 4) + 2$

Solution

(i) $4 \times 50 \div (\mathbf{8 - 3})^2 - 1$ Working on the brackets,

$= 4 \times 50 \div \mathbf{5^2} - 1$ Working on the exponent,

$= \mathbf{4 \times 50} \div 25 - 1$ Performing division and multiplication from left to right,

$= \mathbf{200 \div 25} - 1$

$= 8 - 1$ Subtracting,

$= 7$

(ii) $(100 - \mathbf{3 \times 24}) \div 2\,(\mathbf{6 - 3}) \div 2$ Working on the **bolded** operations within the brackets first,

$= (\mathbf{100 - 72}) \div 2\,(3) \div 2$

$= \mathbf{28 \div 2} \times 3 \div 2$ Performing divisions and multiplications from left to right,

$= \mathbf{14 \times 3} \div 2$

$= \mathbf{42 \div 2}$

$= \mathbf{21}$

(iii) $\sqrt{\mathbf{3^2} + \mathbf{4^2}} \times (7 - 4) + 2$ Working on the exponents,

$= \sqrt{\mathbf{9 + 16}} \times (7 - 4) + 2$ Adding within the radical,

$= \sqrt{\mathbf{25}} \times (7 - 4) + 2$ Working on the square root,

$= \mathbf{5 \times 3} + 2$ Multiplying,

$= 15 + 2$ Adding,

$= 17$

When there are groupings with more than one bracket, start with the inner most bracket, and move outwards to complete evaluating all expressions within the brackets by following the order of operations.

Example 1.4-j **Evaluating Expressions with More than One Bracket**

Evaluate the following:

(i) $4 \times 50 \div [(8 - 3)^2 - 5]$

(ii) $100 - 3\,[24 \div 2(6 - 3)] \div 2$

Solution

(i) $4 \times 50 \div [(\mathbf{8 - 3})^2 - 5]$ Working on the brackets,

$= 4 \times 50 \div [\mathbf{5^2} - 5]$ Working on the exponent and then subtracting within the brackets,

$= 4 \times 50 \div [\mathbf{25 - 5}]$

$= \mathbf{4 \times 50} \div 20$ Performing division and multiplication from left to right,

$= \mathbf{200 \div 20}$

$= 10$

Solution
continued

(ii) $100 - 3[24 \div 2\,(\mathbf{6 - 3})] \div 2$ — Performing division and multiplication from left to right within the brackets,

$= 100 - 3[\mathbf{24 \div 2 \times 3}] \div 2$

$= 100 - 3[\mathbf{12 \times 3}] \div 2$

$= 100 - \mathbf{3 \times 36} \div 2$ — Performing division and multiplication from left to right,

$= 100 - \mathbf{108 \div 2}$

$= \mathbf{100 - 54}$ — Subtracting,

$= 46$

1.4 | Exercises

Answers to odd-numbered problems are available online.

For Problems 1 to 4, express the repeated multiplication in exponential notation.

1. a. $6 \times 6 \times 6 \times 6 \times 6 \times 6$ b. 12×12
2. a. $5 \times 5 \times 5$ b. $7 \times 7 \times 7 \times 7 \times 7$
3. a. $3 \times 3 \times 3 \times 3 \times 3 \times 3$ b. $9 \times 9 \times 9 \times 9 \times 9 \times 9 \times 9 \times 9$
4. a. $8 \times 8 \times 8 \times 8 \times 8$ b. $4 \times 4 \times 4 \times 4 \times 4 \times 4 \times 4$

For Problems 5 to 8, write the base and exponent for the powers.

5. a. 2^9 b. 5^7
6. a. 6^2 b. 10^9
7. a. 1^{20} b. 20^0
8. a. 0^5 b. 12^1

For Problems 9 and 10, express the powers in standard notation and then evaluate.

9. a. 10^6 b. 3^5
10. a. 2^8 b. 5^4
11. If $3^{10} = 59{,}049$, evaluate 3^9 and 3^{11}
12. If $5^8 = 390{,}625$, evaluate 5^7 and 5^9

For Problems 13 to 20, evaluate the expressions.

13. a. $4^2 \times 2^4$ b. $3^2 \times 2^3$ c. $8^0 \times 9^1$
14. a. $5^2 \times 2^3$ b. $4^2 \times 3^3$ c. $12^1 \times 15^0$
15. a. $(7 - 4)^2$ b. $(3 + 2)^3$ c. $10 + 2^3$
16. a. $(8 - 5)^3$ b. $(4 + 1)^2$ c. $3^2 - 4$
17. a. $2^3 + 3^3$ b. $5^2 - 4^2$ c. $2^3 + 3^2 + 4^0$
18. a. $5^2 + 6^2$ b. $8^2 - 6^2$ c. $5^2 + 6^2 + 7^0$
19. a. $6^2 \times 2 - 2$ b. $100 - 5^2 \times 3$ c. $7^2 - (3 + 2)^2$
20. a. $5^2 \times 3 - 15$ b. $144 - 3^3 \times 4$ c. $(5 + 4)^2 - 2^6$

For Problems 21 to 24, find the two identical factors of the numbers.

21. a. 9 b. 36 c. 0

22. a. 16 b. 49 c. 1

23. a. 25 b. 100 c. 121

24. a. 64 b. 81 c. 144

For Problems 25 to 28, evaluate the indicated roots.

25. a. $\sqrt{49}$ b. $\sqrt{16}$ c. $\sqrt{1}$

26. a. $\sqrt{9}$ b. $\sqrt{36}$ c. $\sqrt{0}$

27. a. $\sqrt{81}$ b. $\sqrt{64}$ c. $\sqrt{144}$

28. a. $\sqrt{100}$ b. $\sqrt{25}$ c. $\sqrt{121}$

For Problems 29 to 40, evaluate the expressions.

29. a. $\sqrt{100} + \sqrt{25}$ b. $\sqrt{81} - \sqrt{16}$

30. a. $\sqrt{121} + \sqrt{36}$ b. $\sqrt{144} - \sqrt{9}$

31. a. $\sqrt{9 \times 16}$ b. $\sqrt{36 \times 49}$

32. a. $\sqrt{25 \times 64}$ b. $\sqrt{81 \times 121}$

33. a. $\sqrt{40 - 24}$ b. $\sqrt{75 - 11}$

34. a. $\sqrt{125 - 76}$ b. $\sqrt{48 - 23}$

35. a. $\sqrt{3^2 + 4^2}$ b. $\sqrt{13^2 - 5^2}$

36. a. $\sqrt{5^2 - 4^2}$ b. $\sqrt{12^2 + 5^2}$

37. a. $\sqrt{100 \div 25}$ b. $\sqrt{196 \div 4}$

38. a. $\sqrt{256 \div 4}$ b. $\sqrt{225 \div 25}$

39. a. $\sqrt{8^2}$ b. $\sqrt{20^2}$

40. a. $\sqrt{12^2}$ b. $\sqrt{45^2}$

For Problems 41 to 60, evaluate the expressions.

41. a. $5 \times 4 + 25 \div 25$ b. $64 \div 8 \times 2$

42. a. $7 \times 5 + 20 \div 4$ b. $36 \div 4 \times 9$

43. a. $100 \div 25 \times 4$ b. $18 \div 2 \times 3 + 5$

44. a. $80 \div 10 \times 8$ b. $50 \div 2 \times 5 + 10$

45. a. $32 \div 4 \div 2 \times 4$ b. $96 \div 12 \times 2 + 4$

46. a. $20 \div 4 \times 5 + 2$ b. $56 \div 4 \div 2 \times 5$

47. a. $5^2\sqrt{16} + 10 - 2$ b. $19 - 2^2\sqrt{9} + 3$

48. a. $40 - 3^2\sqrt{16} + 1$ b. $6^2\sqrt{25} + 16 - \sqrt{100}$

49. a. $\sqrt{9} - (8 - 5) + 10 \div 5 + 7$ b. $15 - 15(8 - 6) \div \sqrt{36} + 15$

50. a. $\sqrt{49} - 7(6 - 4) \div (5 - 3)$ b. $\sqrt{16} + (10 - 7) + 20 \div 4 - 3$

51. a. $(8 + 4)(8 - 6) + 10 - (6 + 2)$ b. $15 \div 3 + [4^2 - (6 - 4)^2]$

52. a. $10 \div 2 + [2^2 + (9 - 3)^2]$ b. $(10 - 7)(6 + 4) - (10 + 5) + 3$

53. a. $(4 + 3)^2 - 5^2 + 2^3$ b. $6^2 + 2^3 - (12 - 8)^2$

54. a. $(9 - 6)^2 - 2^2 + 3^3$ b. $3^3 + 2^4 - (15 - 9)^2$

55. a. $12^2 - 5 \times 27 \div (5 - 2)^2 - 3$ b. $3^2[(9 - 6)^2 \div 9 + 7 - 4]$

56. a. $16 \div 8 \times 10^2 + (12 - 7)^2 \times 2$ b. $3^2[(12 - 7)^2 \div 5 + 6 - 2]$

57. a. $7 + (3\sqrt{49} - 1)^2$ b. $16 \div \sqrt{64} + \sqrt{10^2 - 6^2}$

58. a. $15 + (5\sqrt{9} - 8)^2$ b. $\sqrt{12^2 + 5^2} - 27 \div \sqrt{81}$

59. a. $[(20 \div 5) \times 8] \div (2^2 + 4)$ b. $(64 \div 8 \div 4)^2 + (3^2 - 6^0)$

60. a. $[(6^2 \div 4) \times 5] \div (2^2 + 5)$ b. $(81 \div 9 \div 3)^2 + (9^0 + 2^2)$

1 | Review Exercises

Answers to odd-numbered problems are available online.

1. Write the following in (a) expanded form and (b) word form:

   a. 25,047 b. 620,025 c. 3,054,705

2. Write the following in (a) expanded form and (b) word form:

   a. 38,024 b. 405,037 c. 2,601,071

3. Perform the indicated addition and subtraction of the following:

   a. 3,495 + 276 + 85 b. 5,555 + 157 + 60
   c. 7,836 – 655 d. 6,405 – 2,769

4. Perform the indicated addition and subtraction of the following:

   a. 8,655 + 348 + 75 b. 3,450 + 645 + 30
   c. 5,245 – 876 d. 2,056 – 444

5. Estimate the answer to Problem 3 above by first rounding each number to the (a) nearest ten (b) nearest hundred.

6. Estimate the answer to Problem 4 above by first rounding each number to the (a) nearest ten (b) nearest hundred.

7. Perform the indicated multiplication and division of the following:

   a. 465×23 b. 365×24
   c. $314 \div 5$ d. $2,524 \div 12$

8. Perform the indicated multiplication and division of the following:

   a. 345×34 b. 237×25
   c. $276 \div 6$ d. $4783 \div 15$

9. Evaluate the following:

   a. $(12)^2 - (4^2 \times 3)$
   b. $\sqrt{5^2 + 4^2 - 3^2(9^0)}$
   c. $\sqrt{8^2 + 15^2} + 3^2$
   d. $\sqrt{16 \times 49} - \sqrt{25 \times 9}$

10. Evaluate the following:

    a. $\sqrt{(15^2 - 12^2)} + 5^2$
    b. $\sqrt{36 \times 64} - \sqrt{80 - 44}$
    c. $(\sqrt{10^2 + 20}) \div 30$
    d. $12^1 \times 11^0 \times 10^2 + 9^2$

11. After Martha gave 175 stamps to her brother, she had 698 stamps left. How many did she have at the beginning?

12. Amy spent \$349 and had \$167 left. How much did she have at the beginning?

13. Each ticket for a concert costs \$25. A total of \$35,000 was collected from ticket sales for Saturday and Sunday. If five hundred and fifty were sold on Saturday, how many tickets were sold on Sunday?

14. A company manufactured printers for $40 a unit. Over two weeks, $46,000 was spent on manufacturing printers. If five hundred printers were manufactured in the first week, how many printers were manufactured in the second week?

15. At a concert, 245 tickets were sold for $125 each and 325 tickets were sold for $68 each. How much money was collected altogether?

16. Susie held a bake sale. She sold 45 cookies for $2 each and 63 brownies for $3 each. How much money did she make altogether?

17. Allan and Babar have a total of $2,550. Allan has $800 more than Babar. How much money does each of them have?

18. Aycsha saved $5,500 more than Beth. If they saved $32,450 together, how much did each of them save?

19. An elevator can carry a maximum of 540 kg. Two workmen want to move 20 boxes of tiles, each weighing 24 kg. One of the workmen weighs 72 kg and the other weighs 65 kg. What is the largest number of boxes that can be carried in the elevator if both workmen are in the lift?

20. A delivery truck can carry a maximum of 2,000 kg. Two workmen want to move 100 planks of wood, each weighing 30 kg. One of the workmen weighs 85 kg and the other weighs 77 kg. What is the largest number of planks that can be carried by the truck if both workmen are in the truck?

21. Three balls of yarn measuring 24 metres, 60 meters, and 36 metres are to be cut into pieces of equal lengths, without wastage. What is the maximum possible length of each piece?

22. A store has 32 oranges, 48 bananas, and 72 apples. The owner decides to make fruit baskets containing the same number of fruits, without any left over. As well, each basket had to have only one type of fruit in it. Find the maximum possible number of fruits in each basket.

23. Amy, Bob, and Cathy go for a swim every third, seventh, and fourteenth day, respectively. If they met each other on a particular day at the pool, how many days later would they meet again?

24. Three gentlemen decided to go for a walk around a circular park. The first man takes 6 minutes, the second takes 10 minutes, and the third takes 8 minutes. If they start together, when will they meet again?

1 | Self-Test Exercises

Answers to all problems are available online.

1. Estimate the following by first rounding each number to the nearest ten:

   a. 3,950 + 2,540 + 709 + 65

   b. 5,475 + 1,260 + 179 – 50

   c. $1,274 \times 350$

   d. $6,650 \div 112$

2. Estimate the answers of Problem 1 by first rounding each number to the nearest hundred.

3. Evaluate:

   a. $\sqrt{(12^2 \div 4)} + 3 \times 2^4$

   b. $\sqrt{(4^2 \times 5 + 1)} - \sqrt{3^2 + 4^2}$

   c. $16 \times 8 - (4^2 + 8) + \sqrt{(16 \div 4)^2}$

   d. $5(5^2 - 3^2) \div 4 \times 2$

4. Simplify:

   a. $4(1 + 5)^2 \div 8 - (12 + 5)$

   b. $(4 \times 8 - 4^2) \div \sqrt{10^2 - 6^2}$

   c. $2^2 + 2^4 - 15 \times 7^0$

   d. $12^2 \div 4 - 3 \times 3^2$

5. Bob and Hari saved a total of $7,650. If Bob saved 5 times as much as Hari, how much money do each of them have?

6. The number of toasters sold by a manufacturer of kitchen appliances over each of the 4 quarters of last year were 9,092, 9,108, 9,102, and 9,976. Calculate:

   a. Total sales for last year.

   b. Difference between the highest and lowest quarterly sales for last year?

7. A truck can hold 1,275 cartons of milk. Each carton weighs 18 kg and the empty truck weighs 3,045 kg. Calculate the total weight of the truck when it is fully loaded with milk.

8. On Thursday, there were 1,075 shoppers at the Eaton Mall, which was 368 more than that on Friday. On Saturday, there were 125 less shoppers at the Eaton Mall than on Friday. (a) How many shoppers were there on Friday? (b) How many shoppers were there on Saturday?

9. 4,256 people visited the Toronto zoo on Sunday. 1,968 were adults and the rest were children. How many more children than adults visited the zoo?

10. There were some passengers on a train as it left the station in Toronto. At the station in Kitchner, 94 passengers got off and 35 got on. At the station in London, 89 passengers got off and 125 got on. If there were now 194 passengers on board, how many passengers were on the train at the station in Toronto?

11. Four lights, red, blue, green, and yellow, flash at intervals of 12, 16, 18, and 21 seconds, respectively. If they begin flashing at the same time, when will they flash together again?

12. Four wires measuring 12 m, 18 m, 24 m, and 42 m are to be cut into pieces of equal lengths, without wastage. What is the maximum possible length of each piece?

Chapter 2
Fractions and Decimal Numbers

Learning Outcomes

- Identify the types of fractions and perform computations with them.
- Read, write, and round decimal numbers.
- Solve problems involving fractions and decimal numbers.
- Determine the relationship between fractions and decimal numbers.
- Perform arithmetic operations combined with fractions and decimal numbers.

Chapter Outline

2.1 Fractions
2.2 Arithmetic Operations with Fractions
2.3 Decimal Numbers
2.4 Arithmetic Operations with Decimal Numbers
2.5 Arithmetic Operations with Fractions and Decimal Numbers

Fractions and decimal numbers are used to express numbers that are a portion of a whole number. Fractions are very useful for understanding measurement, probability, and data. Decimal numbers are a type of fraction that has the denominator expressed in powers of ten. It is easier to read, write, and perform arithmetic operations with decimal numbers than with fractions. In addition, it is easier to determine the magnitude of numbers when they are expressed as decimal numbers rather than fractions. For example, it is easier to recognize that 7.75 , instead of its fractional form, $\frac{93}{12}$, lies between 7 and 8. In this chapter, we will learn about the different types of decimals and fractions and the methods to convert them from one form to the other. As well, we will learn to perform mathematical operations of fractions and decimal numbers combined with powers and square roots .

2.1 | Fractions

Introduction

In the previous chapter, you learned about whole numbers and how to perform basic operations with whole numbers. However, measurements and calculations of quantities, values, amounts, etc., will not always be in whole numbers. Most of these involve portions of whole numbers and are represented by fractions and a special type of fraction, called a **decimal**. In this section, you will learn about fractions and how to perform basic mathematical operations with fractions.

If we divide one whole unit into several equal portions, then one or several of these equal portions can be represented by a fraction.

A fraction is composed of the following three parts:

1. **Numerator:** Representing the number of equal parts
2. **Fraction bar:** Representing the division sign
3. **Denominator:** Representing the total number of equal parts into which the whole unit is divided.

For example, $\frac{3}{8}$ is a fraction.

fraction bar ⟶ $\frac{3}{8}$ ⟵ numerator / ⟵ denominator

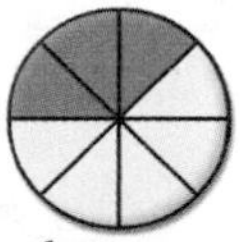

The **numerator** '3' indicates that the fraction represents 3 equal parts of a whole unit and the **denominator** '8' indicates that the whole unit is divided into 8 equal parts, as shown. The **fraction bar** indicates that the numerator '3' is divided by the denominator '8'.

In the above example, $\frac{3}{8}$ is read as "three divided by eight", "three-eighths", or "three over eight". All of these indicate that 3 is the numerator and that 8 is the denominator.

The numerator and denominator are referred to as the terms of the fraction. A **fraction** is another method of representing numbers, where one integer is divided by another non-zero integer.

A fraction where one integer is divided by another non-zero integer is called a '**rational number**'.

For example, $\frac{3}{2}, \frac{5}{2}, \frac{7}{1}, \ldots$ are rational numbers.

We know that 7 is an integer and also a whole number. Since 7 can be written as $\frac{7}{1}$ it is also a '**rational number**'.

The denominator of a fraction cannot be zero, since zero cannot represent a whole unit.

Fractions can be represented on a number line.

For example, $\frac{1}{2}$, $\frac{3}{2}$, $\frac{9}{4}$, $\frac{15}{4}$ are represented on a numberline as:

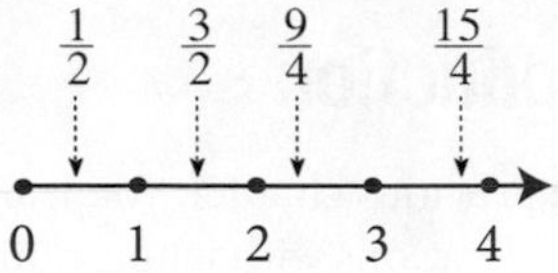

Example 2.1-a

Number Line

Represent the following on a number line:

(i) One unit divided into 2 equal parts

(ii) One unit divided into 3 equal parts

(iii) One unit divided into 5 equal parts

Solution

(i)

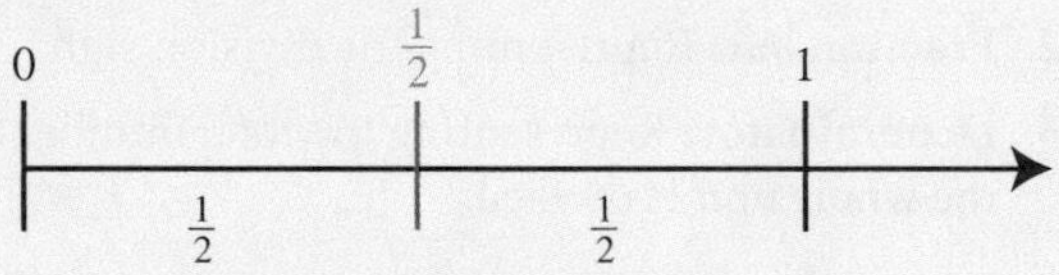

When one unit is divided into two equal portions, then each portion is one half and written as $\frac{1}{2}$.

(ii)

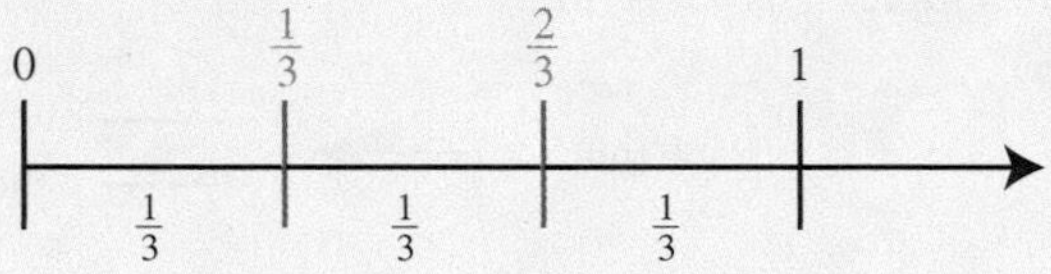

When one unit is divided into three equal portions, then each portion is one third and written as $\frac{1}{3}$.

(iii)

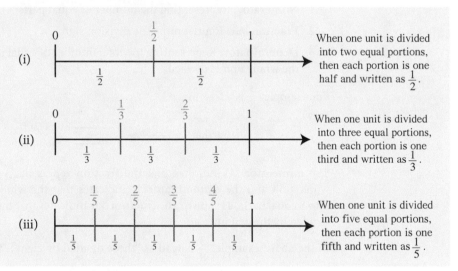

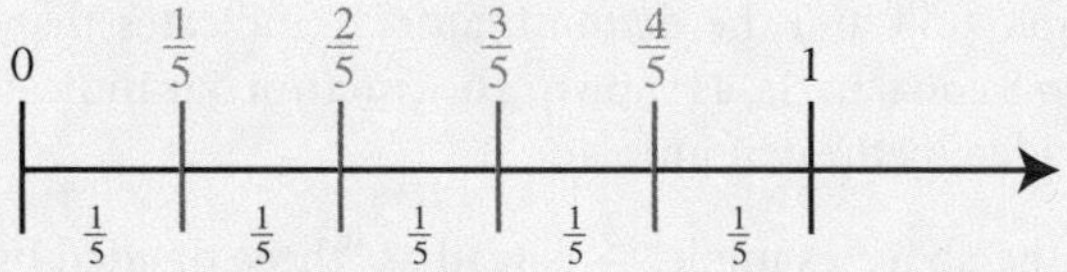

When one unit is divided into five equal portions, then each portion is one fifth and written as $\frac{1}{5}$.

Fractions represent division. For example, $\frac{3}{5}$ is the same as $3 \div 5$.

Proper Fractions

A **proper fraction** is a fraction in which the numerator is less than the denominator.

For example,

$\frac{3}{8}$ is a proper fraction because the numerator, 3, is less than the denominator, 8.

Improper Fractions

An **improper fraction** is a fraction in which the numerator is greater than the denominator; i.e., the value of the entire fraction is more than 1.

For example,

$\frac{7}{4}$ is an improper fraction because the numerator 7 is greater then the denominator 4 (i.e., $7 > 4$).

Mixed Numbers (or Mixed Fractions)

A **mixed number** consists of both a whole number and a proper fraction, written side-by-side, which implies that the whole number and proper fraction are added.

For example, $3\frac{5}{8}$ is a mixed number, where 3 is the whole number, and $\frac{5}{8}$ is the proper fraction.

$3\frac{5}{8}$ implies $3 + \frac{5}{8}$

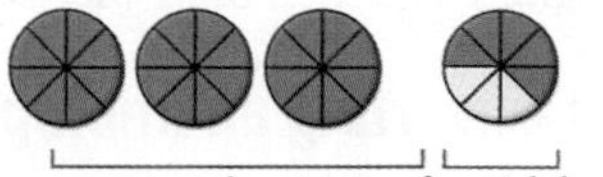

Complex Fractions

A **complex fraction** is a fraction in which one or more fractions are found in the numerator or denominator.

For example:

$\dfrac{1}{\left(\frac{3}{4}\right)}$ is a complex fraction because it has a fraction in the denominator.

$\dfrac{\left(\frac{2}{3}\right)}{6}$ is a complex fraction because it has a fraction in the numerator.

$\dfrac{\left(\frac{2}{5}+\frac{1}{4}\right)}{3}$ is a complex fraction because it has two fractions in the numerator

$\dfrac{\left(\frac{5}{6}\right)}{\left(\frac{1}{8}\right)}$ is a complex fraction because it has a fraction in both the numerator and the denominator.

Relationship Between Mixed Numbers and Improper Fractions

Converting a Mixed Number into an Improper Fraction

Follow these steps to convert a mixed number into an improper fraction:

Step 1: Multiply the whole number by the denominator of the fraction and add this value to the numerator of the fraction.

Step 2: The resulting answer will be the numerator of the improper fraction.

Step 3: The denominator of the improper fraction is the same as the denominator of the original fraction in the mixed number.

For example,

$$3\tfrac{5}{8} = \frac{3(8)+5}{8} = \frac{29}{8}$$

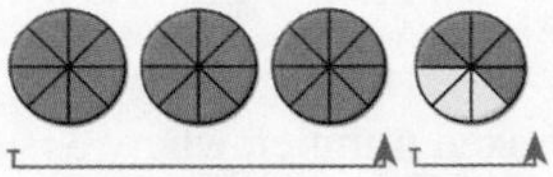

3 × 8 = 24 pieces   5 pieces

There is a total of 29 pieces, each piece being one-eighth in size.

Converting an Improper Fraction into a Mixed Number

Follow these steps to convert an improper fraction into a mixed number:

Step 1: Divide the numerator by the denominator.

Step 2: The quotient becomes the whole number and the remainder becomes the numerator of the fraction.

Step 3: The denominator is the same as the denominator of the original improper fraction.

For example, $\frac{29}{8} = 3\tfrac{5}{8}$ Because

$$\begin{array}{r} 3 \\ 8\overline{)29} \\ 24 \\ \hline 5 \end{array}$$

3 ← Quotient: whole number of the fraction

5 ← Remainder: numerator of the fraction

When two fractions are reduced to their lowest terms and if the resulting fractions are the same, then the two fractions are equivalent.

Converting Fractions to their Equivalent Fractions

When both the numerator and denominator of a fraction are either multiplied by the same number or divided by the same number, the result is a new fraction called an equivalent fraction. Equivalent fractions imply that the old and new fractions have the same value.

Example 2.1-b **Finding Equivalent Fractions**

Find 2 equivalent fractions of $\frac{2}{5}$.

Solution

$\frac{2}{5}$ 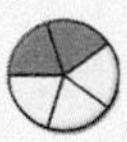 (2 portions of 5 equal parts of the whole)

$\frac{2}{5} = \frac{2 \times 2}{5 \times 2}$ Multiplying both the numerator and denominator by 2,

$= \frac{4}{10}$ 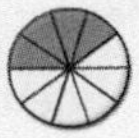 (4 portions of 10 equal parts of the whole)

$$\frac{2}{5} = \frac{2 \times 3}{5 \times 3}$$ Multiplying both the numerator and denominator by 3,

$$= \frac{6}{15}$$  (6 portions of 15 equal parts of the whole)

Therefore, $\frac{4}{10}$ and $\frac{6}{15}$ are equivalent fractions of $\frac{2}{5}$.

Example 2.1-c **Finding Equivalent Fractions**

Find 2 equivalent fractions of $\frac{12}{30}$.

Solution

$$\frac{12}{30} = \frac{12 \div 3}{30 \div 3}$$ Dividing both the numerator and denominator by 3,

$$= \frac{4}{10}$$

$$\frac{12}{30} = \frac{12 \div 6}{30 \div 6}$$ Dividing both the numerator and denominator by 6,

$$= \frac{2}{5}$$

Therefore, $\frac{4}{10}$ and $\frac{2}{5}$ are equivalent fractions of $\frac{12}{30}$.

Simplifying Fractions

Dividing both the numerator and denominator of a fraction by the same number, which results in an equivalent fraction, is called **reducing** or **simplifying** the fraction.

For example, we can simplify $\frac{16}{20}$ as shown:

$$\frac{16}{20}$$ Dividing both the numerator and denominator by 2,

$$= \frac{16 \div 2}{20 \div 2} = \frac{8}{10}$$

$$\frac{16}{20}$$ Dividing both the numerator and denominator by 4,

$$= \frac{16 \div 4}{20 \div 4} = \frac{4}{5}$$

Therefore, $\frac{8}{10}$ and $\frac{4}{5}$ are reduced fractions of $\frac{16}{20}$.

Fraction in Lowest (or Simplest) Terms

A fraction in which the numerator and denominator have no factors in common (other than 1) is said to be a **fraction in its lowest (or simplest) terms.**

Any fraction can be **fully reduced** to its lowest terms by dividing both the numerator and denominator by the highest common factor (HCF).

Example 2.1-d **Reducing Fractions to their Lowest Terms**

Reduce the fraction $\frac{40}{45}$ to its lowest terms.

Solution

The factors of 40 are 1, 2, 4, **5**, 8, 10, 20, and 40.

The factors of 45 are 1, 3, **5**, 9, 15, and 45.

The HCF is **5**.

Therefore, dividing the numerator and denominator by the HCF, 5, results in a fraction in its lowest terms:

$$\frac{40}{45} = \frac{40 \div 5}{45 \div 5} = \frac{8}{9}$$

Therefore, 40 parts out of 45, reduced to its lowest terms, is equal to 8 parts out of 9.

Reciprocal of Fractions

Every non-zero real number has a reciprocal. Two numbers whose products are equal to 1 are called reciprocals of each other.

For example,

$\frac{2}{3}$ and $\frac{3}{2}$ are reciprocals of each other (because $\frac{2}{3} \times \frac{3}{2} = 1$).

When the numerator and denominator of a fraction are interchanged, the resulting fraction is known as the reciprocal of the original fraction.

For example,

5 and $\frac{1}{5}$ are reciprocals (5 can also be written as $\frac{5}{1}$).

Similarly, the reciprocal of $\frac{-2}{5}$ is $\frac{5}{-2} = -\frac{5}{2}$

Reciprocal of a number has the same sign as the number.

Reciprocal of a positive number is always positive and the reciprocal of a negative number is always negative.

Note:

(i) Reciprocal of a number is not the opposite of that number. (Reciprocal of $3 \neq -3$. The reciprocal of $3 = \frac{1}{3}$.)

(ii) Reciprocal of a fraction is not the equivalent fraction of that fraction.

(Reciprocal of $\frac{2}{5} \neq \frac{4}{10}$. The reciprocal of $\frac{2}{5} = \frac{5}{2}$.)

Table 2.1

Examples of Numbers with their Opposites and Reciprocals

When any number is multiplied by its reciprocal, the answer is always 1.

When any number is added with its opposite, the answer is always 0.

Number	5	-3	$\frac{2}{3}$	$-\frac{3}{8}$
Opposite	-5	3	$-\frac{2}{3}$	$\frac{3}{8}$
Reciprocal	$\frac{1}{5}$	$-\frac{1}{3}$	$\frac{3}{2}$	$-\frac{8}{3}$

2.1 | Exercises

Answers to odd-numbered problems are available online.

For Problems 1 to 6, classify the fractions as proper fractions, improper fractions, mixed numbers, or complex fractions.

1. a. $\frac{16}{35}$ b. $3\frac{2}{9}$
2. a. $15\frac{12}{13}$ b. $\frac{29}{30}$
3. a. $\frac{19}{16}$ b. $9\frac{7}{8}$
4. a. $\frac{21}{22}$ b. $\frac{52}{25}$
5. a. $4\frac{2}{5}$ b. $\frac{2\frac{1}{3}}{\frac{1}{8}}$
6. a. $\frac{15}{6\frac{1}{2}}$ b. $\frac{20}{75}$

For Problems 7 to 10, convert the mixed numbers into improper fractions.

7. a. $2\frac{2}{7}$ b. $3\frac{1}{8}$
8. a. $3\frac{2}{5}$ b. $7\frac{5}{8}$
9. a. $5\frac{4}{5}$ b. $6\frac{3}{4}$
10. a. $4\frac{3}{7}$ b. $9\frac{5}{6}$

For Problems 11 to 14, convert the improper fractions into mixed numbers.

11. a. $\frac{19}{7}$ b. $\frac{45}{8}$
12. a. $\frac{23}{7}$ b. $\frac{34}{3}$
13. a. $\frac{23}{3}$ b. $\frac{31}{6}$
14. a. $\frac{26}{4}$ b. $\frac{29}{5}$

For Problems 15 to 20, classify the pair of fractions as 'equal' or 'not equal' by first converting the mixed numbers to improper fractions.

15. $\frac{44}{5}$ and $8\frac{4}{5}$
16. $\frac{47}{8}$ and $5\frac{7}{8}$
17. $11\frac{5}{7}$ and $7\frac{5}{7}$
18. $\frac{41}{4}$ and $10\frac{3}{4}$
19. $\frac{54}{7}$ and $7\frac{5}{7}$
20. $\frac{17}{8}$ and $2\frac{3}{8}$

For Problems 21 to 26, classify the pair of fractions as 'equal' or 'not equal' by first converting the improper fractions to mixed numbers.

21. $\frac{15}{4}$ and $3\frac{1}{4}$
22. $\frac{43}{6}$ and $7\frac{5}{6}$
23. $\frac{18}{5}$ and $3\frac{3}{5}$
24. $\frac{45}{7}$ and $6\frac{3}{7}$
25. $3\frac{8}{9}$ and $\frac{35}{9}$
26. $\frac{34}{8}$ and $4\frac{1}{8}$

For Problems 27 to 30, write the reciprocal of the fractions and reduce them to their lowest terms.

27. a. $\frac{32}{20}$ b. $\frac{48}{84}$
28. a. $\frac{44}{12}$ b. $\frac{42}{70}$
29. a. $\frac{56}{48}$ b. $\frac{84}{21}$
30. a. $\frac{75}{105}$ b. $\frac{144}{48}$

For Problems 31 to 36, classify the pair of fractions as 'equal' or 'not equal' by first reducing the fractions of each pair to their lowest terms.

31. $\frac{6}{12}$ and $\frac{15}{30}$
32. $\frac{6}{10}$ and $\frac{9}{15}$
33. $\frac{8}{10}$ and $\frac{15}{12}$
34. $\frac{12}{18}$ and $\frac{18}{27}$
35. $\frac{15}{12}$ and $\frac{36}{45}$
36. $\frac{35}{15}$ and $\frac{28}{12}$

For Problems 37 to 42 find the missing values.

37. $\frac{4}{9} = \frac{?}{27} = \frac{20}{?}$
38. $\frac{42}{36} = \frac{14}{?} = \frac{?}{30}$
39. $\frac{9}{12} = \frac{18}{?} = \frac{?}{4}$
40. $\frac{45}{75} = \frac{?}{25} = \frac{18}{?}$
41. $\frac{3}{2} = \frac{12}{?} = \frac{?}{12}$
42. $\frac{25}{15} = \frac{?}{3} = \frac{35}{?}$
43. What fraction of 1 year is 4 months? Express your answer as a fraction reduced to its lowest terms.
44. What fraction of 1 hour is 25 minutes? Express your answer as a fraction reduced to its lowest terms.
45. Karen cut a pizza into 16 equal slices and served 12 slices to her friends. What fraction of the pizza was served? Express your answer as a fraction reduced to its lowest terms.

46. Out of 35 students in a math class, 15 recieved an "A" in their final exam. What fraction of the students in the class received an "A" grade? Express your answer as a fraction reduced to its lowest terms.

47. In a survey of 272 people, 68 people responded 'yes' and the remaining respeonded 'no'. What fraction of the people responded 'no'?

48. In a finance math course of 490 students, 70 students failed the final exam. What fraction of the students passed the final exam in this course?

49. Out of the 480 units in a condominium tower, 182 are rented. What fraction of the units are not rented?

50. In a community of 6,000 people, 1,800 were 60 years or older. What fraction of the people were below the age of 60 years?

2.2 | Arithmetic Operations with Fractions

Least or Lowest Common Denominator (LCD)

The **Lowest Common Denominator** (**LCD**) of a set of two or more fractions is the smallest whole number that is divisible by each of the denominators. It is the least common multiple (LCM) of the denominators of the fractions.

In performing addition and subtraction of fractions, it is necessary to find the equivalent fraction using the least common denominator. The best choice for a common denominator is the LCD, because it makes any further simplification easier.

Example 2.2-a

Finding the Lowest Common Denominator

Find the LCD of $\frac{4}{9}$ and $\frac{7}{15}$.

Solution

The LCD of the fractions $\frac{4}{9}$ and $\frac{7}{15}$ is the same as the LCM of the denominators 9 and 15. It is the same as in what you had learned in Chapter 1, Section 1.3.

Therefore, the LCD of $\frac{4}{9}$ and $\frac{7}{15}$ is 45.

Highest Common Factor (HCF)

HCF is the largest integer that divides the set of numbers without remainder.

The factors that are common to two or more numbers are called **common factors** of those numbers.

The **Highest Common Factor (HCF)** of two or more numbers is the largest common number that divides the numbers with no remainder. In other words, the HCF is the largest of all the common factors. HCF is useful when simplifying fractions. For this purpose, HCF is also known as the Greatest Common Divisor (GCD).

Example 2.2-b

Finding the Common Factors

Find the common factors of 12 and 18.

Solution

The factors of 12 are 1, **2**, **3**, 4, **6**, and 12.

The factors of 18 are 1, **2**, **3**, **6**, 9, and 18.

The common factors are **2**, **3**, and **6**.

1 is a factor that is common to all numbers but is not included in the list of common factors.

Example 2.2-c

Finding the Highest Common Factor

Find the HCF of 72, 126, and 216.

Solution

The factors of 72 are 1, **2**, **3**, 4, **6**, 8, **9**, 12, **18**, 24, 36, and 72.

The factors of 126 are 1, **2**, **3**, **6**, 7, **9**, 14, **18**, 21, 42, 63, and 126.

The factors of 216 are 1, **2**, **3**, 4, **6**, 8, **9**, 12, **18**, 24, 27, 36, 54, 72, 108, and 216.

The common factors are **2**, **3**, **6**, **9**, and **18**.

Therefore, the HCF is **18**.

It is best to convert a mixed number into an improper fraction before performing any basic arithmetic operations.

Comparing Fractions

Fractions can easily be compared when they have the same denominator. If they do not have the same denominator, find the LCD of the fractions, then convert them into equivalent fractions with that LCD as their denominator.

Example 2.2-d

Comparing Fractions

Which of the fractions, $\frac{5}{12}$ or $\frac{3}{8}$, is greater?

Solution

Step 1: We first find the LCD of the fractions, which is the same as the LCM of the denominators. The LCM of 12 and 8 is 24.

Step 2: Now convert each of the fractions to its equivalent fraction with 24 as the denominator.

Step 3: Multiply the denominator by 2 to obtain the LCD of 24 and multiply the numerator by 2 as well to maintain an equivalent fraction.

$$\frac{5}{12} = \frac{5 \times 2}{12 \times 2} = \frac{10}{24}$$

5 portions of 12 equal parts of a whole is equal to 10 portions of 24 equal parts of that whole.

Similarly, to convert $\frac{3}{8}$ to an equivalent fraction with 24 as the denominator:

Solution
continued

$$\frac{3}{8} = \frac{3 \times 3}{8 \times 3} = \frac{9}{24}$$

3 portions of 8 equal parts of a whole is equal to 9 portions of 24 equal parts of that whole.

Since the denominators are the same, we can now compare the numerators of the above to identify the greater fraction.

10 > 9, which implies that $\frac{10}{24} > \frac{9}{24}$.

Therefore, $\frac{5}{12} > \frac{3}{8}$.

Addition of Fractions

Addition of fractions requires that the denominators of every fraction be the same. To make them the same, first find the LCD and change each fraction to its equivalent fraction having the same denominator. Now, add the numerators of each of the equivalent fractions. The resulting fraction will have the common denominator, and its numerator will be the result of adding the numerators of the equivalent fractions.

Example 2.2-e **Adding Fractions that have Different Denominators**

Add $3\frac{5}{6}$ and $\frac{4}{9}$.

Solution

$3\frac{5}{6} + \frac{4}{9}$

Converting the mixed number to an improper fraction,

$= \frac{(3 \times 6) + 5}{6} + \frac{4}{9} = \frac{23}{6} + \frac{4}{9}$

Finding the equivalent fraction using the LCD of 18,

$= \frac{69}{18} + \frac{8}{18} = \frac{77}{18}$

Converting the improper fraction to a mixed number,

$= 4\frac{5}{18}$

Therefore, the result from adding $3\frac{5}{6}$ and $\frac{4}{9}$ is $4\frac{5}{18}$.

Subtraction of Fractions

The process for subtraction of fractions is the same as that of addition of fractions. First, find a common denominator, then change each fraction to its equivalent fraction with the common denominator. The resulting fraction will have that denominator and its numerator will be the result of subtracting the numerators of the original fractions.

Example 2.2-f

Subtracting Fractions

Subtract $\frac{2}{3}$ from $12\frac{1}{2}$.

Solution

$12\frac{1}{2} - \frac{2}{3}$

Converting the mixed number to an improper fraction,

$= \frac{(12 \times 2) + 1}{2} - \frac{2}{3} = \frac{25}{2} - \frac{2}{3}$

Finding the equivalent fraction using the LCD of 6,

$= \frac{75}{6} - \frac{4}{6} = \frac{71}{6}$

Converting the improper fraction to a mixed number,

$= 11\frac{5}{6}$

Therefore, the result from subtracting $\frac{2}{3}$ from $12\frac{1}{2}$ is $11\frac{5}{6}$.

Multiplication of Fractions

When multiplying two or more fractions, first convert each mixed number to its improper fraction, then simply multiply the numerators to get the new numerator and multiply the denominators to get the new denominator.

Example 2.2-g

Multiplying Fractions

Multiply:

(i) $\frac{3}{2} \times \frac{4}{11}$ (ii) $\frac{9}{13} \times 4$ (iii) $\frac{7}{12} \times \frac{4}{21}$ (iv) $15 \times \frac{2}{5}$

Solution

(i) $\frac{3}{2} \times \frac{4}{11} = \frac{3}{\cancel{2}_1} \times \frac{\cancel{4}^2}{11} = \frac{3}{1} \times \frac{2}{11} = \frac{6}{11}$

(ii) $\frac{9}{13} \times 4 = \frac{9}{13} \times \frac{4}{1} = \frac{36}{13}$

(iii) $\frac{7}{12} \times \frac{4}{21} = \frac{\cancel{7}^1}{\cancel{12}_3} \times \frac{\cancel{4}^1}{\cancel{21}_3} = \frac{1}{3} \times \frac{1}{3} = \frac{1}{9}$

(iv) $15 \times \frac{2}{5} = \frac{\cancel{15}^3}{1} \times \frac{2}{\cancel{5}_1} = \frac{3}{1} \times \frac{2}{1} = \frac{6}{1} = 6$

Division of Fractions

The division of fractions is done by multiplying the numerator by the reciprocal of the denominator.

When a fraction is inverted, the resulting fraction is called the 'reciprocal' of the original fraction.

For example,

$$\frac{\left(\frac{5}{3}\right)}{\left(\frac{7}{9}\right)} = \frac{5}{3} \div \frac{7}{9} = \frac{5}{\cancel{3}_1} \times \frac{\cancel{9}^3}{7} = \frac{15}{7}$$

Note: Dividing by $\frac{7}{9}$ is the same as multiplying by the reciprocal of $\frac{7}{9}$, which is $\frac{9}{7}$.

When a fraction is a mixed number, convert it to an improper fraction and continue with the arithmetic operation.

For example,

$$\frac{2\frac{1}{4}}{5\frac{5}{8}} = \frac{\left(\frac{9}{4}\right)}{\left(\frac{45}{8}\right)} = \frac{9}{4} \div \frac{45}{8} = \frac{\cancel{9}^1}{\cancel{4}_1} \times \frac{\cancel{8}^2}{\cancel{45}_5} = \frac{2}{5}$$

Note: When multiplying or dividing mixed numbers, it is incorrect to multiply or divide the whole number parts separately from the fractional parts to arrive at the answer.

Example 2.2-h **Dividing Fractions**

Divide $\frac{3}{20}$ by $1\frac{4}{5}$.

Solution

$\frac{3}{20} \div 1\frac{4}{5}$

$= \frac{3}{20} \div \frac{9}{5}$ — Multiplying $\frac{3}{20}$ by the reciprocal of $\frac{9}{5}$,

$= \frac{3}{20} \times \frac{5}{9}$

$= \frac{\cancel{3}^1}{\cancel{20}_4} \times \frac{\cancel{5}^1}{\cancel{9}_3}$ — Simplifying the numerators and the denominators,

$= \frac{1}{12}$

Converting Complex Fractions into Proper or Improper Fractions

A complex fraction can be converted into a proper or improper fraction by dividing the numerator by the denominator and then simplifying the expression.

For example,

$$\frac{\left(\frac{7}{2}\right)}{5} = \frac{7}{2} \div 5 = \frac{7}{2} \times \frac{1}{5} = \frac{7}{10}$$

$$\frac{8}{\left(\frac{9}{2}\right)} = 8 \times \left(\frac{2}{9}\right) = \frac{16}{9}$$

2.2 | Exercises

Answers to odd-numbered problems are available online.

For Problems 1 to 6, identify the greater fraction in each pair.

1. $\frac{2}{5}$ or $\frac{3}{8}$
2. $\frac{4}{3}$ or $\frac{6}{5}$
3. $\frac{12}{15}$ or $\frac{35}{45}$
4. $\frac{5}{4}$ or $\frac{7}{6}$
5. $\frac{8}{7}$ or $\frac{13}{12}$
6. $\frac{5}{13}$ or $\frac{16}{39}$
7. Which of the following fractions are less than $\frac{2}{3}$?
   $\frac{5}{8}, \frac{6}{7}, \frac{3}{5}, \frac{7}{9}$
8. Which of the following fractions are greater than $\frac{3}{4}$?
   $\frac{4}{5}, \frac{7}{9}, \frac{5}{7}, \frac{9}{11}$

For Problems 9 to 12, perform the addition and reduce to lowest terms.

9. a. $\frac{9}{10} + \frac{1}{2}$ b. $\frac{21}{25} + \frac{7}{8}$
10. a. $\frac{3}{4} + \frac{1}{8}$ b. $\frac{35}{18} + \frac{3}{6}$
11. a. $\frac{4}{3} + \frac{5}{6}$ b. $12\frac{4}{3} + 5\frac{1}{3}$
12. a. $\frac{21}{13} + \frac{1}{3}$ b. $18\frac{5}{7} + 2\frac{2}{5}$

For Prɔblems 13 to 16, perform the subtraction and reduce to lowest terms.

13. a. $\frac{2}{3} - \frac{1}{9}$ b. $\frac{9}{12} + \frac{4}{5}$
14. a. $\frac{1}{6} - \frac{1}{8}$ b. $\frac{19}{20} - \frac{8}{10}$
15. a. $\frac{1}{3} + \frac{3}{8}$ b. $16\frac{1}{8} - 1\frac{1}{2}$
16. a. $\frac{17}{9} - \frac{5}{6}$ b. $5\frac{2}{3} - 1\frac{5}{12}$

For Problems 17 to 20, perform the multiplication and reduce to lowest terms.

17. a. $\frac{16}{5} \times \frac{5}{4}$ b. $3 \times \frac{7}{9}$
18. a. $\frac{12}{5} \times \frac{25}{3}$ b. $\frac{6}{9} \times \frac{19}{12}$
19. a. $\frac{3}{8} \times \frac{5}{11}$ b. $9\frac{3}{5} \times 1\frac{29}{96}$
20. a. $\frac{4}{5} \times \frac{23}{9}$ b. $11\frac{4}{3} \times 1\frac{1}{74}$

For Problems 21 to 24, perform the division and reduce to lowest terms.

21. a. $\frac{2}{3} \div \frac{4}{9}$ b. $\frac{3}{8} \div 4$

22. a. $\frac{3}{5} \div \frac{3}{4}$ b. $\frac{1}{7} \div \frac{3}{5}$

23. a. $\frac{10}{15} \div \frac{3}{7}$ b. $23\frac{1}{2} \div 8\frac{13}{16}$

24. a. $\frac{8}{12} \div \frac{2}{4}$ b. $10\frac{1}{4} \div 2\frac{27}{48}$

25. Add the following:

$$\frac{1}{10} + \frac{17}{100} + \frac{39}{1,000}$$

26. Add the following:

$$\frac{3}{10} + \frac{47}{100} + \frac{241}{1,000}$$

27. Subtract the following:

$$\frac{32}{100} - \frac{8}{1,000}$$

28. Subtract the following:

$$\frac{3}{10} - \frac{4}{1,000}$$

For Problems 29 to 50, express your answers as a proper fraction or a mixed number, where appropriate.

29. Peter spent $\frac{5}{12}$ of his money on rent and $\frac{1}{4}$ on food. What fraction of his money did he spend on rent and food?

30. Alan walked $\frac{3}{5}$ km to his friend's house and from there, he walked another $\frac{3}{4}$ km to his school. How far did Alan walk?

31. Last night, Amy spent $3\frac{1}{6}$ hours on her math project and $2\frac{3}{10}$ hours on her design project. How much time did she spend on both projects altogether?

32. A bag contains $2\frac{3}{5}$ kg of red beans and $1\frac{1}{8}$ kg of green beans. What is the total weight of the bag?

33. Thomas baked a $2\frac{1}{2}$ pound cake. He gave $1\frac{5}{8}$ pounds of it to his friend, Yan. How much was left?

34. Alexander bought $4\frac{2}{5}$ litres of milk and drank $1\frac{2}{3}$ litres of it. How much was left?

35. Sarah had $\frac{3}{4}$ kg of cheese. She used $\frac{2}{7}$ kg of the cheese while baking. How many kilograms of cheese was left?

36. Cassidy bought $\frac{5}{8}$ litres of olive oil and used $\frac{1}{3}$ litres of the oil while cooking. What quantity of olive oil was left?

37. David spent $\frac{7}{10}$ of his money on toys and $\frac{1}{3}$ of the remainder on food. What fraction of his money was spent on food?

38. Mary spent $\frac{2}{5}$ of her money on a school bag. She then spent $\frac{1}{3}$ of the remainder on shoes. What fraction of her money was spent on shoes?

39. After selling $\frac{2}{5}$ of its textbooks, a bookstore had 810 books left. How many textbooks were in the bookstore initially?

40. Rose travelled $\frac{3}{5}$ of her journey by car and the remaining 20 km by bus. How far did she travel by car?

41. Cheng can walk $5\frac{1}{4}$ km in $1\frac{1}{2}$ hours. How many kilometres can he walk in 1 hour?

42. $2\frac{3}{4}$ litres of juice weighs $4\frac{2}{3}$ kg. Find the weight (in kilograms) of 1 litre of juice.

43. A chain of length $\frac{7}{8}$ metres is cut into pieces measuring $\frac{1}{16}$ metres each. How many pieces are there?

44. A cake that weighs $\frac{2}{3}$ kg is cut into slices weighing $\frac{1}{12}$ kg each. How many slices are there?

45. A bottle of medicine contains 80 mg of medicine. Each dose of the medicine is $\frac{2}{5}$ mg. How many doses are there in the bottle?

46. A box of cereal contains 917 grams of cereal. How many bowls of cereal will there be if each serving is $32\frac{3}{4}$ grams?

47. Out of 320 bulbs, $\frac{1}{20}$ of the bulbs are defective. How many of them are not defective?

48. If $\frac{4}{15}$ of the 1,800 students enrolled for a mathematics course, how many students did not enroll for the course?

49. The product of two numbers is 9. If one number is $3\frac{3}{4}$, what is the other number?

50. If a wire that is $42\frac{3}{4}$ cm long is cut into several $2\frac{1}{4}$ cm equal pieces, how many pieces would exist?

2.3 | Decimal Numbers

When a number is less than 1, it is usually expressed in its decimal form with 0 in its ones place. For example, .25 is expressed as 0.25.

Introduction

Decimal numbers are used in situations that require more precision than which whole numbers can provide. We use decimal numbers more frequently in our daily lives than whole numbers - money is a good example.

A decimal number may have both a whole number portion and a decimal portion. The whole number portion of a decimal comprises of those digits to the left of the decimal point. The decimal portion is represented by the digits to the right of the decimal point.

For example,

$$\underbrace{345}_{\text{Whole Number Portion}}.\overbrace{678}^{\text{Decimal Number Portion}}$$

The decimal number portion can also be written as a fraction: $\frac{678}{1,000}$.

When a decimal number is expressed as a fraction, the denominator of the fraction is expressed as a power of 10 (10, 100, 1000, etc.).

When decimal numbers are expressed as a fraction using powers of 10, do not reduce them to their lowest terms.

For example, $\frac{678}{1,000}$ if reduced to $\frac{339}{500}$ is no longer expressed as a power of 10.

Similarilty, $1.2 = 1\frac{2}{10}$

$23.45 = 23\frac{45}{100}$

$75.378 = 75\frac{378}{1,000}$

Every whole number can be written as a decimal number by placing a decimal point to the right of the units digits.

For example,

5 in **decimal form** is 5. or 5.0 or 5.00

The number of decimal places in a decimal number depends on the number of digits writen to the right of the decimal point.

For example,

5.	No decimal place
5.0	One decimal place
5.00	Two decimal places
1.250	Three decimal places
2.0050	Four decimal places

Types of Decimal Numbers

There are three different types of decimal numbers.

(i) Non-repeating, terminating decimals numbers:

For example,

0.2

0.3767

0.86452

(ii) Repeating, non-terminating decimal numbers:

For example,

0.222222.... $(0.\overline{2})$

0.255555.... $(0.2\overline{5})$

0.867867.... $(0.\overline{867})$

(iii) Non-repeating, non-terminating decimal numbers:

For example,

0.453740....

π (3.141592...)

e (2.718281...)

Place Value of Decimal Numbers

The position of each digit in a decimal number determines the place value of the digit. Exhibit 2.3 illustrates the place value of the five-digit decimal number: 0.35796.

The place value of each digit is found by decreasing powers of 10, as shown in Table 2.3.

Table 2.3 **Place Value Chart of Decimal Numbers**

$10^{-1} = \frac{1}{10}$	$10^{-2} = \frac{1}{100}$	$10^{-3} = \frac{1}{1,000}$	$10^{-4} = \frac{1}{10,000}$	$10^{-5} = \frac{1}{100,000}$
0.1	0.01	0.001	0.0001	0.00001
Tenths	Hundredths	Thousandths	Ten-thousandths	Hundred-thousandths

Example of the decimal number written in its **standard form:**

0.	3	5	7	9	6

The above can be written in **expanded form** as follows:

0.3 + 0.05 + 0.007 + 0.0009 + 0.00006

Or

3 tenths + 5 hundredths + 7 thousandths + 9 ten-thousandths + 6 hundred-thousandths

Or

$$\frac{3}{10} + \frac{5}{100} + \frac{7}{1,000} + \frac{9}{10,000} + \frac{6}{100,000}$$

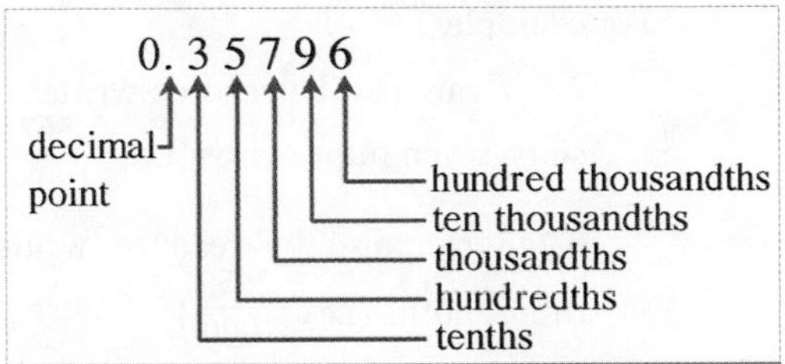

Exhibit 2.3 Place Value of a Five-Digit Decimal Number

Reading and Writing Decimal Numbers

Follow these steps to read and write decimal numbers:

Step 1: Read or write the numbers to the left of a decimal point as a whole number.

Step 2: Read or write the decimal point as "and".

Step 3: Read or write the number to the right of the decimal point also as a whole number, but followed by the name of the place occupied by the digit on the far right.

For example 745.023 is written in word form as:

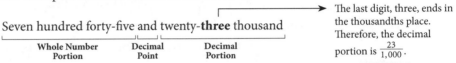

Seven hundred forty-five and twenty-**three** thousand

Whole Number Portion | **Decimal Point** | **Decimal Portion**

The last digit, three, ends in the thousandths place. Therefore, the decimal portion is $\frac{23}{1,000}$.

There are other ways of reading and writing decimal numbers as noted below.

(i) Use the word "point" to indicate the decimal point and thereafter, read or write each digit individually.

For example,

25.67 can also be read or written as: Twenty-five point six seven.

0.245 can also be read or written as: Zero point two four five.

(ii) Use the word "point" indicating the decimal point and thereafter, read or write the decimal potion similar to a whole number.

For example,

25.67 can also be read or written as: Twenty-five point sixty-seven.

0.245 can also be read or written as: Zero point two hundred forty-five

(iii) Ignore the decimal point of the decimal number and read or write the number as a whole number and include the place occupied by the digit on the far right of the decimal number.

For example,

25.67 can also be read or written as: Two thousand, five hundred sixty-seven hundredths (i.e., $\frac{2,567}{100}$).

0.245 can also be read or written as: Two hundred forty-five thousandths (i.e., $\frac{245}{1,000}$).

Note: The above three representations are not used in the examples and /or exercise questions within this chapter.

Use of Hyphens to Express Numbers in Word Form

- A hyphen (-) is used to express the two digit numbers, 21 to 29, 31 to 39, 41 to 49, … 91 to 99, in each group in their word form.
- A hyphen (-) is also used while expressing the place value portion of a decimal number, such as ten-thousandths, hundred-thousandths, ten-millionths, hundred-millionths, and so on.

The following examples illustrate the use of hyphens to express numbers in their word form:

0.893	Eight hundred ninety-three thousandths.
0.0506	Five hundred six ten-thousandths.
0.00145	One hundred forty-five hundred-thousandths.

Example 2.3-a

Writing in Decimal Notation

Express the following in decimal notation:

(i) Two hundred and thirty-five hundredths

(ii) Three and seven tenths

(iii) Eighty-four thousandths

Solution

(i)

Whole Number Portion		Decimal Portion
Two hundred	and	thirty-five hundredths
		The last digit, five, ends in the hundredths place. ($\frac{35}{100}$ = 0.35)
200	.	35

Therefore, the number is written in decimal form as **200.35.**

(ii)

Whole Number Portion		Decimal Portion
Three	and	seven tenths
		The last digit, seven, ends in the tenths place. (i.e., the decimal portion is $\frac{7}{10} = 0.7$)
3	.	7

Therefore, the number is written in decimal form as **3.7**.

(iii)

Whole Number Portion		Decimal Portion
		Eighty-four thousandths
There is no whole number portion. Therefore, it is zero.		The last digit, four, ends in the thousandths place. (i.e., the decimal portion is $\frac{84}{1{,}000} = 0.084$)
0	.	084

Therefore, the number is written in decimal form as **0.084**.

Example 2.3-b

Writing Decimal Numbers in Word Form

Express the following decimal numbers in their word form:

(i) 23.125

(ii) 7.43

(iii) 20.3

(iv) 0.2345

Solution

(i) 23.125

The last digit, 5, is in the thousandths place.

$23\frac{125}{1{,}000}$

Twenty-three and one hundred twenty-five thousandths

(ii) 7.43

The last digit, 3, is in the hundredths place.

$7\frac{43}{100}$

Seven and forty-three hundredths

(iii) 20.3

The last digit, 3, is in the tenths place.

$20\frac{3}{10}$

Twenty and three tenths

(iv) 0.2345

The last digit, 5, is in the ten-thousandths place.

$$\frac{2,345}{10,000}$$

Two thousand three hundred forty-five ten-thousandths

Rounding Decimal Numbers

Rounding Decimal Numbers to the Nearest Whole Number, Tenth, Hundredth, etc.

Rounding decimal numbers refers to changing the value of the decimal number to the nearest whole number, tenth, hundredth, thousandth, etc. It is also referred to as "rounding to a specific number of decimal places", indicating the number of decimal places that will be left when the rounding is complete.

For example,

Rounding to the nearest whole number is the same as rounding without any decimals.

Rounding to the nearest tenth is the same as rounding to one decimal place.

Rounding to the nearest hundredth is the same as rounding to two decimal places.

Rounding to the nearest cent refers to rounding the amount to the nearest hundredth or to two decimal places.

Rules for Rounding Decimal Numbers

Step 1: Identify the digit to be rounded (this is the place value for which the rounding is required).

Step 2: If the digit to the immediate right of the required rounding digit is less than 5 (0, 1, 2, 3, 4), do not change the value of the rounding digit.

If the digit to the immediate right of the required rounding digit is 5 or greater than 5 (5, 6, 7, 8, 9), increase the value of the rounding digit by one (round up by one number).

Step 3: After Step 2, drop all digits that are to the right of the rounding digit.

Example 2.3-c **Rounding Decimal Numbers**

Round the following decimal numbers to the indicated place value:

(i) 268.143 to the nearest hundredth

(ii) $489.677 to the nearest cent

(iii) $39.9985 to the nearest cent

Solution

(i) Rounding 268.143 to the nearest hundredth

Identify the rounding digit in the hundredths place:
268.**143** (4 is the digit in the hundredths place).

The digit to the immediate right of the rounding digit is less than 5; therefore, do not change the value of the rounding digit. Drop all of the digits to the right of the rounding digit, which will result in 268.14.

Therefore, 268.143 rounded to the nearest hundredth (or to two decimal places) is 268.14.

(ii) Rounding $489.677 to the nearest cent

Identify the rounding digit in the hundredths place:
$489.677 (7 is the digit in the hundredths place).

The digit to the immediate right of the rounding digit is greater than 5; therefore, increase the value of the rounding digit by one, from 7 to 8, and drop all digits that are to the right of the rounding digit, which will result in $489.68.

Therefore, $489.677 rounded to the nearest cent (or to two decimal places) is $489.68.

(iii) Rounding $39.9985 to the nearest cent

Identify the rounding digit in the hundredths place:
$39.9985 (9 is the digit in the hundredths place).

The digit to the immediate right of the rounding digit is greater than 5; therefore, increase the value of the rounding digit by one, from 9 to 10, carrying the one to the tenths place, then to the ones, and then to the tens, to increase 3 to 4. Finally, drop all digits that are to the right of the hundredths place.

Therefore, $39.9985 rounded to the nearest cent (or to two decimal places) is $40.00.

2.3 | Exercises

Answers to odd-numbered problems are available online.

For Problems 1 to 8, express in decimal notation.

1. a. $\frac{6}{10}$ b. $\frac{7}{1000}$

2. a. $\frac{9}{1000}$ b. $\frac{41}{1000}$

3. a. $\frac{12}{100}$ b. $\frac{29}{1000}$

4. a. $\frac{75}{100}$ b. $\frac{3}{10}$

5. a. Eighty-seven and two tenths
   b. Three and four hundredths

6. a. Thirty-five and seven tenths
   b. Nine and seven hundredths
7. a. Four hundred one ten-thousandths
   b. Eighty-nine and six hundred twenty-five ten-thousandths
8. a. Fifty-two and three hundred five thousandths
   b. Two hundred eight-thousandths

For Problems 9 to 12, express in standard form.

9. a. One thousand, seven hundred eighty-seven and twenty-five thousandths
   b. Four hundred twelve and sixty-five hundredths
10. a. Nine hundred eighty-seven and twenty hundredths
    b. Seven thousand, two hundred sixty and fifteen thousandths
11. a. One million, six hundred thousand, two hundred
    b. Twenty-three and five tenths
12. a. Six million, two hundred seventeen thousand, five hundred
    b. Twenty-nine hundredths

For Problems 13 to 16, express the decimal numbers in their word form.

13. a. 42.55 b. 734.125
14. a. 7.998 b. 12.77
15. a. 0.25 b. 9.5
16. a. 0.987 b. 311.2
17. Which of the following is the largest number?
    0.034, 0.403, 0.043, 0.304
18. Which of the following is the smallest number?
    1.014, 1.011, 1.104, 1.041

For Problems 19 to 24, round the numbers to one decimal place (nearest tenth).

19. a. 415.1654. b. 7.8725
20. a. 264.1545 b. 25.5742
21. a. 24.1575 b. 112.1255
22. a. 10.3756 b. 0.9753
23. a. 14.3585 b. 0.0645
24. a. 181.1267 b. 19.6916
25. Round the decimal numbers in Problem 19 to two decimal places (nearest hundredth).
26. Round the decimal numbers in Problem 20 to two decimal places (nearest hundredth).
27. Round the decimal numbers in Problem 21 to three decimal places (nearest thousandth).
28. Round the decimal numbers in Problem 22 to three decimal places (nearest thousandth).
29. Round the decimal numbers in Problem 23 to two decimal places (nearest hundredth).
30. Round the decimal numbers in Problem 24 to three decimal places (nearest thousandth).

2.4 | Arithmetic Operations with Decimal Numbers

Addition of Decimal Numbers

Addition of decimal numbers (finding the total or sum) refers to combining numbers. It is similar to adding whole numbers.

To add one decimal number to another decimal number, start by writing the numbers one under the other by aligning the decimal points of these numbers. Add zeros to the right to have the same number of decimal places, if necessary, and draw a horizontal line.

Starting from the right, add all the numbers in that column and continue towards the left.

If the total is less than 10, write the total under the horizontal line. If the total is 10 or more, write the 'ones' digit of the total under the horizontal line and write the tens digit above the tens column. Follow the procedure for each column going right to left. Write the decimal point in the answer.

Example 2.4-a **Adding Decimal Numbers**

Perform the following additions:

(i) 25.125 + 7.14

(ii) 741.87 + 135.456

(iii) 127 + 68.8 + 669.95

Solution

(i) 25.125 + 7.14

$$\begin{array}{r} {}^{1} \\ 25.125 \\ +7.140 \\ \hline 32.265 \end{array}$$

← Add a zero to match the number of decimal places. (7.140)

(ii) 741.87 + 135.456

$$\begin{array}{r} {}^{1}\,{}^{1} \\ 741.870 \\ +\,135.456 \\ \hline 877.326 \end{array}$$

← Add a zero to match the number of decimal places. (741.870)

(iii) 127 + 68.8 + 669.95

$$\begin{array}{r} {}^{1}\,{}^{2}\,{}^{1} \\ 127.00 \\ 68.80 \\ +\,669.95 \\ \hline 865.75 \end{array}$$

← Add two zeros to match the number of decimal places. (127.00)

← Add a zero to match the number of decimal places. (68.80)

Subtraction of Decimal Numbers

Subtraction of decimal numbers refers to finding the difference between decimal numbers. It is similar to subtracting whole numbers.

To subtract one number from another number, start by writing the numbers one under the other by aligning the decimal points of these numbers. Add zeros to the right to have the same number of decimal places, if necessary, and draw a horizontal line. Ensure that the number that is being subtracted from is in the top row and that the number that is being subtracted is below.

Starting from the right, subtract the bottom number from the top number. If the top digit is greater than the bottom digit, subtract and write the number under the line. If the top digit is smaller than the bottom digit, borrow one ten from the digit to the left of this top digit for an additional 10 ones. Add this to the digit on the top, find the difference, and write the difference under the horizontal line. Follow the procedure for each column going right to left. Write the decimal point in the answer.

Example 2.4-b **Subtracting Decimal Numbers**

Perform the following subtractions:

(i) Subtract 29.02 from 135.145

(ii) Subtract 38.7 from 457

Solution

(i) Subtract 29.02 from 135.145

$$\begin{array}{r} {\scriptstyle 2\;15} \\ 1\cancel{3}\cancel{5}.145 \\ -\ 29.020 \\ \hline 106.125 \end{array}$$

(ii) Subtract 38.7 from 457

$$\begin{array}{r} {\scriptstyle 4\;\overset{16}{6}\;\;10} \\ 4\cancel{5}\cancel{7}.\cancel{0} \\ -\ \ 38.7 \\ \hline 418.3 \end{array}$$

Multiplication of Decimal Numbers

When multiplying decimal numbers, line up the numbers on the right without aligning the decimal points. Multiply the number assuming that there are no decimal points; i.e., multiply each digit on the top number by each digit in the bottom number and add the products, similar to the process of multiplying whole numbers. Count the total number of decimal places in the numbers that are being multiplied. Place the decimal point in the answer starting at the right and moving towards the left by the total number of decimal places counted.

Example 2.4-c **Multiplying Decimal Numbers**

Multiply 12.56 and 1.8.

Solution

$$\begin{array}{r l} 12.56 & \text{(2 Decimal places)} \\ \times \quad 1.8 & \text{(1 Decimal places)} \\ \hline 10048 & \\ 12560 & \\ \hline 22.608 & \text{(3 Decimal places)} \end{array} \quad \text{Total of 3 Decimals places}$$

Therefore, the result from multiplying 12.56 and 1.8 is 22.608.

Division of Decimal Numbers

When dividing a decimal number, if the divisor is not a whole number, convert it to a whole number by moving the decimal point to the right and moving the decimal point in the dividend the same number of places.

Divide as usual. Add zeros to the right of the last digit of the dividend and keep dividing until no remainder or a repeating pattern shows up in the quotient.

Example 2.4-d

Dividing Decimal Numbers

Perform the following divisions:

(i) Divide 8.25 by 0.6

(ii) Divide: 0.166 by 0.03

Solution

(i) Divide 8.25 by 0.6

Step 1: $8.25 \div 0.6 = \dfrac{8.25}{0.6}$ Since the denominator contains one decimal place, move the decimal point by one decimal place to the right for both the numerator and the denominator.

$$= \frac{82.5}{6}$$

Step 2:

$$\begin{array}{r} 13.75 \\ 6\overline{)82.50} \\ -6 \\ \hline 22 \\ -18 \\ \hline 45 \\ -42 \\ \hline 30 \\ -30 \\ \hline 0 \end{array}$$

Position the decimal point within the quotient directly above the decimal point within the dividend.

30 ← Add a Zero

Therefore, when 8.25 is divided by 0.6, the quotient is 13.75 and the remainder is 0.

(ii) Divide: 0.166 by 0.03

Step 1: $0.166 \div 0.03 = \frac{0.166}{0.03} = \frac{16.6}{3}$

Since the denominator contains two decimal places, move the decimal point by two decimal places to the right for both the numerator and the denominator.

Step 2:

$$\begin{array}{r} 5.533 \\ 3\overline{)16.600} \\ -15\downarrow \\ \hline 16 \\ -15 \\ \hline 10 \\ -9 \\ \hline 10 \\ -9 \\ \hline 1 \end{array}$$

Position the decimal point within the quotient directly above the decimal point within the dividend.

10 ← Add a Zero

10 ← Add a Zero

> Repeating decimals are usually represented by a horizontal bar on top of the repeating decimal; i.e., 5.533333 is written as $5.5\overline{3}$

Therefore, when 0.166 is divided by 0.03, the quoitent is $5.5\overline{3}$ and the remainder is 1.

2.4 | Exercises

Answers to odd-numbered problems are available online.

For Problems 1 to 4, perform the additions.

1. 927.896 + 659.50 + 128.649
2. 619.985 + 52.82 + 3.187
3. 74 + 129.258 + 0.32 + 666.015
4. 17 + 3.48 + 0.278 + 78.24
5. Find the sum of the following numbers:
   a. Twenty and ninety-five hundredths
   b. Two hundred and seventy-two thousandths
   c. Nineteen and nine tenths
6. Find the sum of the following numbers:
   a. Six and thirty-nine thousandths
   b. Eighty and fourteen hundredths
   c. Sixteen and eight tenths.

For Problems 7 to 10, perform the subtractions.

7. 423.92 – 185.728
8. 7.18 – 9.555
9. 29.28 – 13.4
10. 15.7 – 7.92
11. Subtract three hundred five and thirty-nine hundredths from seven hundred twenty and four tenths.
12. Subtract eight hundred twenty and four hundredths from one thousand, one hundred one and six tenths.

For Problems 13 to 18, perform the multiplications.

13. 137.89 and 5.4
14. 189.945 and 6.3
15. 62.095 and 4.18
16. 92.74 and 3.25
17. 0.43 and 0.8
18. 0.59 and 0.9

For Problems 19 to 24, perform the divisions.

19. 67.78 by 9
20. 261.31 by 7
21. 732.6 by 8
22. 413.9 by 6
23. 14.6 by 0.6
24. 9.155 by 0.7

For Problems 25 to 32, formulate arithmetic expressions and evaluate.

25. $248.76 more than what amount is $627.4?
26. $45.27 more than what amount is $90.75?
27. $235.62 is $115.75 more than what amount?
28. $30.75 is $15.89 more than what amount?
29. $634.25 less than what amount is $412.78?
30. $38.89 less than what amount is $25.67?
31. $252.34 is $297.98 less than what amount?
32. $52.43 is $23.95 less than what amount?
33. The cost of an item is $88.46. If you gave $90 to the cashier, how much change would you receive?
34. The cost of an item is $125.69. If Arun gave $150 to the cashier, how much change would Arun receive?
35. Bill saved $578.50 this week. He saved $124.85 more last week than this week. How much did Bill save during the 2-week period?
36. Last week Carol spent $96.75 more on food than on transport. She spent $223.15 on food. How much did Carol spend on transport?
37. The normal selling price of an item is $237.75. At a sale, Dave paid $49.89 less for that item. How much did Dave pay for that item?
38. A car driver filled gas when the odometer reading was 39,894.4 km. The odometer reading now is 35,894.9 km. How many kilometres did the driver travel, rounded to the nearest kilometre?
39. After spending $38.96 on toys and $1.75 on wrapping paper, Ann still had $45.75. How much money did Ann have initially?
40. After paying $515.09 for a car lease and $379.92 for property tax, my bank balance was $675.45. How much money did I have initially?
41. Simon bought a camera that was on sale for $799.99. He agreed to pay $70.35 every month for 12 months. How much more money than the sale price did Simon pay for the camera?
42. Andy bought a TV that was on sale for $2,249.95. He agreed to pay $130.45 every month for 18 months. How much more money than the sale price did Andy pay for the TV?
43. A salesperson earns a salary of $725.35 every week. During the past 3 weeks, he also received commissions of $375.68, $578.79, and $338.57. Calculate his total income for the past 3 weeks.

44. I leased a car on a 4-year term at $694.38 per month. At the end of the lease period, I paid an additional $18,458.74 to purchase the car. Find the total amount I paid for the car.
45. John bought 2 shirts for $20.95 each and 3 pairs of pants for $34.55 each. He gave $200 to the cashier. Calculate the balance he should receive from the cashier.
46. I bought 3 kg of walnuts for $8.69 per kg and 4 kg of almonds for $7.72 per kg. I gave the cashier a $100 bill. How much balance should I receive from the cashier?
47. A string that measured 0.875 m was cut into pieces of 0.0625 m each. How many pieces did this result in?
48. A cake that weighed 0.82 kg was cut into slices that weighed 0.1025 kg each. How many slices did this result in?
49. Marion bought 3 dresses at $22.49 per dress and 2 pairs of shoes at $14.99 per pair. She gave a $100 bill to the cashier. What change should she expect to receive from the cashier?
50. Gilbert bought 2 kg of grapes at $3.29 per kg and 1.5 kg of strawberries at $5.99 per kg. He gave a $20 bill to the cashier. How much should he expect to receive in change from the cashier?

2.5 | Arithmetic Operations with Fractions and Decimal Numbers

Converting Decimal Numbers to Fractions

It is possible to convert **non-repeating, terminating** decimal numbers (e.g.: 0.567) and **repeating decimal numbers** (e.g.: 0.333333...) to fractions. However, there is no exact equivalent fraction for **non-repeating, non-terminating** decimal numbers (0.837508...).

Converting Non-Repeating, Terminating Decimal Numbers to Fractions

Any non-repeating, terminating decimal number can be converted to a fraction by following these steps:

Step 1: Count the number of decimal places.

Step 2: Move the decimal point by that many places to the right and divide the answer by 10 for every number of places moved; i.e., if there is 1 decimal place, divide by 10, if 2 decimal places, divide by 100, if 3 decimal places, divide by 1000, etc.

Step 3: Simplify (or reduce) the fraction.

Example 2.5-a **Converting Non-Repeating, Terminating Decimal Numbers to Fractions**

Convert the following decimal numbers to their fractional equivalent:

(i) 3.74 (ii) 0.015

Solution

(i) Convert 3.75 to its fractional equivalent

$= 3.\underbrace{75}$ — Contains two decimal places. So move two decimal places to the right.

$= \dfrac{375}{100}$ — Dividing by 25 and simplifying,

$= \dfrac{375^{\div 25}}{100_{\div 25}} = \dfrac{15}{4}$

Therefore, 3.75 converted to its fractional equivalent is $\dfrac{15}{4}$.

(ii) Convert 0.015 to its fractional equivalent

$= 0.\underbrace{015}$ — Contains three decimal places. So move three decimal places to the right.

$= \dfrac{15}{1,000} = \dfrac{15^{\div 5}}{1,000^{\div 5}}$ — Dividing by 5 and simplifying,

$= \dfrac{3}{200}$

Therefore, 0.015 converted to its fractional equivalent is $\dfrac{3}{200}$.

Converting Repeating Decimal Numbers to Fractions

Any repeating decimal number can be converted to a fraction by following the procedure given in the following examples.

Example 2.5-b **Converting Repeating Decimal Numbers to Fractions**

Convert 0.77777... to a fraction.

Solution

Let 0.77777... be equal to a fraction x.

Therefore,

(a) $x = 0.777777... = 0.\bar{7}$ — Multiplying both sides by 10,

(b) $10x = 7.777777... = 7.\bar{7}$

Subtracting (a) from (b) to obtain,

$$10x - x = 7.\bar{7} - 7.\bar{7}$$

$$9x = 7$$

$$x = \frac{7}{9}$$

Therefore, $0.777777... = \dfrac{7}{9}$.

Example 2.5-c **Converting Repeating Decimal Numbers to Fractions**

Convert 0.655555... to a fraction.

Solution

Let 0.655555... be equal to a fraction x.

Therefore,

(a) $x = 0.655555... = 0.6\overline{5}$ Multiplying both sides by 10,

(b) $10x = 6.555555... = 6.\overline{5}$ Multiplying both sides by 10,

(c) $100x = 65.55555... = 65.\overline{5}$

Subtracting (b) from (c) to obtain,

$100x - 10x = 65.\overline{5} - 6.\overline{5}$

$90x = 59$

$x = \dfrac{59}{90}$

Therefore, $0.65555... = \dfrac{59}{90}$.

Example 2.5-d **Converting Repeating Decimal Numbers to Fractions**

Convert 0.353535... to a fraction.

Solution

Let 0.353535... be equal to a fraction x.

(a) $x = 0.3535... = 0.\overline{35}$ Multiplying both sides by 100,

(b) $100x = 35.3535... = 35.\overline{35}$

Subtract (a) from (b) to obtain,

$100x - x = 35.\overline{35} - 0.\overline{35}$

$90x = 35$

$x = \dfrac{35}{90}$

Therefore, $0.3535... = \dfrac{35}{90}$.

From examples 2.5(a) to 2.5(d), you learned that it is possible to convert non-repeating, terminating decimal numbers (e.g., 0.015) and repeating decimal numbers (e.g., $0.6\overline{5}$) into fractions. Therefore, such decimal numbers are also called **rational numbers**.

Irrational Numbers are numbers that cannot be represented by $\frac{a}{b}$, where 'a' and 'b' are integers and $b \neq 0$.

The numbers that cannot be expressed as fractions are called **irrational numbers** (e.g., $\sqrt{2}$, π, $\sqrt{7}$, e). These rational numbers and non-rational numbers are called **'Real Numbers'** in the number system.

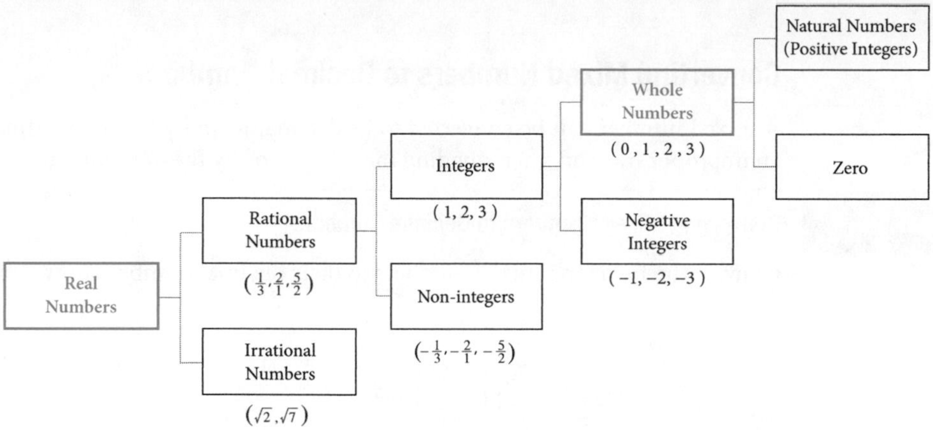

Converting Fractions to Decimal Numbers

Converting Proper and Improper Fractions to Decimal Numbers

A proper or improper fraction can be converted to its equivalent decimal number by dividing the numerator by the denominator.

Example 2.5-e **Converting Proper and Improper Fractions to Decimal Numbers**

Convert the following fractions to their decimal equivalents:

(i) $\frac{3}{8}$ (ii) $\frac{15}{11}$

Solution

(i) $\frac{3}{8}$

$= 3 \div 8$

$= 0.375$

```
     .375
 8 | 3.000
     24
      60
      56
       40
       40
        0
```

Therefore, 0.375 is the decimal equivalent of $\frac{3}{8}$.

(ii) $\frac{15}{11}$

$= 15 \div 11$

$= 1.3636....$

$= 1.\overline{36}$

```
      1.3636
 11 | 15.0000
      11
       40
       33
        70
        66
         40
         33
          70
          66
           4
```

Therefore, $1.\overline{36}$ is the decimal equivalent of $\frac{15}{11}$.

Converting Mixed Numbers to Decimal Numbers

A mixed number can be converted to its decimal form by first converting it to an improper fraction, then dividing the numerator by the denominator.

Example 2.5-f

Converting Mixed Numbers to Decimal Numbers

Convert the following mixed numbers to their decimal number equivalents:

(i) $3\frac{5}{2}$ (ii) $11\frac{3}{7}$

Solution

(i) $3\frac{5}{2} = \frac{3(2)+5}{2} = \frac{11}{2} = 5.5$

(ii) $11\frac{3}{7} = \frac{11(7)+3}{7} = \frac{80}{7} = 11.428571... = 11.43$

Powers of Fractions and Decimal Numbers

Powers of fractions and decimal numbers are expressed the same way as whole numbers. The fractions and decimal numbers are usually writtten within brackets when they are raised to a power.

For example, $\left(\frac{2}{3}\right)^2$ is read as two-thirds squared.

Exponents indicate the number of times the base is to be multiplied.

This means that $\left(\frac{2}{3}\right)$ is used as a factor 2 times.

i.e., $\left(\frac{2}{3}\right)^2 = \frac{2}{3} \times \frac{2}{3} = \frac{4}{9}$

Similarly, $(0.12)^3$ is read as twelve hundredths raised to the power 3.

This means that (0.12) is used as a factor 3 times.

i.e., $(0.12)^3 = (0.12)\,(0.12)\,(0.12) = 0.001728$.

A mixed number that is raised to a power is evaluated by first converting it into an improper fraction and then following the same procedure explained earlier.

For example,

$\left(1\frac{2}{3}\right)^4$ is evaluated by first converting $\left(1\frac{2}{3}\right)^4$ into improper fraction form.

i.e., $\left(1\frac{2}{3}\right)^4 = \left(\frac{5}{3}\right)^4$ Then, expand by using $\left(\frac{5}{3}\right)$ as a factor 4 times.

$= \left(\frac{5}{3}\right)\left(\frac{5}{3}\right)\left(\frac{5}{3}\right)\left(\frac{5}{3}\right)$

$= \frac{625}{81}$

Example 2.5-g

Evaluating Powers of Fractions and Decimal Numbers

Evaluate the following:

(i) $\left(\frac{4}{5}\right)^4$ (ii) $\left(1\frac{1}{2}\right)^5$ (iii) $(1.12)^3$

Solution

(i) $\left(\frac{4}{5}\right)^4 = \left(\frac{4}{5}\right)\left(\frac{4}{5}\right)\left(\frac{4}{5}\right)\left(\frac{4}{5}\right) = \frac{256}{625}$

(ii) $\left(1\frac{1}{2}\right)^5 = \left(\frac{3}{2}\right)^5 = \left(\frac{3}{2}\right)\left(\frac{3}{2}\right)\left(\frac{3}{2}\right)\left(\frac{3}{2}\right)\left(\frac{3}{2}\right) = \frac{243}{32}$

(iii) $(1.12)^3 = (1.12)\ (1.12)\ (1.12) = 1.404928$

Roots of Fractions and Decimal Numbers

In this chapter you will learn about only the **square roots** of **fractions** and **decimals** that have exact roots.

Square roots of fractions are calculated the same way as the square roots of whole numbers but the numerators and denominators are evaluated separately. The answers are expressed in simplified or reduced form.

$\sqrt{\frac{a}{b}}$ is equal to $\frac{\sqrt{a}}{\sqrt{b}}$

For example,

$\sqrt{\frac{9}{16}}$ is the same as $\frac{\sqrt{9}}{\sqrt{16}} = \frac{3}{4}$

Finding roots of decimals becomes easy if the decimal number is converted to a fraction having an even power of ten; i.e., 100, 1,000, etc., and then following the procedure for finding the square roots of fractions.

For example,

$$\sqrt{0.25} = \sqrt{\frac{25}{100}} = \frac{\sqrt{25}}{\sqrt{100}} = \frac{5}{10} = \frac{1}{2} \text{ or } 0.5$$

Example 2.5-h **Evaluating Square Roots of Fractions and Decimal Numbers**

Evaluate the following:

(i) $\sqrt{\frac{25}{144}}$ (ii) $\sqrt{0.49}$

Solution

(i) $\sqrt{\frac{25}{144}} = \frac{\sqrt{25}}{\sqrt{144}} = \frac{5}{12}$

(ii) $\sqrt{0.49} = \sqrt{\frac{49}{100}} = \frac{\sqrt{49}}{\sqrt{100}} = \frac{7}{10} = 0.7$

Combined Order of Operations

The order of operations in evaluating expressions with more than one operation that you learned for whole numbers is also used for fractions and decimal numbers.

Step 1: Evaluate the expressions within the grouping symbols; brackets and radical signs are grouping symbols.

Step 2: Evaluate powers and roots.

Step 3: Perform multiplcation and division in order from left to right.

Step 4: Perform addition and subtraction in order from left to right.

Note: For mutliplication, division, powers, and roots of mixed numbers, they must be converted to improper fractions before proceeding with the Order of Operations.

Example 2.5-i

Evaluating Expressions Using Order of Operations

Evaluate the following:

(i) $\left(1\frac{1}{3}\right)^2 + \sqrt{\frac{5}{6} + \frac{20}{6}}$

(ii) $\left(\frac{2}{3}\right)^2 + \frac{1}{2}\left(4\frac{1}{2}\right)^2 \div \sqrt{81}$

(iii) $\left(\frac{4}{5}\right)^2 + \left(\frac{11}{9} + \sqrt{\frac{49}{81}}\right) \times \frac{3}{25}$

(iv) $\sqrt{1\frac{69}{100}} + \sqrt{0.09} + \sqrt{\frac{64}{25}}$

(v) $\left(1 + \frac{0.08}{4}\right)^2 - 1$

Solution

(i) $\left(1\frac{1}{3}\right)^2 + \sqrt{\frac{5}{6} + \frac{20}{6}}$

$= \left(\frac{4}{3}\right)^2 + \sqrt{\frac{25}{16}}$

$= \left(\frac{4}{3}\right)\left(\frac{4}{3}\right) + \frac{\sqrt{25}}{\sqrt{16}}$

$= \frac{16}{9} + \frac{5}{4}$

$= \frac{64 + 45}{36}$

$= \frac{109}{36}$

(ii) $\left(\frac{2}{3}\right)^2 + \frac{1}{2}\left(4\frac{1}{2}\right)^2 \div \sqrt{81}$

$= \left(\frac{2}{3}\right)\left(\frac{2}{3}\right) + \frac{1}{2}\left(\frac{9}{2}\right)\left(\frac{9}{2}\right) \div 9$

$= \frac{4}{9} + \frac{81}{8} \times \frac{1}{9}$

$= \frac{4}{9} + \frac{9}{8}$

$= \frac{32 + 81}{72}$

$= \frac{113}{72}$

(iii) $\left(\frac{4}{5}\right)^2 + \left(\frac{11}{9} + \sqrt{\frac{49}{81}}\right) \times \frac{3}{25}$

$= \left(\frac{4}{5}\right)^2 + \left(\frac{11}{9} + \frac{7}{9}\right) \times \frac{3}{25}$

$= \left(\frac{4}{5}\right)^2 + \frac{18}{9} \times \frac{3}{25}$

$= \left(\frac{4}{5}\right)\left(\frac{4}{5}\right) + 2 \times \frac{3}{25}$

$= \frac{16}{25} + \frac{6}{25}$

$= \frac{22}{25}$

(iv) $\sqrt{1\frac{69}{100}} + \sqrt{0.09} + \sqrt{\frac{64}{25}}$

$= \sqrt{\frac{169}{100}} + \sqrt{0.09} + \sqrt{\frac{64}{25}}$

$= \sqrt{\frac{169}{100}} + \sqrt{\frac{9}{100}} + \sqrt{\frac{64}{25}}$

$= \frac{\sqrt{169}}{\sqrt{100}} + \frac{\sqrt{9}}{\sqrt{100}} + \frac{\sqrt{64}}{\sqrt{25}}$

$= \frac{13}{10} + \frac{3}{10} + \frac{8}{5}$

$= \frac{13 + 3 + 16}{10}$

$= \frac{32}{10}$

$= \frac{16}{5}$

(v) $\left(1 + \frac{0.08}{4}\right)^2 - 1$

$= (1 + 0.02)^2 - 1$

$= (1.02)^2 - 1$

$= (1.02)(1.02) - 1$

$= 1.0404 - 1$

$= 0.0404$

2.5 | Exercises

Answers to odd-numbered problems are available online.

For Problems 1 to 4, express the decimal numbers in their word form.

1. a. 0.5 b. 0.007
2. a. 0.008 b. 0.04
3. a. 0.12 b. 0.029
4. a. 0.75 b. 0.3

For Problems 5 to 12, convert the decimal numbers to proper fractions and the proper fractions to decimal numbers.

5. Convert

	Decimal Number	Proper Fraction
a.	0.2	?
b.	?	$\frac{3}{4}$
c.	0.06	?

6. Convert

	Decimal Number	Proper Fraction
a.	0.26	?
b.	?	$\frac{41}{50}$
c.	0.92	?

7. Convert

	Decimal Number	Proper Fraction
a.	?	$\frac{9}{25}$
b.	0.004	?
c.	?	$\frac{7}{50}$

8. Convert

	Decimal Number	Proper Fraction
a.	?	$\frac{16}{25}$
b.	0.225	?
c.	?	$\frac{19}{20}$

9. Convert

	Decimal Number	Proper Fraction
a.	?	$\frac{1}{2}$
b.	0.4	?
c.	?	$\frac{3}{50}$

10. Convert

	Decimal Number	Proper Fraction
a.	?	$\frac{13}{20}$
b.	0.425	?
c.	?	$\frac{14}{25}$

11. Convert

	Decimal Number	Proper Fraction
a.	0.005	?
b.	?	$\frac{9}{25}$
c.	0.01	?

12. Convert

	Decimal Number	Proper Fraction
a.	0.66	?
b.	?	$\frac{43}{50}$
c.	0.78	?

For Problems 13 to 16, convert the decimal numbers to improper fractions and the improper fractions to decimal numbers.

13. Convert

	Decimal Number	Improper Fraction
a.	3.5	?
b.	?	$\frac{8}{5}$
c.	5.6	?

14. Convert

	Decimal Number	Improper Fraction
a.	7.2	?
b.	?	$\frac{37}{5}$
c.	8.4	?

15. Convert

	Decimal Number	Improper Fraction
a.	?	$\frac{101}{20}$
b.	6.8	?
c.	?	$\frac{11}{4}$

16. Convert

	Decimal Number	Improper Fraction
a.	?	$\frac{107}{50}$
b.	4.8	?
c.	?	$\frac{22}{4}$

For Problem 17 to 20, convert the decimal numbers to mixed numbers and the mixed numbers to decimal numbers.

17. Convert

	Decimal Number	Mixed Number
a.	2.25	?
b.	?	$1\frac{3}{4}$
c.	4.02	?

18. Convert

	Decimal Number	Mixed Number
a.	5.04	?
b.	?	$12\frac{3}{5}$
c.	14.025	?

19. Convert

	Decimal Number	Mixed Number
a.	?	$8\frac{7}{20}$
b.	16.005	?
c.	?	$15\frac{1}{2}$

20. Convert

	Decimal Number	Mixed Number
a.	?	$3\frac{5}{8}$
b.	4.75	?
c.	?	$5\frac{9}{20}$

For Problems 21 to 24, convert the repeating decimal numbers to proper fractions and the proper fractions to repeating decimal numbers.

21. Convert

	Decimal Number	Proper Fraction
a.	$0.\overline{6}$	?
b.	?	$0.2\overline{5}$
c.	$0.2\overline{5}$	?

22. Convert

	Decimal Number	Proper Fraction
a.	?	$\frac{2}{3}$
b.	$0.\overline{2}$	?
c.	?	$\frac{8}{11}$

23. Convert

	Decimal Number	Proper Fraction
a.	$0.\overline{27}$	?
b.	?	$\frac{4}{7}$
c.	$0.8\overline{3}$	?

24. Convert

	Decimal Number	Proper Fraction
a.	?	$\frac{5}{11}$
b.	$0.\overline{75}$	?
c.	?	$\frac{2}{7}$

For Problems 25 to 34 evaluate the powers of the fractions.

25. a. $\left(\frac{3}{5}\right)^2$ b. $\left(\frac{6}{7}\right)^2$

26. a. $\left(\frac{3}{4}\right)^2$ b. $\left(\frac{2}{9}\right)^2$

27. a. $\left(\frac{3}{4}\right)^3$ b. $\left(\frac{5}{3}\right)^4$

28. a. $\left(\frac{2}{7}\right)^3$ b. $\left(\frac{6}{5}\right)^4$

29. a. $\left(1\frac{1}{3}\right)^2$ b. $\left(3\frac{1}{2}\right)^3$

30. a. $\left(2\frac{1}{4}\right)^2$ b. $\left(1\frac{2}{3}\right)^3$

31. a. $\left(\frac{3}{5}\right)^2\left(\frac{2}{3}\right)^3$ b. $\left(\frac{3}{4}\right)^3\left(\frac{1}{6}\right)^2$

32. a. $\left(\frac{5}{2}\right)^3\left(\frac{1}{3}\right)^2$ b. $\left(\frac{3}{8}\right)^2\left(\frac{4}{3}\right)^3$

33. a. $\left(\frac{1}{4}\right)^2 \div \left(\frac{1}{8}\right)^2$ b. $\left(\frac{5}{3}\right)^2 \div \left(\frac{10}{9}\right)^2$

34. a. $\left(\frac{1}{2}\right)^2 \div \left(\frac{1}{3}\right)^2$ b. $\left(\frac{2}{3}\right)^2 \div \left(\frac{4}{9}\right)^2$

For Problems 35 to 44 evaluate the roots of the fractions.

35. a. $\sqrt{\frac{1}{9}}$ b. $\sqrt{\frac{1}{49}}$

36. a. $\sqrt{\frac{1}{16}}$ b. $\sqrt{\frac{1}{36}}$

37. a. $\sqrt{\frac{4}{25}}$ b. $\sqrt{\frac{81}{16}}$

38. a. $\sqrt{\frac{36}{100}}$ b. $\sqrt{\frac{9}{49}}$

39. a. $\sqrt{\frac{100}{121}}$ b. $\sqrt{\frac{1}{100}}$

40. a. $\sqrt{\frac{144}{81}}$ b. $\sqrt{\frac{1}{10,000}}$

41. a. $\sqrt{\frac{5}{9}+\frac{4}{9}}$ b. $\sqrt{\frac{2}{25}+\frac{14}{25}}$

42. a. $\sqrt{\frac{15}{36}+\frac{10}{36}}$ b. $\sqrt{\frac{1}{16}+\frac{8}{16}}$

43. a. $\sqrt{3\frac{1}{16}}$ b. $\sqrt{6\frac{1}{4}}$

44. a. $\sqrt{1\frac{11}{25}}$ b. $\sqrt{1\frac{21}{100}}$

For Problems 45 to 48, evaluate the powers of decimal numbers.

45. a. $(0.1)^3$ b. $(0.3)^2$
46. a. $(1.1)^3$ b. $(1.2)^3$
47. a. $(0.4)^2$ b. $(0.02)^3$
48. a. $(0.9)^2$ b. $(0.05)^3$

For Problems 49 to 54, evaluate the roots of decimal numbers.

49. a. $\sqrt{0.25}$ b. $\sqrt{0.49}$
50. a. $\sqrt{0.36}$ b. $\sqrt{0.64}$
51. a. $\sqrt{1.21}$ b. $\sqrt{1.69}$
52. a. $\sqrt{2.56}$ b. $\sqrt{1.44}$
53. a. $\sqrt{0.01}$ b. $\sqrt{0.0049}$
54. a. $\sqrt{0.09}$ b. $\sqrt{0.0004}$

For Problems 55 to 60, evaluate the expressions.

55. a. $\left(\frac{3}{5}\right)^2 + \left(1\frac{1}{5}\right)\left(\sqrt{144}\right)$ b. $\left(\frac{2}{5}\right)^2 + \left(\frac{3}{2}\right)^3$
56. a. $\left(\frac{4}{7}\right)^2 + \sqrt{\frac{3}{9} + \frac{1}{9}}$ b. $\left(\frac{3}{8}\right)^2 + \left(\frac{1}{2}\right)^3$
57. a. $\sqrt{4\frac{21}{25}} \times \left(\frac{5}{3}\right)^2$ b. $\left(\frac{1}{4}\right)^2 \div \left(\frac{1}{8}\right)^2$
58. a. $\sqrt{1\frac{9}{16}} \times \left(\frac{4}{5}\right)^2$ b. $\left(\frac{1}{3}\right)^2 \div \left(\frac{1}{6}\right)^2$
59. a. $(1.3)^2 \times \sqrt{0.04}$ b. $(0.1)^3 \div \sqrt{\frac{1}{100}}$
60. a. $(0.01)^2 \times \sqrt{0.09}$ b. $(0.5)^3 \div \sqrt{\frac{1}{100}}$

2 | Review Exercises

Answers to odd-numbered problems are available online.

1. Find the missing values:

   a. $\frac{6}{12} = \frac{?}{6} = \frac{24}{?}$ b. $\frac{12}{45} = \frac{?}{15} = \frac{16}{?}$

   c. $\frac{20}{25} = \frac{?}{5} = \frac{12}{?}$ d. $\frac{36}{48} = \frac{?}{36} = \frac{18}{?}$

2. Find the missing values:

   a. $\frac{9}{15} = \frac{?}{45} = \frac{15}{?}$ b. $\frac{18}{27} = \frac{?}{18} = \frac{10}{?}$

   c. $\frac{21}{35} = \frac{?}{25} = \frac{12}{?}$ d. $\frac{12}{28} = \frac{?}{70} = \frac{15}{?}$

3. Identify the pair(s) of fractions that are equal:

   a. $\frac{24}{21}$ and $\frac{11}{5}$ b. $\frac{20}{44}$ and $\frac{6}{15}$

   c. $\frac{18}{45}$ and $\frac{16}{4}$

4. Identify the pair(s) of fractions that are equal:

   a. $\frac{15}{18}$ and $\frac{30}{42}$ b. $\frac{21}{24}$ and $\frac{35}{40}$

   c. $\frac{40}{48}$ and $\frac{35}{42}$

5. Change the improper fractions to mixed numbers in simplest form:

   a. $\frac{15}{10}$ b. $\frac{39}{26}$

   c. $\frac{88}{12}$ d. $\frac{102}{9}$

6. Change the improper fractions to mixed numbers in simplest form:

   a. $\frac{18}{8}$ b. $\frac{98}{12}$

   c. $\frac{88}{10}$ d. $\frac{48}{15}$

7. Reduce the following to their lowest terms:

   a. $\frac{75}{345}$ b. $\frac{124}{48}$

   c. $\frac{70}{15}$

8. Reduce the following to their lowest terms:

   a. $\frac{36}{144}$ b. $\frac{68}{10}$

   c. $\frac{80}{12}$

9. Write the following in word form:

   a. 32.04 b. 200.2

   c. 45,005.001 d. 1,005,071.25

10. Write the following in word form:

    a. 27.602 b. 470.5

    c. 32,010.07 d. 3,500,007.45

11. Perform the indicated operations:

    a. 478.82 + 85.847 b. 65.09 – 24.987

    c. 54.37 × 1.46 d. 77.09 ÷ 8

12. Perform the indicated operations:

    a. 716.03 + 49.936 b. 15.71 – 3.509

    c. 15.71 × 3.26 d. 39.83 ÷ 9

13. What is the difference between the smallest and the largest number of the following?

    0.012, 0.201, 0.02, 0.102

14. What is the sum of the smallest and the largest number of the following?

    0.041, 0.011, 0.014, 0.01

15. Which of the following is closest to 2?

    2.011, 2.005, 1.996, 1.995

16. Which of the following is closest to 1?

    2.011, 2.004, 1.997, 1.996

For Problems 17 and 18, convert the decimal numbers to fractions in lowest terms and the fractions to decimal numbers.

17. Convert

	Decimal Number	Proper Fraction
a.	0.025	?
b.	?	$\frac{5}{8}$
c.	0.08	?
d.	?	$\frac{7}{25}$
e.	0.002	?
f.	?	$\frac{39}{50}$

18. Convert

	Decimal Number	Proper Fraction
a.	0.06	?
b.	?	$\frac{23}{50}$

	Decimal Number	Proper Fraction
c.	0.075	?
d.	?	$\frac{27}{40}$
e.	0.004	?
f.	?	$\frac{17}{25}$

19. Find the total weight of three items that weigh $3\frac{2}{3}$ kg, $4\frac{1}{2}$ kg, and $5\frac{3}{8}$ kg.
20. I used $2\frac{1}{5}$ litres of paint for my bedroom, $1\frac{1}{4}$ litres for my study room, and $7\frac{1}{3}$ litres for my living room. How many litres of paint did I use for the three rooms?
21. Henry is $8\frac{1}{4}$ years old. Amanda is $2\frac{5}{12}$ years old. How many years younger is Amanda than Henry?
22. I purchased $12\frac{1}{3}$ hectares of land and sold $4\frac{2}{5}$ hectares. How many hectares do I own now?
23. A car can travel $8\frac{1}{4}$ km with 1 litre of gas. How many kilometres can it travel using $45\frac{3}{5}$ litres of gas?
24. Samantha can walk $5\frac{3}{8}$ km in 1 hour. How far can she walk in $4\frac{1}{3}$ hours?
25. Alisha and Beyonce saved a total of $580. Two-fifth's of Alisha's savings equals $144. How much did each of them save?
26. Andy and Bob had $128. One-third of Bob's amount is $25. How much did each of them have?
27. Barbie's hourly pay is $23.07. If Barbie worked 37.75 hours last week, calculate her gross pay for last week.
28. Carol's overtime rate of pay is $57.45 per hour. If Carol worked 12.5 hours overtime last week, calculate her overtime pay for last week.
29. Lakshmi had $2,675.68 in her chequing account. She deposited 2 cheques in the amounts of $729.27 and $72.05 and withdrew $1,275.60. How much did she have in her account after the withdrawal?
30. George's car had 12.47 litres of gas at the start of his trip to the United States. He added the following quantity of gas during his trip: 34.25 litres, 15.2 litres, and 20.05 litres. At the end of the trip, there were 7.9 litres of gas left in the car. How much gas was used during the trip?
31. Three-fourths of the number of boys at a school is equal to half of the number of girls. The school has 480 students in total. How many more girls are there than boys?
32. There are 3,400 spectators at a soccer match. Three-fifth's of the number of men equals six-seventh's of the number of women. How many spectators are women?

Evaluate the following

33. $5 + \left(\frac{6}{10}\right)^3 + \sqrt{6^2 + 8^2}$
34. $\left(\frac{5}{7}\right)^2 \div 5 + \sqrt{3^2 + 4^2}$
35. $\sqrt{1.21} - (0.5)^2 + \sqrt{\frac{4}{25}}$
36. $\sqrt{0.81} - (0.2)^2 + \sqrt{\frac{9}{36}}$
37. $\left(\frac{1}{5}\right)^3 + \left(\frac{4}{25}\right)^2$
38. $\left(\frac{2}{3}\right)^3 + \left(\frac{2}{9}\right)^2$
39. $\left(\frac{5}{12}\right)^3 \left(\frac{4}{5}\right)^2$
40. $\left(\frac{4}{7}\right)^2 \left(\frac{1}{4}\right)^3$

2 | Self-Test Exercises

Answers to all problems are available online.

1. Find the missing values:

   a. $\frac{8}{5} = \frac{?}{20} = \frac{24}{?}$ b. $\frac{12}{22} = \frac{6}{?} = \frac{?}{55}$

   c. $\frac{48}{72} = \frac{12}{?} = \frac{?}{144}$

2. Reduce the following to their lowest terms:

   a. $\frac{225}{30}$ b. $\frac{156}{18}$

   c. $\frac{256}{144}$

3. Perform the indicated operations:

   a. $7\frac{2}{2} + 6\frac{1}{4}$ b. $5\frac{1}{3} - 3\frac{7}{15}$

   c. $\frac{3}{4} \times \frac{26}{27} \times \frac{9}{13}$ d. $2\frac{1}{4} \div \frac{3}{8}$

4. Perform the indicated operations:

   a. 0.165 + 10.8478 + 14.7 + 2.19
   b. 34.09 – 25.957
   c. 0.524 × 4.08
   d. 6.893 ÷ 3

5. Write in word form:

   a. 0.004   b. 6.05
   c. 300.02   d. 7.071

6. Convert the decimal numbers to fractions:

	Decimal Number	Fraction
a.	0.625	?
b.	3.2	?
c.	3.4	?
d.	0.72	?
e.	2.3	?
f.	1.73	?

7. Convert the fractions to decimal numbers:

	Fraction	Decimal Number
a.	$\frac{7}{20}$	?
b.	$\frac{11}{5}$	?
c.	$1\frac{4}{5}$	?
d.	$\frac{8}{9}$	?
e.	$\frac{16}{15}$	?
f.	$2\frac{1}{3}$	?

8. On a certain map, 1 cm represents 125 km. How many km are represented by 4.75 cm? How many cm on the map will represent a distance of 4,725 km?

9. Henry took 3 days to make 69 deliveries. On the first day, he completed one-third of the deliveries. On the second day, he made 10 more deliveries than on the first day. How many deliveries did he make on the third day?

10. Kyle had $4,000 and gave half of it to Bob. Bob spent a quarter of the money he received from Kyle. How much money does Bob have left?

11. Niveda spent one-third of her money on a handbag and half of the remainder on shoes. What fraction of her money did she spend on shoes? If she has \$40 left, how much did she spend?

12. Adrian's annual salary is \$52,000. Calculate his hourly rate if he works 37.5 hours per week. (Hint: 1 year = 52 weeks)

13. An item in a store sells for \$279.75. The same item is sold online for \$245.99. How much cheaper is the item online?

14. The cost per day to rent a car is \$24.45 plus \$0.37 per kilometre driven. What would be the cost to rent a car for 5 days if Sally plans to drive 325.50 km?

15. I walked for $\frac{3}{4}$ hour at $5\frac{1}{2}$ km per hour and jogged for $\frac{1}{2}$ hour at 10 km per hour. What was the total distance that I covered?

Evaluate the following:

16. $\sqrt{0.0025} + \left(\frac{2}{5}\right)^2 - \sqrt{\frac{49}{16}}$

17. $\sqrt{\frac{81}{64}} - \left(\frac{5}{4}\right)^3 \div \left(\frac{25}{16}\right)^2 + \sqrt{7^2 + 24^2}$

18. $\sqrt{\frac{1}{9}} + \sqrt{\frac{4}{36}} - \left(\frac{2}{3}\right)^2$

19. $\left(\frac{3}{5}\right)^3\left(\frac{25}{6}\right)^2 + (\sqrt{0.25})\sqrt{100}$

20. $\sqrt{5^2 + 12^2} - (\sqrt{0.49})\sqrt{\frac{25}{144}}$

Chapter 3
Exponents, Roots, and Order of Operations

Learning Outcomes

- Identify the types and properties of exponents.
- Perform arithmetic operations with exponents.
- Identify types of roots.
- Perform computation with roots and fractional exponents.
- Apply operations in their proper order using BEDMAS.

Chapter Outline

An exponent is a notation that demonstrates the number of times a number or expression is multiplied by itself. It allows us to represent extremely large and extremely small numbers and perform arithmetic operations more easily than having to use the standard form of a number. Exponents are used in equations in calculating compound interest on loans and investments. Roots (or radicals) and exponents are the opposites of each other. If 3 raised to the power of 2 equals 9, then the square root of 9, $\sqrt{9}$, is 3. Fractional exponents simplify calculations involving radicals, such as square roots, cubic roots, etc. When we have expressions involving more than one operation, we follow rules for the operation, known as order of operations. In this chapter, we will learn about the properties and rules associated with exponents, roots, fractional exponents, signed numbers, and order of operations.

3.1 | Exponents

Introduction

In Section 1.4 (Chapter 1) and Section 2.5 (Chapter 2), you learned about powers and roots of whole numbers, fractions, and decimal numbers.

Recall that the power of a number is the product of repeated multiplication of that number. This is expressed using exponential notation, which is the shorter way to represent the repeated multiplication.

For example, the number 2 multiplied by itself 5 times, $2 \times 2 \times 2 \times 2 \times 2$, is written in exponential notation as $\mathbf{2^5}$:

2^5 ← exponent (5), base (2)

The whole representation, 2^5, is known as the power.

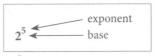

$$\underbrace{2^5}_{\text{Power using Exponents and Bases}} = \underbrace{2 \times 2 \times 2 \times 2 \times 2}_{\text{Repeated Multiplication}} = \underbrace{32}_{\text{Standard Notation}}$$

Similarily, the fraction $\left(\frac{4}{5}\right)$ multiplied by itself 4 times,

$\left(\frac{4}{5}\right) \times \left(\frac{4}{5}\right) \times \left(\frac{4}{5}\right) \times \left(\frac{4}{5}\right)$, is written in exponential notation as:

$\left(\frac{4}{5}\right)^4$ ← exponent (4), base $\left(\frac{4}{5}\right)$

The whole representation, $\left(\frac{4}{5}\right)^4$, is the power.

$$\left(\frac{4}{5}\right)^4 = \frac{4}{5} \times \frac{4}{5} \times \frac{4}{5} \times \frac{4}{5} = \frac{256}{625}$$

Similarily, the decimal number 1.2 multiplied by itself 3 times,

$(1.2) \times (1.2) \times (1.2)$, is written in exponential notation as:

$(1.2)^3$ ← exponent (3), base (1.2)

The whole representation, $(1.2)^3$, is the power.

$(1.2)^3 = 1.2 \times 1.2 \times 1.2 = 1.728$

Properties (Rules) of Exponents

The following properties of exponents, called the **rules** or **laws** of exponents, simplify expressions that involve exponents.

When multiplying powers of the same bases, add the exponents.

Product of Powers (Product Rule)

To multiply powers with the same base, add the exponents.

For example, $7^5 \times 7^3$

$$= \underbrace{(7 \times 7 \times 7 \times 7 \times 7)}_{\text{5 Factors of 7}} \times \underbrace{(7 \times 7 \times 7)}_{\text{3 Factors of 7}}$$

$$= \underbrace{7 \times 7 \times 7 \times 7 \times 7 \times 7 \times 7 \times 7}_{\text{8 Factors of 7}}$$

$$= 7^{(5+3)} = 7^8$$

You will note that the resulting exponent, 8, is obtained by adding the exponents 5 and 3. That is, the exponents are added when powers with the same base are multiplied.

In general, for any number (base) '*a*' and exponents '*m*' and '*n*',

$$a^m \times a^n = a^{(m+n)}$$

Example 3.1-a

Simplifying in Exponential Form Using the Product Rule

Express the following as a single exponent:

(i) $2^3 \times 2^4 \times 2^2$

(ii) $\left(\frac{3}{5}\right)^6 \times \left(\frac{3}{5}\right)^2$

(iii) $(0.2)^3 \times (0.2)^2$

Solution

(i) $2^3 \times 2^4 \times 2^2 = 2^{(3+4+2)} = 2^9$

(ii) $\left(\frac{3}{5}\right)^6 \times \left(\frac{3}{5}\right)^2 = \left(\frac{3}{5}\right)^{(6+2)} = \left(\frac{3}{5}\right)^8$

(iii) $(0.2)^3 \times (0.2)^2 = (0.2)^{(3+2)} = (0.2)^5$

When dividing powers wtih the same bases, subtract the exponent of the denominator from that of the numerator.

Quotient of Powers (Quotient Rule)

To divide powers with the same base, subtract the exponents.

For example, $4^7 \div 4^2 = \dfrac{\overbrace{4 \times 4 \times 4 \times 4 \times 4 \times 4 \times 4}^{\text{7 Factors of 4}}}{\underbrace{4 \times 4}_{\text{2 Factors of 4}}}$

$$= \frac{4 \times 4}{4 \times 4} \times 4 \times 4 \times 4 \times 4 \times 4$$

$$= \underbrace{4 \times 4 \times 4 \times 4 \times 4}_{\text{5 Factors of 4}} = 4^{(7-2)} = 4^5$$

You will note that the resulting exponent, 5, can be obtained by subtracting the denominator from the numerator (7 – 2 = 5) since the powers have the same base.

In general, for any non-zero number (base) 'a' and exponents 'm' and 'n',

$$\frac{a^m}{a^n} = a^{(m-n)}$$

Example 3.1-b

Simplifying in Exponential Form Using the Quotient Rule

Express the following as a single exponent:

(i) $3^9 \div 3^5$

(ii) $\left(\frac{2}{3}\right)^6 \div \left(\frac{2}{3}\right)^4$

(iii) $(1.15)^5 \div (1.15)^2$

Solution

(i) $3^9 \div 3^5 = 3^{(9-5)} = 3^4$

(ii) $\left(\frac{2}{3}\right)^6 \div \left(\frac{2}{3}\right)^4 = \left(\frac{2}{3}\right)^{6-4} = \left(\frac{2}{3}\right)^2$

(iii) $(1.15)^5 \div (1.15)^2 = (1.15)^{(5-2)} = (1.15)^3$

To raise the product of factors "a" and "b" to the power "n", raise each factor to the nth power.

Power of a Product (Power of a Product Rule)

To find the **Power of a Product**, each factor of the product is raised to the indicated power.

For example, $(3 \times 5)^4 = (3 \times 5)(3 \times 5)(3 \times 5)(3 \times 5)$

$$= \underbrace{3 \times 3 \times 3 \times 3}_{\text{4 Factors of 3}} \times \underbrace{5 \times 5 \times 5 \times 5}_{\text{4 Factors of 5}}$$

$$= 3^4 \times 5^4$$

You will note from the result that each factor of the product is raised to the 4th power.

In general, if any product of factors 'a' and 'b' are raised to a power 'n' then each factor of the product is also raised to the same power,

$$(a \times b)^n = a^n \times b^n$$

Example 3.1-c

Simplify in Exponential Form Using the Power of a Product Rule

Express the following in expanded form using the power of a product rule:

(i) $(8 \times 6)^3$ (ii) $\left(\frac{3}{5} \times \frac{2}{7}\right)^3$ (iii) $(1.12 \times 0.6)^3$

Solution

(i) $(8 \times 6)^3 = 8^3 \times 6^3$

(ii) $\left(\frac{3}{5} \times \frac{2}{7}\right)^3 = \left(\frac{3}{5}\right)^3 \times \left(\frac{2}{7}\right)^3$

(iii) $(1.12 \times 0.6)^3 = (1.12)^3 \times (0.6)^3$

Power of a Quotient (Power of a Quotient Rule)

To raise the quotient of a numerator 'a' and denominator 'b' to the power 'n', raise both the numerator and denominator to the nth power.

This is similar to the power of a product rule. To find the **Power of a Quotient**, raise the numerator to the indicated power and divide by the denominator raised to the indicated power.

For example, $\left(\frac{5}{8}\right)^3 = \underbrace{\left(\frac{5}{8}\right)\times\left(\frac{5}{8}\right)\times\left(\frac{5}{8}\right)}_{\text{3 Factors of } \left(\frac{5}{8}\right)}$

$$= \frac{5\times5\times5}{8\times8\times8} \quad \begin{matrix}\leftarrow \text{3 factors of 5} \\ \leftarrow \text{3 factors of 8}\end{matrix}$$

$$= \frac{5^3}{8^3}$$

You will note from the result that the numerator and the denominator of the expression is raised to the power of 3.

In general, if any quotient with numerator '*a*' and denominator '*b*' is raised to a power '*n*', this means that the numerator '*a*' and denominator '*b*' are both raised to that power,

$$\left(\frac{a}{b}\right)^n = \frac{a^n}{b^n}$$

Example 3.1-d

Simplify in Exponential Form Using Power of a Quotient Rule

Express the following in expanded form using the power of a quotient rule:

(i) $\left(\frac{7}{4}\right)^3$ (ii) $\left[\frac{\left(\frac{2}{3}\right)}{\left(\frac{3}{5}\right)}\right]^4$ (iii) $\left(\frac{1.05}{0.05}\right)^3$

Solution

(i) $\left(\frac{7}{4}\right)^3 = \frac{7^3}{4^3}$

(ii) $\left[\frac{\left(\frac{2}{3}\right)}{\left(\frac{3}{5}\right)}\right]^4 = \left(\frac{2}{3}\div\frac{3}{5}\right)^4 = \left(\frac{2}{3}\right)^4\div\left(\frac{3}{5}\right)^4$

(iii) $\left(\frac{1.05}{0.05}\right)^3 = \frac{(1.05)^3}{(0.05)^3}$

Power of a Power (Power of a Power Rule)

To raise a power to a power, multiply the exponents.

In order to find the **Power of a Power** of a number, multiply the two exponents of the powers together to get the new exponent of the power.

For example, $(9^3)^2$

$$= (9^3) \times (9^3)$$
$$= (9 \times 9 \times 9) \times (9 \times 9 \times 9)$$
$$= 9 \times 9 \times 9 \times 9 \times 9 \times 9$$
$$= 9^6\text{, which is the same as } 9^{(3 \times 2)}$$

In general, to raise the power of a number, 'a' to a power 'm' and then to raise it to a power 'n' [i.e., $(a^m)^n$], raise the power of the number 'a' to the product of the power 'm' and 'n',

$$(a^m)^n = a^{mn}$$

Example 3.1-e **Simplifying in Exponential Form Using Power of a Power Rule**

Solve the following:

(i) $(5^4)^3$ (ii) $\left[\left(\frac{3}{8}\right)^3\right]^2$ (iii) $[(1.04)^4]^2$

Solution

(i) $(5^4)^3 = 5^{(4 \times 3)} = 5^{12}$

(ii) $\left[\left(\frac{3}{8}\right)^3\right]^2 = \left(\frac{3}{8}\right)^{(3 \times 2)} = \left(\frac{3}{8}\right)^6$

(iii) $[(1.04)^4]^2 = (1.04)^{(4 \times 2)} = (1.04)^8$

Table 3.1(a) summarizes the properties (rules) of exponents.

Table 3.1-a **Properties (Rules) of Exponents**

Property (Rule)	Rule in Exponential Form	Example
Product Rule	$a^m \times a^n = a^{(m+n)}$	$3^5 \times 3^4 = 3^{(5+4)} = 3^9$
Quotient Rule	$\frac{a^m}{a^n} = a^{(m-n)}$	$\frac{3^7}{3^4} = 3^{(7-4)} = 3^3$
Power of a Product Rule	$(a \times b)^n = a^n \times b^n$	$(3 \times 5)^2 = 3^2 \times 5^2$
Power of a Quotient Rule	$\left(\frac{a}{b}\right)^n = \frac{a^n}{b^n}$	$\left(\frac{3}{5}\right)^3 = \frac{3^3}{5^3}$
Power of a Power Rule	$(a^m)^n = a^{(m \cdot n)}$	$(3^2)^3 = 3^{2 \times 3} = 3^6$

For Addition or Subtraction of Powers, there is no special rule for exponents with either the same or different bases. Evaluate each operation separately and then perform the addition or subtraction.

For example,

Addition of exponential expressions with the same base:

(i) $2^3 + 2^4$ Evaluating 2^3 and 2^4 separately, and then adding

$= 8 + 16 = 24$

Addition of exponential expressions with different bases:

(ii) $2^2 + 3^3$ Evaluating 2^3 and 3^3 separately, and then adding

$= 4 + 27 = 31$

Subtraction of exponential expressions with the same base:

(iii) $5^3 - 5^2$ Evaluating 5^3 and 5^2 separately, and then subtracting

$= 125 - 25 = 100$

Subtraction of exponential expressions with different bases:

(iv) $4^3 - 2^3$ Evaluating 4^3 and 2^3 separately, and then subtracting

$= 64 - 8 = 56$

There is also no special rule for the **product or quotient of powers having exponents of different bases.** Evaluate each operation separately and then perform the multipication or division.

For example,

Product of exponential expressions with different bases:

(i) $2^4 \times 3^2$ Evaluating 2^4 and 3^2 separately and then multiplying,

$= 16 \times 9 = 144$

Quotient of exponential expressions with of different bases:

(ii) $\frac{3^3}{2^4}$ Evaluating 3^3 and 2^4 separately and then dividing,

$= \frac{27}{16}$

Properties of Exponents and Bases of One and Zero

Table 3.1(b) explains the properties of exponents and bases of one and zero:

Table 3.1-b **Exponents and Bases of One (1) and Zero (0)**

Property (Rule)	Description	Rule in Exponential Form	Example
Base 'a' Exponent 1	Any number of base 'a' raised to the exponent '1' equals the number itself.	$a^1 = a$	$8^1 = 8$
Base 'a' Exponent 0	Any non-zero number of base 'a' raised to the exponent '0' equals 1.	$a^0 = 1$	$8^0 = 1$
Base '1' Exponent 'n'	A base of '1' raised to any exponent 'n' equals 1.	$1^n = 1$	$1^5 = 1$
Base '0' Exponent 'n'	A base of '0' raised to any positive exponent 'n' equals 0.	$0^n = 0$	$0^5 = 0$
Base '0' Exponent '0'	A base of '0' raised to the exponent '0' is undefined (∞).	0^0 = undefined (∞)	0^0 = undefined (∞)
Base '0' Exponent '$-n$'	A base of '0' raised to any negative exponent 'n' is undefined (∞).	0^{-n} = undefined (∞)	0^{-5} = undefined (∞)

Example 3.1-f **Solving Expressions that have Exponents with Different Bases**

Solve the following:

(i) $4^2 + 3^4 - 2^3$

(ii) $5^3 \times 2^4$

(iii) $(-2)^3 + (-3)^2$

(iv) $8^2 \div 4^3$

Solution

(i) $4^2 + 3^4 - 2^3$

$= 16 + 81 - 8$

$= 89$

(ii) $5^3 \times 2^4$

$= 125 \times 16$

$= 2{,}000$

(iii) $(-2)^3 + (-3)^2$

$= -8 + 9$

$= 1$

(iv) $8^2 \div 4^3$

$= \dfrac{8^2}{4^3}$

$= \dfrac{64}{64} = 1$

Calculator Method in Solving Expressions with Exponents

The exponent key on different calculators can be identified by symbols such as y^x, x^y, ^ , etc.

The sequence of operations involved in solving expressions with exponents also depends on the calculator.

In this section, you will learn to solve expressions with exponents using the Texas Instruments BA II Plus calculator.

The exponent button on the Texas Instruments BA II Plus calculator is the y^x button, as shown in this picture.

Example 3.1-g **Solving Expressions that have Exponents using Texas Instruments BA II Plus Calculator**

Calculate: (i) 5^6 (ii) $\left(\frac{3}{2}\right)^3$ (iii) $(1.02)^4$

Solution

(i) 5^6

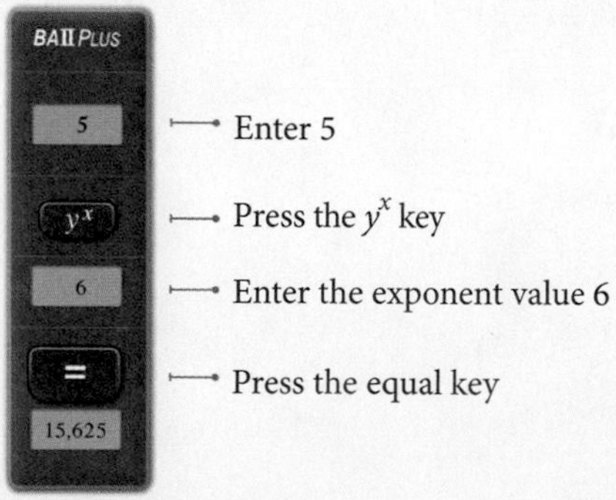

(ii) $\left(\frac{3}{2}\right)^3$

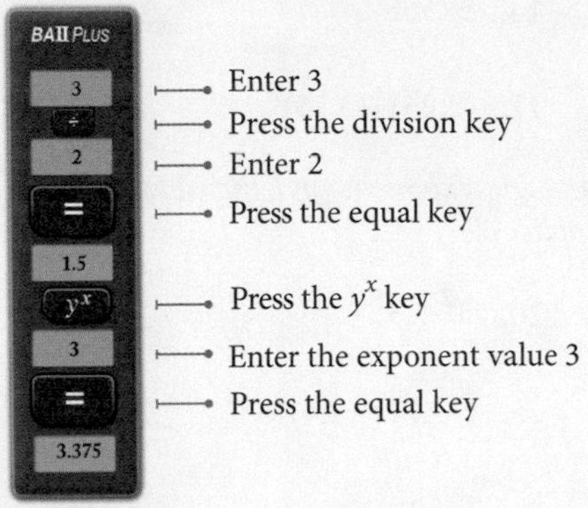

(iii) $(1.02)^4$

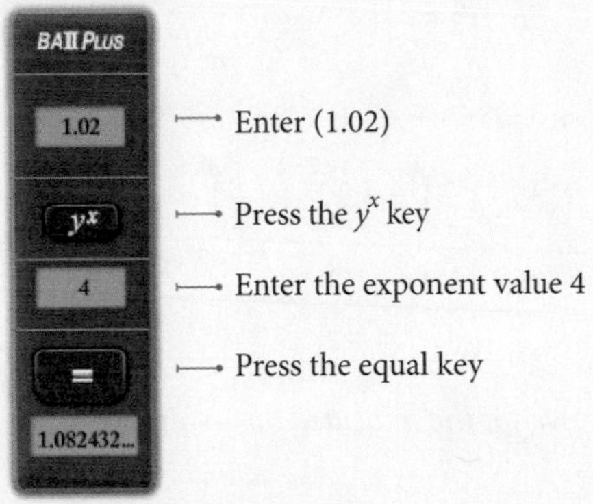

3.1 | Exercises

Answers to odd-numbered problems are available online.

Express Problems 1 to 6 in single exponential notation.

1. $7 \times 7 \times 7 \times 7$
2. $2 \times 2 \times 2 \times 2 \times 2 \times 2 \times 2 \times 2$
3. $\frac{2}{5} \times \frac{2}{5} \times \frac{2}{5} \times \frac{2}{5} \times \frac{2}{5} \times \frac{2}{5}$
4. $\frac{2}{7} \times \frac{2}{7} \times \frac{2}{7} \times \frac{2}{7} \times \frac{2}{7}$
5. $(1.15) \times (1.15) \times (1.15) \times (1.15)$
6. $(2.5) \times (2.5) \times (2.5) \times (2.5) \times (2.5)$

Express Problems 7 to 12 as repeated multiplication.

7. 9^5
8. 6^7
9. $\left(\frac{5}{7}\right)^4$
10. $\left(\frac{7}{8}\right)^5$
11. $(1.05)^3$
12. $(1.12)^5$

Express Problems 13 to 18 as a single exponent and then evaluate using a calculator. Round your answer to two decimals, where applicable.

13. $4^3 \times 4^6$
14. $5^4 \times 5^6$
15. $\left(\frac{1}{2}\right)^4 \left(\frac{1}{2}\right)^3$
16. $\left(\frac{2}{3}\right)^2 \left(\frac{2}{3}\right)^3$
17. $(3.25)^4 (3.25)^2$
18. $(0.75)^3 (0.75)^4$

Express Problems 19 to 42 as a single exponent and then evaluate using a calculator. Round your answer to two decimals, where applicable.

19. $6^8 \div 6^3$
20. $3^7 \div 3^5$
21. $\left(\frac{2}{5}\right)^3 \div \left(\frac{2}{5}\right)^1$
22. $\left(\frac{3}{2}\right)^4 \div \left(\frac{3}{2}\right)^3$
23. $(1.4)^5 \div (1.4)^2$
24. $(3.25)^6 \div (3.25)^5$
25. $(6^2)^3$
26. $(5^3)^2$
27. $\left[\left(\frac{2}{3}\right)^4\right]^3$
28. $\left[\left(\frac{3}{4}\right)^4\right]^2$
29. $\left[(2.5)^2\right]^3$
30. $\left[(1.03)^3\right]^2$
31. $3^4 + 3^2 + 3^0$
32. $4^2 + 4^4 + 4^0$
33. $2^4 + 3^4 - 1^4$
34. $3^3 + 2^3 - 1^3$
35. $\left(\frac{1}{2}\right)^3 + \left(\frac{1}{2}\right)^2 + \left(\frac{1}{2}\right)^0$
36. $\left(\frac{1}{5}\right)^2 + \left(\frac{1}{5}\right)^0 + \left(\frac{1}{5}\right)^4$
37. $(2.1)^2 + (2.1)^0$
38. $(3.2)^2 + (3.2)^1$
39. $4^3 \times 3^4$
40. $7^2 \times 2^2$
41. $6^4 \div 5^4$
42. $8^2 \div 7^2$

Express Problems 43 to 46 as a power of the indicated base value.

43. 4^5 as a power of 2
44. 9^6 as a power of 3
45. $9(27)^2$ as a power of 3
46. $8(16)^2$ as a power of 2

3.2 | Roots and Fractional Exponents

Roots

Roots are the inverse of exponents.

For example, the square of 2 (or raising 2 to the exponent 2) is 4; i.e., $2^2 = 4$. The inverse of squaring a number is finding the square root of that number. Therefore, the square root of 4 is 2.

Similarly, the square of 3 is 9; i.e., $3^2 = 9$. Therefore, the square root of 9 is 3.

Two types of notations are used to represent the above. One is using the symbol '$\sqrt{\ }$', which represents a radical. The other is using fractional exponents.

The square root of 9 can be represented as $\sqrt{9}$ in radical form, or as $9^{\frac{1}{2}}$ in fractional exponent form.

Square root of 9 = $\sqrt{9} = 9^{\frac{1}{2}}$

We know $9 = 3 \times 3 = 3^2$ Therefore, the square root (2nd root) of 9 is 3.

Similarly, $8 = 2 \times 2 \times 2 = 2^3$ Therefore, the cube root (3rd root) of 8 is 2.

$16 = 2 \times 2 \times 2 \times 2 = 2^4$ Therefore, the 4th root of 16 is 2.

A radical is an indicated root of a number (or expression).

$\sqrt[2]{9}$ indicates the 2nd root (square root) of 9.

$\sqrt[3]{8}$ indicates the 3rd root (cube root) of 8.

$\sqrt[4]{16}$ indicates the 4th root of 16.

$\sqrt[n]{a}$ refers to the nth root of a.

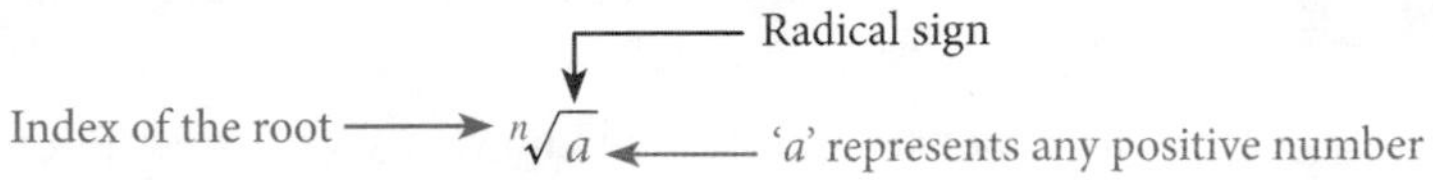

Index is written as a small number on the left of the radical symbol. It indicates which root is to be taken. $\sqrt[2]{25}$ indicates the 2nd root or square root of 25. For square roots, the index 2 does not need to be written as it is understood to be there, i.e., $\sqrt[2]{25} = \sqrt{25}$.

Principal Roots

Principal Root of Even Roots

Any even root of a positive number will have two solutions, with one being the negative of the other.

For example, 9 has the following two roots:

+ 3 because $3 \times 3 = 9$, and

− 3 because $(-3) \times (-3) = 9$

This is usually written as ± 3 and read as "plus or minus 3". **The positive root is called the principal root.**

Principal Root of Odd Roots

There is only one solution for any odd root of positive numbers and this root is called its principal root.

For example,

$\sqrt[3]{27} = 3$ because $(3)(3)(3) = 27$

Perfect Roots

Roots of a whole number may not be a whole number. A whole number is a perfect root if its root is also a whole number.

For example,

4 is a perfect square root of 16 because $4^2 = 16$; i.e., $\sqrt{16} = 4$

3 is a perfect cube root of 27 because $3^3 = 27$; i.e., $\sqrt[3]{27} = 3$

Table 3.2 **Examples of Perfect Roots**

Roots	1	2	3	4	5	6	7	8	9	10
Square Roots	$\sqrt{1}$	$\sqrt{4}$	$\sqrt{9}$	$\sqrt{16}$	$\sqrt{25}$	$\sqrt{36}$	$\sqrt{49}$	$\sqrt{64}$	$\sqrt{81}$	$\sqrt{100}$
Cube Roots	$\sqrt[3]{1}$	$\sqrt[3]{8}$	$\sqrt[3]{27}$	$\sqrt[3]{64}$	$\sqrt[3]{125}$	$\sqrt[3]{216}$	$\sqrt[3]{343}$	$\sqrt[3]{512}$	$\sqrt[3]{729}$	$\sqrt[3]{1,000}$
Fourth Roots	$\sqrt[4]{1}$	$\sqrt[4]{16}$	$\sqrt[4]{81}$	$\sqrt[4]{256}$	$\sqrt[4]{625}$	$\sqrt[4]{1,296}$	$\sqrt[4]{2,401}$	$\sqrt[4]{4,096}$	$\sqrt[4]{6,561}$	$\sqrt[4]{10,000}$

The Product Rule and the knowledge of Perfect Roots are used in simplifying square roots, cube roots, etc.

For Example,

(i) To simplify $\sqrt{12}$, we could write 12 as 4×3 as a combination of two factors where one of them, 4, is a perfect square.

i.e., $\sqrt{12} = \sqrt{4} \times \sqrt{3} = 2\sqrt{3}$

(ii) To simplify $\sqrt[3]{54}$, we could write 54 as 27×2 as a combination of two factors where one of them, 27, is a perfect cube of 3.

i.e., $\sqrt[3]{54} = \sqrt[3]{27} \times (\sqrt[3]{2}) = 3(\sqrt[3]{2})$

Example 3.2-a **Finding Perfect Roots**

Simplify using perfect roots of a number:

(i) $\sqrt{72}$ (ii) $\sqrt[3]{40}$

Solution

(i) $\sqrt{72}$

$= \sqrt{36} \times \sqrt{2}$ $72 = 36 \times 2$

$= 6\sqrt{2}$ 36 is a perfect square of 6

(ii) $\sqrt[3]{40}$

$= \sqrt[3]{8} \times (\sqrt[3]{5})$ $40 = 8 \times 5$

$= 2(\sqrt[3]{5})$ 8 is a perfect cube of 2

Fractional Exponents

Fractional exponents are easier to write than radical notations. As explained earlier, **square (or 2nd) root** is written as the power '$\frac{1}{2}$' in fractional exponent notation.

For example, $\sqrt{5} = 5^{\frac{1}{2}}$

Cube (or 3rd) root is written as the power '$\frac{1}{3}$' in fractional exponent notation.

For example, $\sqrt[3]{8} = 8^{\frac{1}{3}}$

The **fourth (4th) root** is written as the power '$\frac{1}{4}$' in fractional exponent notation.

For example, $\sqrt[4]{5^3} = (5^3)^{\frac{1}{4}} = 5^{\frac{3}{4}}$

An appropriate radical will "undo" an exponent.

For example,

$$\sqrt{5^2} = (5^2)^{\frac{1}{2}} = 5$$
$$\sqrt[3]{7^3} = (7^3)^{\frac{1}{3}} = 7$$

When we enter a fractional exponent in a calculator, we must put **brackets** around the fractional exponent.

For example,

In order to evaluate $25^{\frac{2}{5}}$ we must put brackets around $\frac{2}{5}$.

On a calculator to evalute $25^{\frac{2}{5}}$ it would be entered as;

$$\boxed{2} \boxed{5} \boxed{y^x} \boxed{(} \boxed{2} \boxed{\div} \boxed{5} \boxed{)} \boxed{=}$$

$$\boxed{3.623898...} = 3.62$$

(Without the brackets, the operation will mean $(25)^2 \div 5$, which is incorrect.)

Example 3.2-b	**Evaluating Using a Calculator**

Solve the following:

(i) $15^{\frac{3}{2}}$ (ii) $\left(\frac{3}{5}\right)^{\frac{1}{4}}$ (iii) $(2.5)^{\frac{3}{7}}$

Solution

(i) $15^{\frac{3}{2}} =$

$=$ [58.094750...] $= 58.09$

(ii) $\left(\frac{3}{5}\right)^{\frac{1}{4}} =$ (3 ÷ 5) y^x (1 ÷ 4) =

$=$ [0.880111...] $= 0.88$

(iii) $(2.5)^{\frac{3}{7}} =$ (2 . 5) y^x (3 ÷ 7) =

$=$ [1.480968...] $= 1.48$

Arithmetic Operations with Fractional Exponents

All the rules of exponents learned in Section 3.1 and as outlined in Table 3.1(a) are applicable to fractional exponents.

Example 3.2-c

Solving Expressions with Fractional Exponents using the Product Rule

Simplify the following using the product rule then evaluate to two decimal places using your calculator:

(i) $2^{\frac{1}{2}} \times 2^{\frac{1}{3}}$ (ii) $3^{\frac{3}{4}} \times 3^{\frac{9}{4}} \times 3^{0}$ (iii) $\left(\frac{3}{5}\right)^{\frac{7}{3}} \times \left(\frac{3}{5}\right)^{\frac{2}{3}}$

Solution

(i) $2^{\frac{1}{2}} \times 2^{\frac{1}{3}} = 2^{\left(\frac{1}{2}+\frac{1}{3}\right)} = 2^{\left(\frac{3+2}{6}\right)} = 2^{\frac{5}{6}} = 1.781797... = 1.78$

(ii) $3^{\frac{3}{4}} \times 3^{\frac{9}{4}} \times 3^{0} = 3^{\left(\frac{3}{4}+\frac{9}{4}+0\right)} = 3^{\frac{12}{4}} = 3^{3} = 27.00$

(iii) $\left(\frac{3}{5}\right)^{\frac{7}{3}} \times \left(\frac{3}{5}\right)^{\frac{2}{3}} = \left(\frac{3}{5}\right)^{\left(\frac{7+2}{3}\right)} = \left(\frac{3}{5}\right)^{\frac{9}{3}} = \left(\frac{3}{5}\right)^{3} = 0.216 = 0.22$

Example 3.2-d

Solving Expressions with Fractional Exponents using the Quotient Rule

Simplify the following using the quotient rule then evaluate to two decimal places using your calculator:

(i) $4^{\frac{2}{3}} \div 4^{\frac{1}{3}}$ (ii) $(1.2)^{\frac{5}{2}} \div (1.2)^{\frac{1}{2}}$ (iii) $\left(\frac{1}{3}\right)^{\frac{1}{4}} \div \left(\frac{1}{3}\right)^{\frac{3}{4}}$

Solution

(i) $4^{\frac{2}{3}} \div 4^{\frac{1}{3}} = 4^{\left(\frac{2}{3}-\frac{1}{3}\right)} = 4^{\left(\frac{2-1}{3}\right)} = 4^{\frac{1}{3}} = 1.587401... = 1.59$

(ii) $(1.2)^{\frac{5}{2}} \div (1.2)^{\frac{1}{2}} = (1.2)^{\left(\frac{5}{2}-\frac{1}{2}\right)} = (1.2)^{\frac{4}{2}} = (1.2)^2 = 1.44$

(iii) $\left(\frac{1}{3}\right)^{\frac{1}{4}} \div \left(\frac{1}{3}\right)^{\frac{3}{4}} = \left(\frac{1}{3}\right)^{\left(\frac{1-3}{4}\right)} = \left(\frac{1}{3}\right)^{\frac{2}{4}} = \left(\frac{1}{3}\right)^{-\frac{1}{2}} = 3^{\frac{1}{2}} = 1.732050... = 1.73$

Example 3.2-e

Solving Expressions with Fractional Exponents using the Power of a Product Rule

Simplify the following using the power of a product rule then evaluate to two decimal places using your calculator:

(i) $(16 \times 9)^{\frac{1}{2}}$ (ii) $\left(49 \times \frac{1}{9}\right)^{\frac{1}{2}}$ (iii) $(64 \times 9)^{\frac{3}{2}}$

Solution

(i) $(16 \times 9)^{\frac{1}{2}} = 16^{\frac{1}{2}} \times 9^{\frac{1}{2}} = (4^2)^{\frac{1}{2}} \times (3^2)^{\frac{1}{2}} = 4 \times 3 = 12.00$

(ii) $\left(49 \times \frac{1}{9}\right)^{\frac{1}{2}} = \dfrac{49^{\frac{1}{2}}}{9^{\frac{1}{2}}} = \dfrac{(7^2)^{\frac{1}{2}}}{(3^2)^{\frac{1}{2}}} = \dfrac{7}{3} = 2.333333... = 2.33$

(iii) $(64 \times 9)^{\frac{3}{2}} = 64^{\frac{3}{2}} \times 9^{\frac{3}{2}} = (8^2)^{\frac{3}{2}} \times (3^2)^{\frac{3}{2}}$

$= 8^3 \times 3^3 = 512 \times 27 = 13{,}824.00$

Example 3.2-f

Solving Expressions with Fractional Exponents using the Power of a Quotient Rule

Simplify the following using the power of a quotient rule then evaluate to two decimal places using your calculator:

(i) $\left(\frac{16}{9}\right)^{\frac{1}{2}}$ (ii) $\left(\frac{125}{64}\right)^{\frac{1}{3}}$

Solution

(i) $\left(\frac{16}{9}\right)^{\frac{1}{2}} = \dfrac{16^{\frac{1}{2}}}{9^{\frac{1}{2}}} = \dfrac{(4^2)^{\frac{1}{2}}}{(3^2)^{\frac{1}{2}}} = \dfrac{4}{3} = 1.333333... = 1.33$

(ii) $\left(\frac{125}{64}\right)^{\frac{1}{3}} = \dfrac{125^{\frac{1}{3}}}{64^{\frac{1}{3}}} = \dfrac{(5^3)^{\frac{1}{3}}}{(4^3)^{\frac{1}{3}}} = \dfrac{5}{4} = 1.25$

Example 3.2-g

Solving Expressions with Fractional Exponents Using the Power of a Power Rule

Simplify the following using the power of a power rule then evaluate to two decimal places using your calculator:

(i) $\left(6^{\frac{1}{2}}\right)^3$ (ii) $\left(18^{\frac{1}{3}}\right)^{\frac{1}{4}}$ (iii) $\left[\left(\frac{2}{3}\right)^3\right]^2$

Solution

(i) $\left(6^{\frac{1}{2}}\right)^3 = 6^{\left(\frac{1}{2}\times 3\right)} = 6^{\frac{3}{2}} = 14.696938... = 14.70$

(ii) $\left(18^{\frac{1}{3}}\right)^{\frac{1}{4}} = 18^{\left(\frac{1}{3}\times\frac{1}{4}\right)} = 18^{\frac{1}{12}} = 1.272348... = 1.27$

(iii) $\left[\left(\frac{2}{3}\right)^3\right]^2 = \left(\frac{2}{3}\right)^{3\times 2} = \left(\frac{2}{3}\right)^6 = \frac{2^6}{3^6} = \frac{64}{729} = 0.0877915... = 0.09$

Example 3.2-h Solving Expressions with Fractional Exponents and Different Bases

Solve the following to two decimal places using your calculator:

(i) $16^{\frac{1}{2}} + 8^{\frac{1}{2}}$ (ii) $25^{\frac{1}{2}} - 27^{\frac{1}{3}}$ (iii) $\left(\frac{7}{8}\right)^{\frac{1}{4}} - \left(\frac{2}{3}\right)^{\frac{1}{3}}$

(iv) $(5)^{\frac{1}{2}} \times (3)^{\frac{1}{2}}$ (v) $(2)^{\frac{3}{4}} \div (3)^{\frac{1}{2}}$

Solution

(i) $16^{\frac{1}{2}} + 8^{\frac{1}{2}} = 4 + 2.828427... = 6.828427... = 6.83$

(ii) $25^{\frac{1}{2}} - 27^{\frac{1}{3}} = 5 - 3 = 2.00$

(iii) $\left(\frac{7}{8}\right)^{\frac{1}{4}} - \left(\frac{2}{3}\right)^{\frac{1}{3}} = 0.967168... - 0.873580... = 0.093587... = 0.09$

(iv) $(5)^{\frac{1}{2}} \times (3)^{\frac{1}{2}} = 2.236067 \times 1.732050... = 3.872979... = 3.87$

(v) $(2)^{\frac{3}{4}} \div (3)^{\frac{1}{2}} = 1.681792... \div 1.732050... = 0.970983 = 0.97$

3.2 | Exercises

Answers to odd-numbered problems are available online.

Express Problems 1 to 4 in their radical form.

1. $64^{\frac{1}{2}}$
2. $81^{\frac{1}{2}}$
3. $\left(\frac{25}{16}\right)^{\frac{1}{2}}$
4. $\left(\frac{8}{25}\right)^{\frac{1}{2}}$

Express Problems 5 to 20 in their fractional exponent form and then evaluate and round your answers to two decimal places.

5. $\sqrt{144}$
6. $\sqrt{81}$
7. $\sqrt[3]{64}$
8. $\sqrt[3]{125}$
9. $\sqrt{2^6}$
10. $\sqrt{3^4}$
11. $\sqrt{40}$
12. $\sqrt{50}$
13. $\sqrt{8} \times \sqrt{12}$
14. $\sqrt{12} \times \sqrt{10}$
15. $\sqrt{7} \times \sqrt{14}$
16. $\sqrt{9} \times \sqrt{27}$

17. $\sqrt{\frac{25}{49}}$ 18. $\sqrt{\frac{36}{64}}$ 19. $\sqrt{\frac{64}{9}}$ 20. $\sqrt{\frac{24}{6}}$

Simplify Problems 21 to 36 by expressing it as a single exponent (using the property of exponents) and then evaluate and round your answers to two decimal places.

21. $5^{\frac{1}{2}} \times 5^{\frac{3}{4}}$ 22. $3^{\frac{7}{8}} \times 3^{\frac{5}{9}}$ 23. $3^{\frac{1}{2}} \times 3^{\frac{1}{4}}$

24. $11^{\frac{3}{4}} \times 11^{\frac{2}{3}}$ 25. $8^{\frac{4}{5}} \times 8^{\frac{2}{5}} \times 8^{\frac{1}{5}}$

26. $5^{\frac{4}{7}} \times 5^{\frac{4}{7}} \times 5^{\frac{6}{7}}$ 27. $5^{\frac{1}{3}} \times 5^{\frac{1}{2}} \times 5^{0}$ 28. $9^{\frac{5}{8}} \times 9^{\frac{2}{3}} \times 9^{0}$

29. $8^{\frac{1}{3}} \times 8^{\frac{2}{3}} \times 8^{1}$ 30. $2^{\frac{2}{3}} \times 2^{\frac{1}{2}} \times 2^{1}$ 31. $\frac{4^{\frac{5}{7}}}{4^{\frac{2}{7}}}$

32. $\frac{2^{\frac{4}{5}}}{2^{\frac{3}{5}}}$ 33. $\left(3^{2}\right)^{\frac{1}{3}}$ 34. $\left(10^{3}\right)^{0}$

35. $\left(12^{\frac{1}{2}}\right)^{4}$ 36. $\left(5^{\frac{2}{3}}\right)^{6}$

Evaluate Problems 37 to 50 and express your answers rounded to two decimal places.

37. $5^{\frac{1}{2}} + 7^{\frac{1}{2}}$ 38. $125^{\frac{1}{3}} + 64^{\frac{1}{3}}$ 39. $16^{\frac{1}{2}} - 9^{\frac{1}{2}}$

40. $50^{\frac{1}{2}} - 40^{\frac{1}{2}}$ 41. $5 \times 3^{\frac{1}{2}} + 2^{0} + 2^{\frac{1}{2}}$ 42. $12 \times 10^{\frac{1}{2}} + 3^{0} + 5^{\frac{1}{2}}$

43. $8^{\frac{1}{2}} \times 9^{\frac{1}{2}}$ 44. $6^{\frac{1}{2}} \times 3^{\frac{1}{2}}$ 45. $45^{\frac{1}{2}} \times 60^{\frac{1}{2}}$

46. $24^{\frac{1}{2}} \times 75^{\frac{1}{2}}$ 47. $\frac{5 + 4^{\frac{1}{2}}}{36^{\frac{1}{2}}}$ 48. $\frac{6^{\frac{1}{2}} + 6^{\frac{1}{2}}}{9^{\frac{1}{2}}}$

49. $\frac{10^{\frac{1}{2}} - 5^{\frac{1}{2}}}{25^{\frac{1}{2}}}$ 50. $\frac{7 - 7^{\frac{1}{2}}}{4^{\frac{1}{2}}}$

3.3 | Order of Operations (BEDMAS)

Introduction

In the previous chapter, you learned the order in which arithmetic operations are performed for expressions or problems with more than one arithmetic operation involving whole numbers, integers, fractions, and decimal numbers. In this section, you will learn in greater detail how to evaluate combined operations involving grouping symbols (brackets), exponents, divisions, multiplications, additions, and subtractions associated with real numbers of the number system.

The types of real numbers of the number system and a diagram showing the various elements of the number system are illustrated at the end of this section.

When arithmetic expressions in real numbers contain multiple operations with brackets or grouping symbols, exponents, divisions, multiplications, additions, and subtractions, the arithmetic operation is performed in the following sequence:

(i) Perform all operations within the **brackets** or **grouping** symbols. If there is more than one bracket, start with the innermost bracket and move outwards. Evaluate the expression within the brackets in the order of (ii) to (iv), as outlined below, and replace the expressions with the result of this operation.

(ii) Perform operations with **exponents.**

(iii) Perform the necessary **divisions** and **multiplications** in the order in which they appear from left to right.

(iv) Complete the operation by performing the necessary **additions** and **subtractions** in the order in which they appear from left to right.

The order of operations: Brackets, Exponents, Divisions, Multiplications, Additions and Subtractions, can be remembered by the acronym, **BEDMAS**.

Computing Expressions Involving Integers

Example 3.3-a **Evaluating Expressions by Following the Order of Operations (BEDMAS)**

Solve the following arithmetic expressions:

(i) $100 - 3[24 \div 2\,(6 - 3)] \div 2$ (ii) $10^2 \times 4 + 50 \div (8 - 3)^2 - 4^0$

Solution

(i) $100 - 3[24 \div 2\,(\mathbf{6 - 3})] \div 2$ — Working on inner brackets,

$= 100 - 3[\mathbf{24 \div 2} \times 3] \div 2$

$= 100 - 3[\mathbf{12 \times 3}] \div 2$ — Performing division and multiplication from left to right within the brackets,

$= 100 - \mathbf{3 \times 36} \div 2$

$= 100 - \mathbf{108 \div 2}$ — Performing division and multiplications from left to right within the bracket

$= \mathbf{100 - 54}$ — Subtracting,

$= 46$

(ii) $10^2 \times 4 + 50 \div (\mathbf{8 - 3})^2 - 4^0$ — Working on the brackets,

$= \mathbf{10^2} \times 4 + 50 \div \mathbf{5^2} - \mathbf{4^0}$ — Working on the exponents,

$= \mathbf{100 \times 4} + 50 \div 25 - 1$ — Performing division and multiplication from left to right,

$= 400 + \mathbf{50 \div 25} - 1$

$= \mathbf{400 + 2} - 1$ — Performing addition and subtraction from left to right,

$= \mathbf{402 - 1}$

$= 401$

Computing Expressions Involving Integers, Exponents, Fractions, and Decimal Numbers

Example 3.3-b **Evaluating Expressions by Following the Order of Operations (BEDMAS)**

Solve the following arithmetic expressions:

(i) $12 + 3^2\left[\frac{8 \times 5}{2^3 - 6}\right]^2 - 7$ (ii) $(12 + 3^2)\left[\frac{8 \times 5}{2^3 - 6}\right]^2 - 7$

Solution

(i) $12 + 3^2\left[\frac{8 \times 5}{2^3 - 6}\right]^2 - 7$ Working on the exponents in the brackets,

$= 12 + 3^2\left[\frac{\mathbf{8 \times 5}}{8 - 6}\right]^2 - 7$ Working on the multiplication in the bracket,

$= 12 + 3^2\left[\frac{40}{\mathbf{8 - 6}}\right]^2 - 7$ Working on the subtraction in the brackets,

$= 12 + 3^2\left[\frac{\mathbf{40}}{\mathbf{2}}\right]^2 - 7$ Working on the fraction in the brackets,

$= 12 + \mathbf{3^2} \times \mathbf{20^2} - 7$ Working on the exponents,

$= 12 + \mathbf{9} \times \mathbf{400} - 7$ Multiplying,

$= \mathbf{12 + 3{,}600 - 7}$ Performing addition and subtraction from left to right,

$= 3{,}605$

(ii) $(12 + \mathbf{3^2})\left[\frac{8 \times 5}{\mathbf{2^3} - 6}\right]^2 - 7$ Working on the exponents in the brackets,

$= (12 + 9)\left[\frac{\mathbf{8 \times 5}}{8 - 6}\right]^2 - 7$ Working on the multiplication in the brackets,

$= (21)\left[\frac{40}{\mathbf{8 - 6}}\right]^2 - 7$ Working on the subtraction in the brackets,

$= (21)\left[\frac{\mathbf{40}}{\mathbf{2}}\right]^2 - 7$ Working on the division in the brackets,

$= (21)\ \mathbf{20^2} - 7$ Working on the exponent,

$= \mathbf{(21)400} - 7$ Multiplying,

$= \mathbf{8{,}400} - \mathbf{7}$ Subtracting,

$= 8{,}393$

Example 3.3-c

Evaluating Expressions by following the Order of Operations (BEDMAS)

Solve the following: $\frac{4}{2^3}\left[(0.5 \times 5^2 + 2.5)^2 \div 3^2\right] + 5$

Solution

$\frac{4}{2^3}\left[(0.5 \times \mathbf{5^2} + 2.5)^2 \div 3^2\right] + 5$ — Working on the exponent in the inner brackets,

$= \frac{4}{2^3}\left[(\mathbf{0.5 \times 25} + 2.5)^2 \div 3^2\right] + 5$ — Working on the multiplication in the inner brackets,

$= \frac{4}{2^3}\left[(\mathbf{12.5 + 2.5})^2 \div 3^2\right] + 5$ — Working on the addition in the inner bracket,

$= \frac{4}{2^3}\left[\mathbf{15^2 \div 3^2}\right] + 5$ — Working on the exponents in the bracket,

$= \frac{4}{2^3}\left[\mathbf{225 \div 9}\right] + 5$ — Working on the division in the bracket,

$= \frac{4}{2^3} \times 25 + 5$ — Working on the exponent,

$= \frac{4}{8} \times 25 + 5$ — Performing division and multiplication from left to right,

$= \mathbf{0.5 \times 25} + 5$ — Multiplying,

$= \mathbf{12.5 + 5}$ — Adding,

$= 17.5$

Example 3.3-d

Computing Expressions Involving Radicals

Solve the following arithmetic expressions:

(i) $35 \div 7 + \sqrt{4^2 + 9}$ (ii) $4^2 - \sqrt{13^2 - 5^2} + 3^2\sqrt{25}$

Solution

(i) $35 \div 7 + \sqrt{\mathbf{4^2 + 9}}$ — Evaluating the grouping within the radical sign,

$= 35 \div 7 + \sqrt{\mathbf{16 + 9}}$

$= 35 \div 7 + \sqrt{\mathbf{25}}$

$= 35 \div 7 + 5$ — Dividing,

$= 5 + 5$ Adding,

$= 10$

(ii) $4^2 - \sqrt{13^2 - 5^2} + 3^2\sqrt{2}$ Evaluating the grouping within the radical sign,

$= 4^2 - \sqrt{169 - 25} + 3^2\sqrt{25}$

$= 4^2 - \sqrt{144} + 3^2\sqrt{25}$

$= 4^2 - 12 + 3^2 \times 5$ Working on the exponents,

$= 16 - 12 + 9 \times 5$ Multiplying,

$= 16 - 12 + 45$ Performing addition and subtraction from left to right,

$= 4 + 45$

$= 49$

Arithmetic Operations with Signed Numbers

In the previous chapters you learned that positive real numbers can be represented by points on a number line from zero to the right of the zero. That is, whole numbers, positive integers, and positive rational and irrational numbers can be represented on a number line from zero to the right of the zero.

Every positive number has an opposite, called a negative number. Zero, '0', is neither positive nor negative. The numbers that are to the left of the zero on the number line represent negative numbers. We use the negative sign, '–', to represent negative integers, and the positive sign, '+', to represent positive integers.

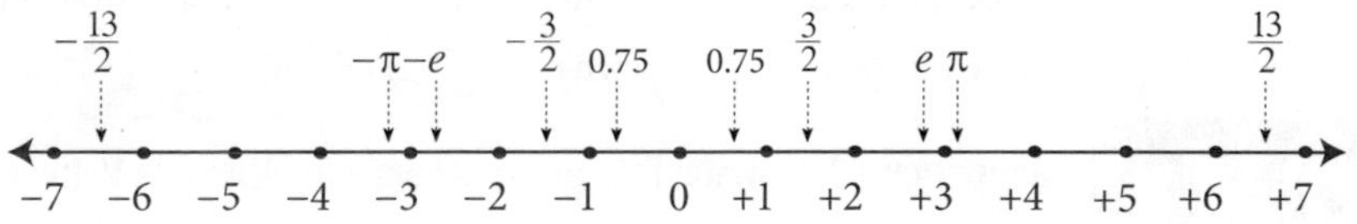

The arrowhead on either end shows that the line continues indifinitely in both the positive and negative directions.

Real numbers include all positive numbers and negative numbers. Numbers that lie to the left of a number on the number line are smaller than the numbers that lie to the right of that number.

For example,

3 is greater than −2,

−3 is greater than −5,

−5 is smaller than −4,

−1 is smaller than 2

Positive and negative numbers are referred to as signed numbers. Since numbers are naturally positive, when we read or write positive numbers, we usually omit the word **'positive'** or the positive sign **'+'**. But when the number is negative, we must read or write it as **'negative'** or include the negative sign **'–'**. For example, **'+ 7'** is read as **'seven'** and written as '7'. But **'– 7'** should be read as **'negative seven'** or should be written with the **'negative'** sign as **'– 7'**.

Two integers that are at equal distances from the origin and in opposite directions are called opposites.

Any positive number and its opposite will be at an equal distance from zero on the number line.

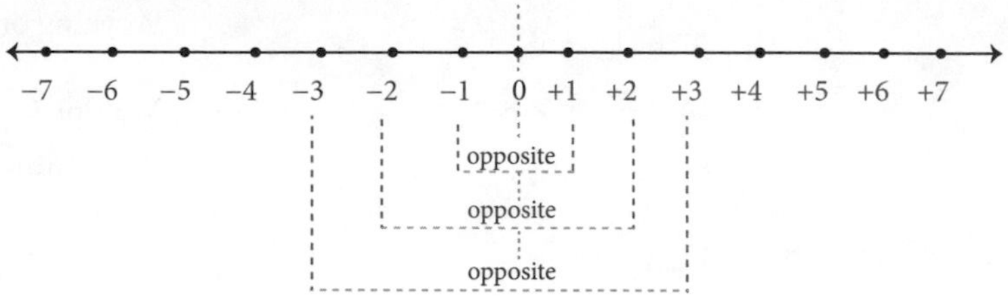

A negative number is the opposite of a positive number. For example, – 3 is the opposite of + 3.

Absolute Value

The absolute value of a number is its distance from the origin '0' on the number line. Since it is a distance, it is always positive and the direction does not matter.

For example, – 5 and +5 are 5 units from the origin '0'.

i.e., $|-5| = 5$ and $|5| = 5$

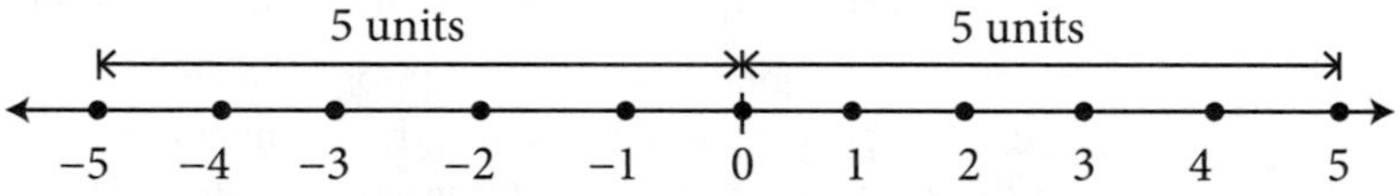

The absolute value of a number *'a'* is denoted by $|a|$. The vertical bars used in the representation of the absolute value differ from how brackets are used.

For example, $|-4| = 4$ whereas $(-4) = -4$

Example 3.3-e **Simplifying Arithmetic Expressions Involving Absolute Values**

Simplify: $-\left|\frac{-4}{3}\right|$

Solution

$-\left|\frac{-4}{3}\right|$ Simplifying the absolute value portion,

$= -\left(\frac{4}{3}\right)$ Simplifying the bracket portion,

$= \frac{-4}{3}$

Therefore, $-\left|\frac{-4}{3}\right| = \frac{-4}{3}$.

Example 3.3-f

Subtracting Numbers Involving Absolute Values

Simplify: $10 - |8 - 15|$

Solution

$10 - \mathbf{|8 - 15|}$	Simplifying within the absolute value portion,
$= 10 - \mathbf{|-7|}$	Simplifying the absolute value portion,
$= 10 - \mathbf{(7)}$	Simplifying the bracket portion,
$= \mathbf{10 - 7}$	Subtracting,
$= 3$	

Therefore, $10 - |8 - 15| = 3$.

Addition and Subtraction of Signed Numbers

- When adding two positive numbers, the answer is always positive (+).

  For example,

  Adding + 5 and + 3:

  $(+5) + (+3) = 5 + 3 = \mathbf{8}$ This is the same as **+ 8.**

- When adding two negative numbers, the answer is always negative (–).

  For example,

  Adding – 4 and – 3:

  $(-4) + (-3) = -4 - 3 = \mathbf{-7}$

- When adding numbers that have different signs, subtract the smaller number from the larger number and the answer will have the sign of the larger, dominant number.

  For example,

  (i) Adding + 8 and – 12 (or – 12 and + 8):

  $+8 + (-12) = 8 - 12 = \mathbf{-4}$

  (ii) Adding – 5 and + 8 (or + 8 and – 5):

  $-5 + (+8) = -5 + 8 = +3 = \mathbf{3}$

- When subtracting negative numbers, first change all the subraction problems to addition problems, then follow the rule for the addition of signed numbers.

  For example,

  (i) Subtracting –12 from 18:

  $18 - (-12) = 18 + 12 = \mathbf{30}$

  (ii) Subtracting – 5 from – 7:

  $(-7) - (-5) = -7 + 5 = \mathbf{-2}$

  (iii) Subtracting – 2 from – 6:

  $(-6) - (-2) = -6 + 2 = \mathbf{-4}$

Multiplying two signed numbers:

(+) (+) = (+)

(–) (–) = (+)

(+) (–) = (–)

(–) (+) = (–)

Multiplication and Division of Signed Numbers

When signed numbers are multiplied or divided, the result will be a number with either a '+' or a '–' sign.

The following are rules to be followed when multiplying or dividing **two signed numbers:**

(a) When both numbers are positive, the final answer will be positive.

For example,

(i) $(+5)(+4) = +20$

(ii) $\frac{+12}{+3} = +4$

(b) When both numbers are negative, the final answer will be positive.

For example,

(i) $(-5)(-4) = +20$

(ii) $\frac{-12}{-3} = +4$

(c) When any one of the numbers is negative, the final answer will be negative.

For example,

(i) $(+5)(-4) = -20$

(ii) $(-5)(+4) = -20$

(iii) $\frac{+12}{-3} = -4$

(iv) $\frac{-12}{+3} = -4$

(v) $\frac{-25}{+15} = \frac{-5}{3}$ *or* $-\frac{5}{3}$

(vi) $\frac{+30}{-4} = \frac{+15}{-2} = \frac{-15}{2}$ *or* $-\frac{15}{2}$

Dividing two signed numbers:

$\frac{(+)}{(+)} = (+)$

$\frac{(-)}{(-)} = (+)$

$\frac{(-)}{(+)} = (-)$

$\frac{(+)}{(-)} = (-)$

Note: When multiplying or dividing more than 2 signed numbers, group them into pairs and determine the sign using the rules for signed numbers.

For example,

(i) $(-3)(-2)(+4)(-1)(-5)$

$= (6)(-4)(-5)$

$= (-24)(-5)$

$= 120$

(ii) $\frac{(-15)(+8)(-15)}{(-25)(14)} = \frac{-(15 \times 8)(-50)}{-(25 \times 14)}$

$= \frac{+15 \times 8 \times 50}{-25 \times 14} = -\frac{15 \times 8 \times \overset{2}{\cancel{50}}}{\underset{1}{\cancel{25}} \times 14}$

$= -\frac{15 \times 8 \times \overset{1}{\cancel{2}}}{\underset{7}{\cancel{14}}} = -\frac{15 \times 8}{7}$

$= -\frac{120}{7}$

$a^{-n} = \frac{1}{a^n}$,

where 'n' is a positive integer.

Negative Exponents

In the exponential notation of a number, the base of the number may be raised to a negative exponent. When the exponent is negative, it is represented by a^{-n}. The negative exponent is the reciprocal of a positive exponent.

Positive Exponent: $a^n = a \times a \times a \times a \times a \times \ldots \times a$ (multiplication of 'n' factors of 'a')

Negative Exponent: $a^{-n} = \frac{1}{a^n} = \frac{1}{a \times a \times a \times a \times a \times \ldots \times a}$ (division of 'n' factors of 'a')

Therefore, a^n and a^{-n} are reciprocals.

Repeated Multiplication	Positive Exponential Notation
$5 \times 5 \times 5 \times 5$ =	5^4
$5 \times 5 \times 5$ =	5^3
5×5 =	5^2
5 =	5^1
1 =	5^0

If this pattern is continued further...

Factors are divided by 5 | Exponents are reduced by 1

Repeated Division	Negative Exponential Notation
$\frac{1}{5}$ =	5^{-1}
$\frac{1}{5 \times 5}$ =	5^{-2}
$\frac{1}{5 \times 5 \times 5}$ =	5^{-3}

Exhibit 3.3 Repeated Multiplication of a Number and its Exponential Notation

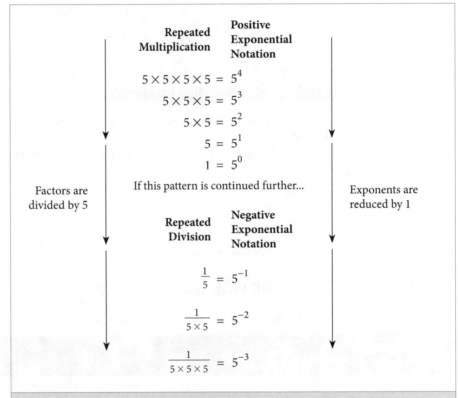

Any positive number with a negative exponent will always result in a positive answer. For example,

Negative Exponential Notation	Positive Exponential Notation	Repeated Division	Standard Notation
5^{-1}	$\frac{1}{5^1}$	$\frac{1}{5}$	$\frac{1}{5}$
5^{-2}	$\frac{1}{5^2}$	$\frac{1}{5\times5}$	$\frac{1}{25}$
5^{-3}	$\frac{1}{5^3}$	$\frac{1}{5\times5\times5}$	$\frac{1}{125}$

Fractions with Negative Exponents

When a fraction has a negative exponent, change the fraction to its reciprocal and drop the sign of the exponent. After this change, the number in the exponent indicates the number of times the numerator and denominator should be multiplied.

For example,

$$\left(\frac{2}{5}\right)^{-3} = \left(\frac{5}{2}\right)^{3} = \left(\frac{5}{2}\right)\left(\frac{5}{2}\right)\left(\frac{5}{2}\right) = \frac{5\times5\times5}{2\times2\times2} = \frac{125}{8}$$

Note: The reciprocal of $\frac{2}{5}$ is $\frac{5}{2}$.

Exponents with Negative Bases

When an exponent has a negative base there are four possible scenarios:

Negative Base with Exponents	Example	Sign of Answer
Positive and Even	$(-2)^6 = (-2)(-2)(-2)(-2)(-2)(-2) = 64$	+
Positive and Odd	$(-2)^5 = (-2)(-2)(-2)(-2)(-2) = -32$	–
Negative and Even	$(-2)^{-6} = \frac{1}{(-2)^6} = \frac{1}{(-2)(-2)(-2)(-2)(-2)(-2)} = \frac{1}{64} = 0.015625$	+
Negative and Odd	$(-2)^{-5} = \frac{1}{(-2)^5} = \frac{1}{(-2)(-2)(-2)(-2)(-2)} = \frac{1}{-32} = -0.03125$	–

Note: A negative base of an exponent expressed within a bracket, as in $(-5)^4$, results in a different answer compared to a negative base expressed without a bracket, as in -5^4.

In $(-5)^4$, the exponent applies to both the negative sign and 5 within the bracket.

For example,

(i) $(-5)^4$ is (-5) multiplied 4 times;
i.e., $(-5)^4 = (-5)(-5)(-5)(-5) = 625$

(ii) $(-5)^3$ is (-5) multiplied 3 times; i.e., $(-5)^3 = (-5)(-5)(-5)$
$= -125$

In -5^4, the exponent applies only to the number 5.

For example,

(i) -5^4 is the negative answer of 5 multiplied 4 times;
i.e., $-5^4 = -[5 \times 5 \times 5 \times 5] = -625$

(ii) -5^3 is the negative answer of 5 multiplied 3 times;
i.e., $-5^3 = -[5 \times 5 \times 5] = -125$

$$\left(\frac{a}{b}\right)^{-n} = \left(\frac{b}{a}\right)^{n}$$

Arithmetic Operations of Exponential Expressions with Signed Numbers

Example 3.3-g **Solving Expressions using the Product Rule**

Solve the following:

(i) $(-5)^4 \times (-5)^{-1}$

(ii) $(-2)^5 \times (-2)^2 \times (-2)^0 \times 2$

Solution

(i) $(-5)^4 \times (-5)^{-1}$
$= (-5)^{(4-1)}$
$= (-5)^3$
$= -125$

(ii) $(-2)^5 \times (-2)^2 \times (-2)^0 \times 2$
$= (-2)^{(5+2+0)} \times 2$
$= (-2)^7 \times 2$
$= -128 \times 2$
$= -256$

Example 3.3-h **Solving Expressions using the Quotient Rule**

Solve the following:

(i) $(-3)^7 \div (-3)^2$

(ii) $(-5)^3 \div (-5)^0$

Solution

(i) $(-3)^7 \div (-3)^2$
$= (-3)^{(7-2)}$
$= (-3)^5 = -243$

(ii) $(-5)^3 \div (-5)^0$
$= (-5)^{(3-0)}$
$= (-5)^3 = -125$

Example 3.3-i

Solving Expressions using the Power of a Product Rule

Solve the following:

(i) $(-5\times 2)^3$ (ii) $(3\times 2)^{-2}$

Solution

(i) $(-5\times 2)^3$

$=(-5)^3\times 2^3$

$=-125\times 8$

$=-1{,}000$

or, $(-10)^3$

$=-1{,}000$

(ii) $(3\times 2)^{-2}$

$=3^{-2}\times 2^{-2}$

$=\frac{1}{3^2}\times\frac{1}{2^2}$

$=\frac{1}{9}\times\frac{1}{4}$

$=\frac{1}{36}$

or, $(6)^{-2}$

$=\frac{1}{36}$

Example 3.3-j

Solving Expressions using the Power of a Quotient Rule

Solve the following:

(i) $(2\div 3)^{-2}$ (ii) $(-2)^{-3}$

Solution

(i) $(2\div 3)^{-2}$

$=\left(\frac{2}{3}\right)^{-2}$

$=\left(\frac{3}{2}\right)^{2}$

$=\frac{3^2}{2^2}=\frac{9}{4}$

(ii) $(-2)^{-3}$

$=\frac{1}{(-2)^3}$

$=\frac{1}{-8}=-\frac{1}{8}$

Example 3.3-k

Evaluating Exponents with Powers

Solve the following:

(i) $(4^3)^2$ (ii) $(-3^3)^2$

Solution

(i) $(4^3)^2$

$=4^{3\times 2}$

$=4^6$

$=4{,}096$

(ii) $(-3^3)^2$

$=(-3)^{3\times 2}$

$=(-3)^6$

$=729$

Roots of Negative Numbers

There is no real solution to any even root of a negative number.

For example,

$\sqrt[2]{-4}$ has no real roots.

$\sqrt[4]{-81}$ has no real roots.

There is a solution to an odd root of a negative number.

$\sqrt[5]{-32} = -2$ because $(-2)(-2)(-2)(-2)(-2) = -32$

$\sqrt[3]{-27} = -3$ because $(-3)(-3)(-3) = -27$

Table 3.3 **Types of Real Numbers**

Type	Description	Examples
Natural Numbers	Counting numbers (numbers starting from 1).	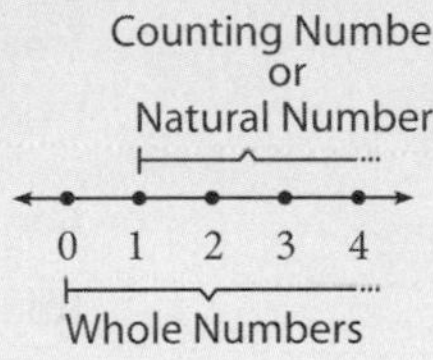
Whole Numbers	Natural numbers, including zero.	
Integers	Natural numbers (positive integers), their negatives (negative integers), and zero.	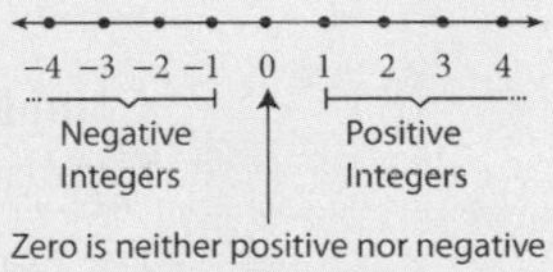
Rational Numbers*	Numbers that can be expressed as one integer divided by another non-zero integer; i.e., numbers that can be written as a quotient of integers with non-zero divisors.	$-\frac{5}{2}, \frac{0}{1}, \frac{3}{2}, \frac{3}{1}$
Irrational Numbers	Numbers that cannot be expressed as a rational number.	$\sqrt{2}, \pi, \sqrt{7}, e$

Natural numbers are positive integers. Zero is neither positive nor negative.

Rational numbers can be expressed as $\frac{a}{b}$, where a and b are integers and $b \neq 0$.

Irrational numbers cannot be expressed as $\frac{a}{b}$, where a and b are integers and $b \neq 0$.

- Terminating decimals and repeating decimals are also rational numbers because they can be expressed as a quotient of integers.

* **Terminating decimals** are decimals that end.

For example, $0.325 = \frac{3}{8}$

Repeating decimals are decimals that do not end but show a repeating pattern.

For example, 0.185185... is usually written as $0.185 = \frac{5}{27}$

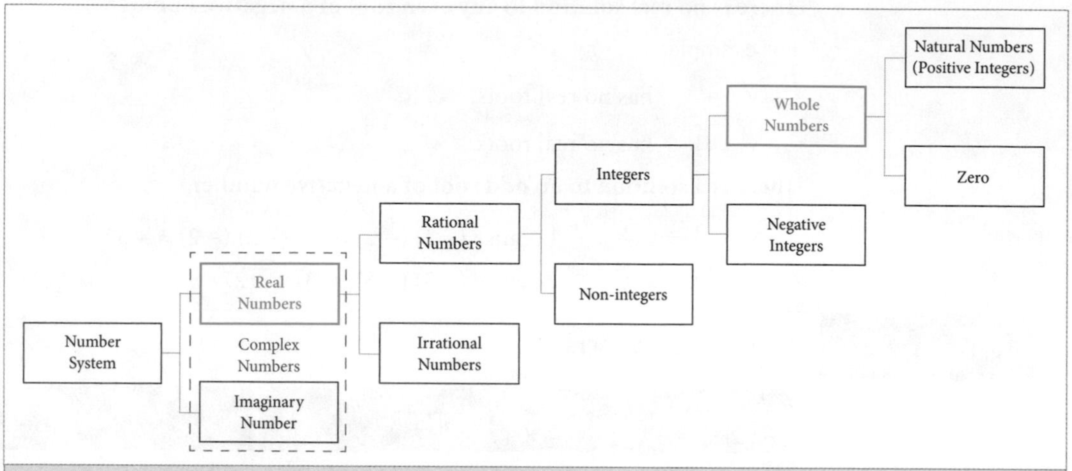

Exhibit 3.3-b Number System

Imaginary Numbers are numbers, which when raised to the power of 2, result in negative real numbers.

For example, $\sqrt{-2}$ is an imaginary number as $(\sqrt{-2})^2 = -2$

Imaginary numbers are denoted by 'ai', where $i = \sqrt{-1}$

For example, $\sqrt{-4} = \sqrt{4 \times (-1)} = \sqrt{4} \times \sqrt{-1} = 2i$

$\sqrt{-5} = \sqrt{5} \times \sqrt{-1} = \sqrt{5}i$

Complex Numbers are numbers that consist of real numbers and imaginary numbers. They are denoted by $a + bi$, where a and b are real numbers.

For example, $2 + 3i$ and $7 - 4i$.

3.3 | Exercises

Answers to odd-numbered problems are available online.

Simplify and express your answers rounded to two decimal places wherever applicable.

1. a. $64 \div 4 \div 2 \times 8$ b. $48 \div 3 \div 4 \times 2$
2. a. $18 - 8 \div 2 + 6$ b. $4 \times 6 \div 2 - 5$
3. $16 \div 4 \times 4 + 6$
4. $50 \div 25 \times 2 + 2$
5. $[18(4 - 7) + 19] - [50 - (14 \times 3)]$
6. $(24 - 8 \times 4) - [24(6 + 2) - 200]$
7. $(-1)(-3)(2)(-5)(-6)$
8. $(-5)(-3)(12)(-3)(-1)$
9. $4{,}500\left(1 + 0.005 \times \frac{240}{365}\right)$
10. $600\left(1 + 0.002 \times \frac{180}{365}\right)$
11. $1{,}500\left(1 + 0.004 \times \frac{7}{12}\right)$
12. $960\left(1 + 0.05 \times \frac{3}{12}\right)$

13. $\dfrac{2,500}{\left(1+0.01\times\dfrac{150}{365}\right)}$

14. $\dfrac{1,250}{\left(1+0.02\times\dfrac{160}{365}\right)}$

15. $\dfrac{1,800}{\left(1+0.05\times\dfrac{5}{12}\right)}$

16. $\dfrac{2,700}{\left(1+0.04\times\dfrac{7}{12}\right)}$

17. $(5+7)^2-5^2-7^2$

18. $(9-12)^2-9^2-12^2$

19. $2^3+2^4-20\times 3$

20. $7\times 8-3^2-2^3$

21. $(20\times 4-8^2)^2+9$

22. $-12^2\div 4-3\times 2^4$

23. $(3\times 9-3^2)-12$

24. $-5\times 3^3\div 9+5^2$

25. $11^2-4\times 54\div(5-2)^3-3$

26. $[(1+12)(1-5)]^2\div(5+3\times 2^2-4)$

27. $31-[(15\div 3)\times 32\div 2^2(26\div 13)]$

28. $3(7^2+2\times 15\div 3)-(1+3\times 4)^2$

29. $1,275(1.03)^7$

30. $5,400(1.005)^8$

31. $2,400(1.02)^{-10}$

32. $4,650(1.04)^{-6}$

33. $\dfrac{800[(1.04)^{10}-1]}{0.04}$

34. $\dfrac{750[(1.02)^{25}-1]}{0.02}$

35. $\dfrac{2,400[1-(1.02)^{-8}]}{0.02}$

36. $\dfrac{400[1-(1.05)^{-12}]}{0.05}$

37. $128\div(-16)\div(-2)$

38. $200\div(-10)\div 5$

39. $\dfrac{[(-6)\times 7+(-12)\div(-4)+3]\div 6}{[(-24)\div 8+4]\div[14-16+3]}$

40. $\dfrac{8\{9-(-2)-7[4+(-1)]\}}{-12+4[-4+(-3)]\div 7}$

41. $\dfrac{6^{-\frac{5}{4}}}{6^{\frac{3}{4}}}$

42. $\dfrac{5^{\frac{4}{9}}}{5^{-\frac{2}{9}}}$

43. $\dfrac{7^{\frac{4}{3}}}{7^{-\frac{2}{3}}}$

44. $\dfrac{3^{-\frac{6}{7}}}{3^{\frac{2}{7}}}$

45. $\dfrac{10^{-\frac{3}{5}}\times 10^{\frac{4}{5}}}{10^{\frac{2}{5}}}$

46. $\dfrac{5^{\frac{2}{7}}\times 5^{\frac{4}{7}}}{5^{-\frac{6}{7}}}$

47. $\dfrac{2^{\frac{5}{7}}\times 2^{-\frac{6}{7}}}{2^{-\frac{8}{7}}}$

48. $\dfrac{3^{\frac{2}{3}}\times 3^{-\frac{4}{3}}}{3^{\frac{5}{3}}}$

49. $\dfrac{6^{-\frac{5}{9}}\times 6^{0}}{6^{-\frac{7}{9}}}$

50. $\dfrac{9^{\frac{2}{5}}\times 9^{0}}{9^{-\frac{3}{5}}}$

51. $(5^{-2})^{\frac{4}{3}}$

52. $(4^{-2})^{\frac{5}{2}}$

53. $\left(6^{-\frac{1}{2}}\right)^{-6}$

54. $\left(2^{-\frac{4}{5}}\right)^{-5}$

55. $\left(8^{-\frac{2}{3}}\right)^{-6}$

56. $\left(6^{-\frac{2}{3}}\right)^{-3}$

57. $\left(7^{-\frac{1}{3}}\right)^{9}$

58. $\left(3^{\frac{4}{9}}\right)^{0}$

59. $\left(\dfrac{4^{2}}{3^{\frac{1}{2}}}\right)^{-1}$

60. $\left(\dfrac{3^{-2}}{5^{-\frac{1}{3}}}\right)^{3}$

61. $\left(\dfrac{3^{\frac{3}{4}}}{2^{-\frac{1}{3}}}\right)^{12}$

62. $\left(\dfrac{6^{\frac{1}{2}}}{3^{\frac{1}{4}}}\right)^{4}$

63. $\left(\dfrac{5^{-\frac{2}{3}}}{4^{-4}}\right)^{2}$

64. $\left(\dfrac{2^{-\frac{1}{4}}}{4^{-\frac{1}{2}}}\right)^{4}$

Express Problems 65 and 66 in positive exponent form.

65. a. $\left(\frac{2}{3}\right)^{-4}$ b. $-\left(\frac{3}{4}\right)^{-1}$

66. a. $\left(-\frac{3}{7}\right)^{-5}$ b. $\left(\frac{4}{5}\right)^{-3}$

Express Problems 67 and 68 as a single exponent and then evaluate using a calculator.

67. a. $(-6)^5 \times (-6)^3$ b. $8^{-6} \times 8^9$

68. a. $(-2)^5 \times (-2)^6$ b. $4^{-7} \times 4^8$

Express Problems 69 and 70 as a single exponent and then evaluate using a calculator:

69. a. $\left(\frac{1}{2}\right)^4\left(\frac{1}{2}\right)^3$ b. $3^4 \times 3^{-7} \times 3^5$

70. a. $\left(\frac{2}{3}\right)^2\left(\frac{2}{3}\right)^3$ b. $7^3 \times 7^{-8} \times 7^9$

Express Problems 71 to 74 as a single exponent and then evaluate using a calculator.

71. a. $(-4)^5 \div (-4)^3$ b. $-5^4 \div -5^2$

72. a. $(-2)^7 \div (-2)^4$ b. $-4^6 \div -4^4$

73. a. $-\left(\frac{1}{2}\right)^2 \div \left(\frac{1}{2}\right)^3$ b. $\left(-\frac{3}{5}\right)^3 \div \left(-\frac{3}{5}\right)^1$

74. a. $-\left(\frac{1}{4}\right)^4 \div \left(\frac{1}{4}\right)^2$ b. $\left(-\frac{5}{8}\right)^2 \div \left(-\frac{5}{8}\right)^0$

Express Problems 75 and 76 as a single exponent and then evaluate using a calculator.

75. a. $(-2^3)^2$ b. $\left[\left(\frac{2}{3}\right)^2\right]^3$

76. a. $(-3^2)^3$ b. $\left[\left(\frac{1}{4}\right)^2\right]^3$

Evaluate Problems 77 to 80.

77. a. $4^2 + 4^4 + 4^0$ b. $5^{-1} + 3^{-1} + 1^{-1}$
78. a. $3^4 + 3^2 + 3^0$ b. $6^{-1} + 3^{-2} + 1^0$
79. a. $5^2 \times (-6^2)$ b. $6^4 \div 5^4$
80. a. $(-4)^3 \times 3^2$ b. $8^2 \div 7^2$

3 | Review Exercises

Answers to odd-numbered problems are available online.

For the following problems, simplify and express your answers rounded to two decimal places wherever applicable:

1. Find the difference between 2^5 and 5^2.
2. Find the difference between 3^4 and 4^3.
3. Express 243 as a power of 3 and then evaluate $243^{\frac{3}{5}}$.
4. Express 512 as a power of 2 and then evaluate $512^{\frac{4}{9}}$.
5. Express as a single exponent using laws of exponents, and then evaluate:
   a. $(3^2)^{\frac{1}{2}} \times (3^3)^{\frac{2}{3}}$ b. $(6^2)^{\frac{1}{3}} \times (6^3)^{\frac{1}{9}}$
6. Express as a single exponent using laws of exponents, and then evaluate:
   a. $(2^2)^{\frac{1}{4}} \times (2^5)^{\frac{3}{10}}$ b. $(5^3)^{\frac{2}{3}} \times (5^2)^{\frac{1}{2}}$
7. Simplify using laws of exponents and then evaluate:
   a. $\frac{2^3 \times 3^4 \times 2^2}{3 \times 2^5}$ b. $\frac{(5^2)^3 \times 5^4}{5^7}$
8. Simplify using laws of exponents and then evaluate:
   a. $\frac{5^2 \times 7^3 \times 5^4}{7 \times 5^6}$ b. $\frac{(2^5)^4 \times 2^2}{2^{17}}$
9. Simplify using laws of exponents and then evaluate:
   a. $(125)^{-\frac{1}{3}}$ b. $(49)^{-\frac{1}{2}}$ c. $\sqrt{\frac{64}{81}}$
10. Simplify using laws of exponents and then evaluate:
    a. $(16)^{-\frac{1}{4}}$ b. $(27)^{-\frac{1}{3}}$ c. $\sqrt{\frac{25}{36}}$
11. a. $\frac{16 + 4(3)}{10 - 4 + 1} + \frac{(16 + 4)3}{10 - (4 + 1)}$
    b. $14 - 3\{[(6 - 9)(-4) + 12](-2)\}$
12. a. $\frac{2(6) + 4}{24 - (7 + 3)} + \frac{2(6 + 4)}{24 - 7 + 3}$
    b. $5(-4) - 3[(-9 + 6) + (-3) - 4]$
13. a. $4{,}500\left(1 + 0.04 \times \frac{240}{365}\right)$
    b. $\frac{1{,}250}{\left(1 + 0.02 \times \frac{150}{365}\right)}$
14. a. $600\left(1 + 0.06 \times \frac{180}{365}\right)$
    b. $\frac{5{,}600}{\left(1 + 0.04 \times \frac{210}{365}\right)}$
15. a. $[(1 + 12)(1 - 5)]^2 \div (5 + 3 \times 2^2 - 4)$
    b. $2^2[(9 - 7) \div 2 + 9 - 4]$
16. a. $8 \div 4 + (6^2 - 4) \div (13 - 5) \times 64$
    b. $6 \div [4 \times (8 - 2) \div (3^2 + 3)] \div 4$
17. a. $\frac{10}{3} - \left(\frac{3}{2} + \frac{4}{5} \div \frac{6}{5}\right) \div 2$
    b. $\left(\frac{2}{3} + \frac{4}{3}\right)^5$

18. a. $\left(\frac{7}{2}\times\frac{6}{5}\div\frac{8}{5}\right)+\left(6\times\frac{11}{6}\right)$

 b. $\left(\frac{1}{2}\right)^2\div 7(12-8)$

19. a. $6{,}000\left(1+\frac{0.06}{12}\right)^{36}$

 b. $2{,}000(1+0.004)^{-24}$

20. a. $4{,}000\left(1+\frac{0.075}{12}\right)^{60}$

 b. $5{,}000(1+0.003)^{-48}$

21. $\frac{3{,}000\,[(1.06)^{25}-1]}{0.06}$

22. $\frac{1{,}400\,[(1.03)^{30}-1]}{0.03}$

23. $\frac{950\,[1-(1.03)^{-15}]}{0.03}$

24. $\frac{1{,}200\,[1-(1.04)^{-20}]}{0.04}$

25. a. $-15-(-15)$

 b. $-14-(-7)$

26. a. $13-(-11)+0$

 b. $22-(-4)-6$

27. a. $8+|2-7|$

 b. $-|-23|-|10-15|$

28. a. $15-|3-9|$

 b. $-|-42|-|35-18|$

3 | Self-Test Exercises

Answers to all problems are available online.

For the following problems, simplify and express your answers rounded to two decimal places wherever applicable:

1. Express the following as a power of the indicated bases:

 a. 625 as a power of 5.

 b. 729 as a power of 3.

 c. 128 as a power of 2.

2. Simplify using laws of exponents and then evaluate:

 a. $\frac{2^3\times(3^2)^3\times 3^4}{2^3\times(2^3)^2\times 3^5}$ b. $\frac{2^4\times(3^2)^4\times 2^2}{2^5\times(3^3)^2\times 2^0}$

3. Simplify using laws of exponents and then evaluate:

 a. $(2^2\times 3\times 5^0)^{-1}$ b. $(3^2\times 2^{-2}\times 5)^0$

4. a. $\left(\frac{3}{2}\right)^2+\frac{3}{8}$

 b. $\frac{3}{2}\div\frac{15}{8}\times\sqrt{16}$

 c. $4\times\frac{8}{5}\div\frac{4}{3}+\sqrt{4}-1$

5. a. $\frac{2}{5}\times\sqrt{100}+2^4\div\frac{5}{3}$

 b. $\frac{3}{4}+\left(\frac{3}{2}\right)^3$

 c. $\sqrt{36}\times\frac{4}{3}\div\frac{8}{6}-7+2$

6. a. $\left(\frac{2}{3}+\frac{4}{3}\right)^5$

 b. $\left(\frac{7}{2}\times\frac{6}{5}\div\frac{8}{5}\right)+\left(6\times\frac{11}{6}\right)$

7. a. $\frac{10}{3}-\left(\frac{3}{2}+\frac{4}{5}\div\frac{6}{5}\right)\div 2$

 b. $2^2\left(3-\frac{3}{4}\right)$

8. a. $\left(\frac{3}{2}\times\frac{3}{2}+7-\frac{5}{4}\right)^2$

 b. $45-(5+7)^2$

 c. $4(-3^2)+4$

9. a. $5^4+2^4-3^4$

 b. $(-4)^5\div(-2)^6$

 c. $-\frac{3^{-2}}{7}$

10. a. $200(1.08)^7$

 b. $450(1.03)^{-2}$

11. a. $2{,}000\left[1+\frac{0.075}{12}\right]^{60}$

b. $4{,}500\left[1+\frac{0.048}{4}\right]^{-15}$

12. $\frac{3{,}600\,[(1.06)^{5}-1]}{0.06}$

13. $\frac{4{,}400\left[1-(1.03)^{-20}\right]}{0.03}$

14. Evaluate:

a. $-9+(-4)+(-2)$

b. $8-(-5)-(-3)$

c. $|12-8\times 2|-|-4|$

15. Evaluate:

a. $\frac{16^{\frac{1}{2}}\times 6}{81^{\frac{1}{2}}}$

b. $\frac{9^{\frac{1}{2}}\times 81^{\frac{1}{2}}}{13^{2}-5^{2}}$

Chapter 4
Ratios and Proportions

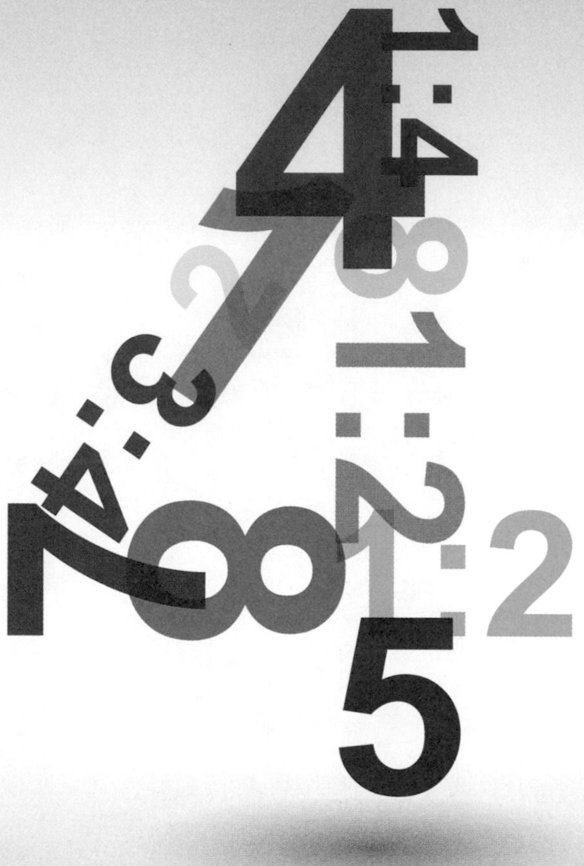

Learning Outcomes

- Identify ratios and rates to compare quantities.
- Set up ratios and use them to solve problems involving allocation and sharing of quantities.
- Solve problems by finding unknown quantities using proportions as equivalent sets of ratios.
- Allocate quantities on a proportionate basis using pro-ration as an application of proportions.

Chapter Outline

One of the ways in which we use mathematics in our daily lives is through the comparison of numbers and quantities of two or more items. Data expressed in numbers becomes more meaningful and easier to evaluate when relevant comparisons are made. We use ratios to find the unit price in determining the best price for an item, when different quantities of the same item are offered at different prices. Also, we use proportions to calculate unknown quantities that would be otherwise, difficult to estimate. For example, if you wanted to calculate the amount of gas needed to travel 375 km, knowing that the fuel efficiency of your car is 9.8 litres per 100 km, then you would have to set up a proportion equation to determine the amount of gas needed. In this chapter, you will learn the concept and be able to solve problems relating to ratios, proportions, and pro-rations.

4.1 | Ratios

Introduction

A **ratio** is a comparison or relationship between two or more quantities with the same unit. Therefore, the reason that ratios do not have units is because they are quantities of the same unit.

Ratio is a comparison or relationship between two or more quantities.

For example, Andy (A) invested \$5,000 and Barry (B) invested \$4,000 in a business. The comparison of A's investment to B's investment is called the ratio of their investments.

Expressing a Ratio of Two Quantities

When comparing two quantities, there are different ways to express the ratio. In the example above, the ratio of A's investment to B's may be expressed in any of the following forms:

5,000 to 4,000 (separate the quantities using the word 'to')

5,000 : 4,000 (using a colon and read as '5,000 is to 4,000')

$\frac{5,000}{4,000}$ (as a fraction and read as '5,000 over 4,000')

In the above example, if the decimal equivalent of the fraction is used, then it must be stated as "*A's* invesment is 1.25 times B's investment".

Similarily, if a percentage equivalent of a decimal or fraction is used, then it must be stated as "*A's* investment is 125% of B's investment".

Note:

When representing a ratio as a fraction, if the denominator is 1, the denominator (1) must still be written.

For example, if the ratio of two quantities is $\frac{3}{1}$ then it is incorrect to say that the ratio is 3. It should be stated as $\frac{3}{1}$ or 3 : 1.

Expressing a Ratio of More than Two Quantities

When comparing more than two quantities, we use a colon to represent a ratio.

For example, if A's investment is \$5,000, B's investment is \$4,000, and C's investment is \$1,000 in a business, then the ratio of their investments is expressed as,

$$A : B : C = 5,000 : 4,000 : 1,000$$

When two ratios are equal, they result in the same answer when reduced to their lowest terms.

Terms of a Ratio

The quantities in the ratio are called the terms of a ratio.

For example, the terms of the ratio 5 : 7 : 19 are 5, 7, and 19.

Equivalent Ratios

When all the terms of the ratio are multiplied by the same number or divided by the same number, the result will be an equivalent ratio.

For example, when the terms of a ratio 12 : 15 are multiplied by 2, we obtain an equivalent ratio of 24 : 30.

$$12 : 15$$

$$12 \times \mathbf{2} : 15 \times \mathbf{2}$$

$$24 : 30$$

When the terms of the ratio 12 : 15 are divided by the common factor 3, we obtain the equivalent ratio of 4 : 5.

$$12 : 15$$

$$12 \div 3 : 15 \div 3$$

$$4 : 5$$

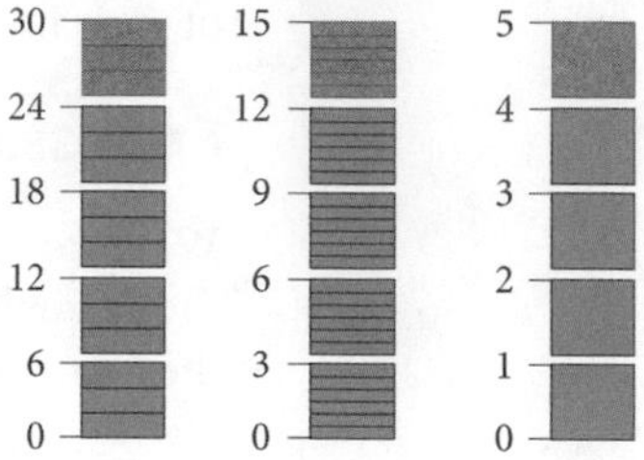

$$12 : 15 \quad = \quad 24 : 30 \quad = \quad 4 : 5$$

$$\frac{12}{15} = \frac{24}{30} = \frac{4}{5}$$

Therefore, the ratios 12 : 15, 24 : 30, and 4 : 5 are called equivalent ratios.

Example 4.1-a **Determining Equivalent Ratios**

Determine whether the given pairs of ratios are equivalent.

(i) 18 : 12 and 12 : 8

(ii) 20 : 24 and 15 : 20

Solution

(i) 18 : 12   12 : 8

= 18 ÷ 6 : 12 ÷ 6   = 12 ÷ 4 : 8 ÷ 4

= 3 : 2   = 3 : 2

Therefore, the given pair of ratios is equivalent.

(ii) 20 : 24   15 : 20

= 20 ÷ 4 : 24 ÷ 4   = 15 ÷ 5 : 20 ÷ 5

= 5 : 6   = 3 : 4

Therefore, the given pair of ratios is not equivalent.

Reducing a Ratio to its Simplest or Lowest Terms

Comparisons are easier when ratios are reduced to their lowest terms. When all the terms of a ratio are integers, the ratio can be reduced to its lowest terms by dividing all the terms by their common factors.

For example, if 'A' earns \$3,000, 'B' earns \$4,500, and 'C' earns \$6,000, then the equivalent ratio of their earnings reduced to the lowest terms is calculated as follows:

$A : B : C$	
3,000 : 4,500 : 6,000	Dividing each term by the common factor 100,
= 30 : 45 : 60	Dividing each term by the common factor 15,
= 2 : 3 : 4	Now, the ratio is in its lowest terms.

A ratio is in its simplest form when the terms do not have a common factor other than one.

By reducing to its lowest terms, we can say that the earnings of A : B : C are in the ratio of 2 : 3 : 4.

Comparing Quantities of Items That Have the Same Kind of Measure but Different Units

When writing ratios to compare quantities of items that have the same kind of measure, the units have to be the same.

For example, the ratio of 45 minutes to 2 hours is not 45 : 2. We are comparing 'time' in both these cases; therefore, the units used have to be the same.

45 minutes : 2 hours	Converting 2 hours to minutes using 1 hour = 60 minutes,
= 45 minutes : 120 minutes	Dividing by the common factor 15,
= 3 : 8	

Consider another example to determine the ratio of 2.5 kilometres to 3,000 metres.

2.5 km : 3,000 m	Converting km to m, 2.5 km = 2500 m,
= 2,500 m : 3,000 m	Dividing by the common factor 100,
= 25 : 30	Dividing by the common factor 5,
= 5 : 6	

Example 4.1-b **Comparing Quantities**

Express each of the following ratios in their simplest forms:

(i) 1.2 L to 800 mL

(ii) 16 weeks to 2 years

Solution

(i) 1.2 L : 800 mL	Converting 1.2 to mL, 1.2 L = 1,200 mL
= 1,200 mL : 800 mL	Dividing both terms by the common factor 400,
= 3 : 2	

Therefore, the ratio of 1.2 L to 800 mL is 3 : 2.

Solution
continued

(ii)	16 weeks : 2 years	Converting 2 years to weeks, 2 years = 104 weeks
	= 16 weeks : 104 weeks	Dividing both terms by the common factor 8,
	= 2 : 13	

Therefore, the ratio of 16 weeks to 2 years is 2 : 13.

Reducing Ratios When One or More of the Terms of the Ratio Are Fractions

To reduce the ratio, first convert all the terms to integers by multiplying all the terms by their lowest common denominator, and then reduce to their lowest terms.

For example,

$3 : \frac{9}{2} : 6$	Multiplying each term by the common denominator 2,
$6 : 9 : 12$	Dividing each term by the common factor 3,
$2 : 3 : 4$	

The ratio remains the same when all the terms are multiplied and divided by the same number.

Reducing Ratios When One or More of the Terms of the Ratio Are Decimal Numbers

To reduce the ratio, first convert all the terms to integers by moving the decimal of all the terms to the right by the same number of places, and then reduce to their lowest terms.

For example,

2.25 : 3.5 : 5	Moving the decimal by 2 places to the right,
225 : 350 : 500	Dividing each term by the common factor 25,
9 : 14 : 20	

Reducing Ratios When the Terms of the Ratio Are a Combination of Fractions and Decimals

To reduce the ratio, first convert all the fractional terms to decimals or decimal terms to fractions, then convert all the terms to integers. Finally, reduce to their lowest terms.

For example,

$5.8 : \frac{9}{2} : 4$	Multiplying each term by the common denominator 2,
$11.6 : 9 : 8$	Moving the decimal by 1 place to the right,
$116 : 90 : 80$	Dividing each term by the common factor 2,
$58 : 45 : 40$	

Reducing Ratios to an Equivalent Ratio Whose Smallest Term is 1

To make the comparison of quantities easier, we can also reduce a ratio to its equivalent ratio whose smallest term is equal to 1, by dividing all the terms by the smallest value.

For example, if the investment amounts of 3 partners '*A*', '*B*', and '*C*' are \$35,000, \$78,750, and \$59,500, respectively, then the equivalent ratio of their investments, whose smallest term is 1, is calculated as follows:

A : B : C	
35,000 : 78,750 : 59,500	Dividing each term by the smallest term, 35,000,
1 : 2.25 : 1.7	Now, the ratio is reduced to its equivalent ratio with the smallest term equal to 1.

By reducing it so that the smallest term is equal to 1, we can say: (i) *B*'s investment is 2.25 times *A*'s investment and (ii) *C*'s investment is 1.7 times *A*'s investment.

Example 4.1-c **Reducing to Lowest Terms**

Express the following ratios as equivalent ratios in their lowest whole numbers and then reduce them to ratios whose smallest term is one (1):

(i) $2\frac{1}{2} : 6\frac{1}{4} : 5$ (ii) $2.5 : 1.75 : 0.625$

Solution

(i) $2\frac{1}{2} : 6\frac{1}{4} : 5$	Converting the mixed number to an improper fraction,
$\frac{5}{2} : \frac{25}{4} : 5$	Multiplying each term by the common denominator 4,
$10 : 25 : 20$	Dividing each term by the common factor 5,
$2 : 5 : 4$	Dividing each term by the smallest term 2,
$1 : 2.5 : 2$	

Therefore, $2\frac{1}{2} : 6\frac{1}{4} : 5$ reduced to its lowest terms is 2 : 5 : 4 and the equivalent ratio whose smallest term is 1 is 1 : 2.5 : 2.

Solution
continued

(ii) 2.5 : 1.75 : 0.625

2.5 : 1.75 : 0.625	Moving all the decimals by 3 places to the right,
2,500 : 1,750 : 625	Dividing each term by the common factor 125,
20 : 14 : 5	Dividing each term by the smallest term 5,
4 : 2.8 : 1	

Therefore, 2.5 : 1.75 : 0.625 reduced to its lowest terms is 20 : 14 : 5 and the equivalent ratio whose smallest term is 1 is 4 : 2.8 : 1.

Order of a Ratio

The order of presenting terms in a ratio is important. For example, if A saves \$800, B saves \$1,500, and C saves \$1,200, then the ratio of the savings of $A : B : C$ is:

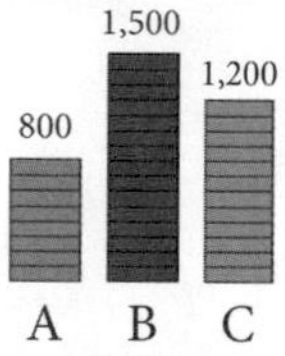

A : B : C = 800 : 1,500 : 1,200 Dividing each term by the common factor 100,

= 8 : 15 : 12

In the previous example, the ratio of the savings of $C : B : A$ is:

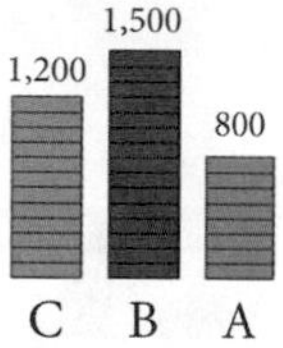

$C : B : A$ = 1,200 : 1,500 : 800 Dividing each term by the common factor 100,

= 12 : 15 : 8

Note that $C : B : A$ is not the same as $A : B : C$.

Ratios compare the numbers in order. The ratio 12 : 15 : 8 expresses a different comparison than the ratio 8 : 15 : 12.

Comparing Quantities

When using ratios to compare quantities of items that have different units of measure, the units of measurement of each quantity must be included in the ratio.

For example, when baking a cake, Maggie uses 4 kilograms of flour, 2 litres of water, and 6 eggs. Therefore, the ratio of flour to water to eggs is given by,

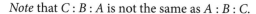

	flour (kg)	:	water (L)	:	eggs (numbers)	
=	4	:	5	:	6	Dividing each term by the common factor 2,
=	2	:	1	:	3	i.e., 2 kg flour : 1 litre water : 6 eggs

Rate, Unit Rate, and Unit Price

If the denominator of a **ratio** is 1, the 1 must be written in the denominator.
If the denominator of a **rate** is 1, we usually do not write the 1 in the denominator.

Rate

A rate is a special ratio that is used to compare two quantities or amounts having different units of measure. The quantities of measurements being compared are called the terms of the ratio.

For example, if a car travels 100 km using 9 L of gas, then the rate is 100 km : 9 L. The 1st term of the ratio is measured in kilometres and the 2nd term is measured in litres. The word 'per' indicates that it is a rate and it is usually denoted by a slash "/". Therefore, 100 km : 9 L is usually written as 100 km per 9 L or 100 km/9 L.

Rates are used in our day-to-day activities such as travelling, working, shopping, etc. For example: travelled 90 km in 1.5 hours, worked 75 hours in 2 weeks, paid $4.80 for 3 L of milk, etc.

Example 4.1-d

Calculating Rate as a Ratio of Different Units of Measurements

A laser printer printed 88 pages in 6 minutes. Express the rate in simplified form.

Solution

The unit of the first term is in number of pages and the unit of the second term is in minutes.

Therefore, the rate of printing = 88 pages : 6 minutes (or 88 pages / 6 minutes).

Then, in simplified form = 44 pages : 3 minutes (or 44 pages / 3 minutes).

Therefore, the printing rate is 44 pages / 3 minutes.

Unit Rate

Unit rate represents the number of units of the first quantity (or measurements) that corresponds to one unit of the second quantity. That is, unit rate is a rate in which the rate is expressed as a quantity which has a denominator of 1.

Rate can be converted to unit rate simply by dividing the first term by the second term.

For example,

A rate of 90 km in 1.5 hours, converted to unit rate:

= 90 km/1.5 hours

= 60 km/1 hour

= 60 km/hour

Simlarly,

A rate of 75 hours in 2 weeks, converted to unit rate:

= 75 hours/2 weeks

= 37.5 hours/1 week

= 37.5 hours/week

Example 4.1-e

Calculating Speed

A car travelled 300 kilometres in 5 hours. Calculate its speed.

Solution

Distance (km) : Time (hr)

= 300 : 5 — Dividing each term by 5 to reduce the second unit to 1,

= 60 : 1

Therefore, the speed of the car is 60 km per hour or 60km/hr.

Example 4.1-f

Calculating Hourly Rate of Pay

Peter worked 9 hours and earned $247.50. Calculate his hourly rate of pay.

Solution

Earnings ($) : Working Period (hrs)

= 247.50 : 9 — Dividing each term by 9 to reduce the second unit to 1,

= 27.50 : 1

Therefore, his hourly rate of pay is $27.50 per hour or $27.50/hr.

Example 4.1-g

Using Unit Rates to Solve a World Problem

A car travels 90 km in 1.5 hours. At this rate, how many kilometres will it travel in 5 hours?

Solution

This can be done using the unit rate.

The unit rate corresponds to 90 km in 1.5 hours

= 90 km / 1.5 hours

= 60 km/hour

That is, the distance travelled in 1 hour = 60 km.

Therefore, the distance travelled in 5 hours = 60 × 5 = 300 km.

Example 4.1-h

Comparing Unit Rate

Car A requires 8.9 litres of gas to travel 100 km. Car B requires 45 litres of gas to travel 475 km. Which car has the better fuel economy?

Solution

Car A : 100 km requires 8.9 litres of gas. Therefore, the number of km per litre:

$$\frac{100 \text{ km}}{8.9 \text{ litres}} = 11.24 \text{ km/litre of gas}$$

Car B : 475km requires 45 litres of gas. Therefore, the number of km per litre:

$$\frac{475 \text{ km}}{45 \text{ litres}} = 10.56 \text{ km/litre of gas}$$

Therefore, Car A has the better fuel economy.

Unit Price

Unit price is the unit rate when it is expressed in unit currency, dollars, cents, etc. Unit price shows the cost of an item for one unit of that item. The price is always the numerator and the unit is the denominator. That is, price is expressed as a quantity of 1.

Price of gas is \$1.36 per litre (\$1.36/litre), price of grapes is \$2 per kg (\$2/kg), price of juice is \$0.75 per can, etc., are examples of unit price.

If the total price of a given quantity of an item is known, then to find its unit price, divide the total price of the item by its quantity.

The unit price is used in comparing and making decisions in purchasing items when various options are available. We save money when we compare the unit price of the same item in different sized containers or different packages to determine the cheaper price per unit for our purchases.

Example 4.1-i

Calculating the Unit Price of an Item

If 3 litres of milk costs \$4.80, then what is the unit price of milk?

Solution

Divide the total price of the given quantity milk by its quantity to find the unit price of milk.

That is, \$4.80 should be divided by 3 litres.

Therefore the unit price of milk = \$4.80 / 3 litres = \$1.60 per litre (\$1.60/litre).

Example 4.1-j **Comparing Unit Price**

5 kg of almonds cost $43.50 and 4 kg of almonds cost $34.20. Which is the better buy based on unit price?

Solution

5 kg of almonds cost $43.50.

$$\text{Therefore, unit price} = \frac{\$43.50}{5\text{ kg}}$$

$$= \$8.70 \text{ per kg}$$

4 kg of almonds cost $34.20

$$\text{Therefore, unit price} = \frac{\$34.20}{4\text{ kg}}$$

$$= \$8.55 \text{ per kg}$$

Therefore, based on unit price, buying 4 kg of almonds for $34.20 is cheaper than buying 5 kg of almonds for $43.50.

Note: Unit rate and unit price problems can also be solved using the method of proportions that you will learn in the next section.

The total of the amount shared individually will be equal to the original amount shared. The ratio of the amount shared individually, when reduced, will be equal to the original ratio.

Sharing Quantities

This refers to the allocation or distribution of a quantity into two or more portions (or units) based on a given ratio.

For example, to allocate last year's $1,000 profit among A, B, and C in the ratio of 2 : 3 : 5, first add the terms in the ratio (i.e., 2, 3, and 5), which results in a total of 10 units. These 10 units represent the total profit of $1,000, where A's share constitutes 2 units, B's 3 units, and C's 5 units, as shown in the diagram.

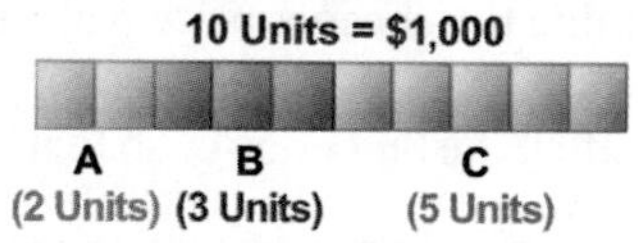

Each person's share can then be calculated, as follows:

$$A\text{'s share} = \frac{2}{10} \times 1{,}000 = \$200.00$$

$$B\text{'s share} = \frac{3}{10} \times 1{,}000 = \$300.00$$

$$C\text{'s share} = \frac{5}{10} \times 1{,}000 = \$500.00$$

Note:

- The total of A, B, and C's shares will be equal to the profit amount $1,000.

That is, the shares of $A + B + C = 200 + 300 + 500 = 1{,}000$.

- If we reduce the ratio of the amounts shared by A, B, and C to its lowest terms, the result would be the original ratio. That is, 200 : 300 : 500 reduced to the lowest terms would be 2 : 3: 5.

Suppose this year, the ratio of *A*'s share : *B*'s share : *C*'s share is changed to 5 : 3 : 2 (instead of last year's 2 : 3 : 5), and the profit amount $1,000 remained the same, then their individual shares will change.

Their shares are recalculated as shown below:

$$A\text{'s share} = \frac{5}{10} \times 1{,}000 = \$500.00$$

$$B\text{'s share} = \frac{3}{10} \times 1{,}000 = \$300.00$$

$$C\text{'s share} = \frac{2}{10} \times 1{,}000 = \$200.00$$

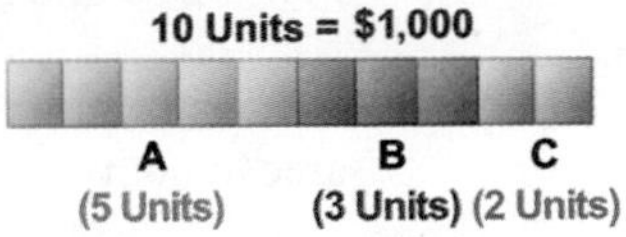

Note:

- The total of *A*, *B*, and *C*'s shares this year will be equal to the profit amount of $1,000. That is, the shares of $A + B + C = 500 + 300 + 200 = \$1{,}000$
- If we reduce the ratio of the amounts shared by A, B, and C to its lowest terms, the result would be the original ratio. That is, 500 : 300 : 200 reduced to the lowest terms is 5 : 3 : 2.

Example 4.1-k **Sharing Using Ratios**

A, *B*, and *C* start a business and invest $3,500, $2,100, and $2,800, respectively. After a few months, if *C* decides to sell his shares to *A* and *B*, how much would *A* and *B* have to pay for *C*'s shares if they want to maintain their initial investment ratio?

Solution

Investments of *A*, *B*, and *C* are in the ratio of 3,500 : 2,100 : 2,800, which can be reduced to 5 : 3 : 4.

If *A* and *B* want to maintain their investment ratio at 5 : 3, then *C*'s share (of $2800) has to be paid for by *A* and *B* in this ratio. By adding the ratio of *A* and *B*, we know that *C*'s share is to be divided into a total of 8 units, as illustrated:

$$A \text{ would have to pay } C: \frac{5}{8} \times 2{,}800 = \$1{,}750.00$$

$$B \text{ would have to pay } C: \frac{3}{8} \times 2{,}800 = \$1{,}050.00$$

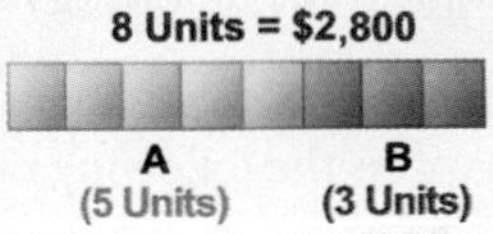

Therefore, A would have to pay $1,750.00 and B would have to pay $1,050.00 in order to maintain their initial investment ratio.

Example 4.1-l **Application Using Equivalent Ratios**

Andrew, Barry, and Cathy invested their savings in a bank. The ratio of the investments of Andrew to Barry is 2 : 3 and that of Barry to Cathy is 4 : 5. What is the investment ratio of Andrew: Barry: Cathy?

Solution

$A : B = 2 : \mathbf{3}$ and $B : C = \mathbf{4} : 5$

Find the equivalent ratio for $A : B$ and $B : C$ so that the number of units in B is the same in both cases.

This can be done by finding the equivalent ratio of $A : B$ by multiplying by 4 and that of $B : C$ by multiplying by 3.

$A : B = 2 : 3$ Multiplying each term by 4,

$= 8 : 12$

$B : C = 4 : 5$ Multiplying each term by 3,

$= 12 : 15$

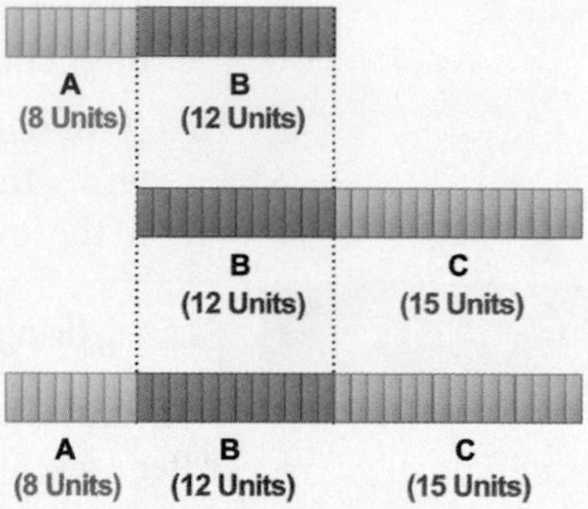

Therefore, the investment ratio of Andrew : Barry : Cathy is 8 : 12 : 15.

4.1 | Exercises

Answers to all problems are available online.

1. Express the following ratios as equivalent ratios in their lowest whole number:

   a. 18 : 48 : 30 b. 175 : 50 : 125 c. 0.45 : 1 : 2

2. Express the following ratios as equivalent ratios in their lowest whole number:

   a. 27 : 45 : 72 b. 180 : 60 : 150 c. 2.4 : 0.75

3. Express the following ratios as equivalent ratios in their lowest whole number:

   a. $\frac{2}{3} : \frac{1}{5}$ b. $12 : \frac{5}{3} : 3$ c. $1.7 : 8.5 : \frac{34}{3}$

4. Express the following ratios as equivalent ratios in their lowest whole number:

   a. $\frac{3}{4} : \frac{2}{5}$ b. $65 : 91 : \frac{13}{2}$ c. $12 : 1.5 : \frac{3}{2}$

5. Express the ratio in Problem 1 as an equivalent ratio having the smallest term 1.
6. Express the ratio in Problem 2 as an equivalent ratio having the smallest term 1.
7. Express the ratio in Problem 3 as an equivalent ratio having the smallest term 1.
8. Express the ratio in Problem 4 as an equivalent ratio having the smallest term 1.

9. Which of the following ratios are equal?

   a. 4 : 6 and 6 : 10 b. 8 : 10 and 28 : 35

   c. 6 : 8 and 27 : 32 d. 16 : 22 and 64 : 88

10. Which of the following ratios are equal?

    a. 16 : 20 and 24 : 30 b. 10 : 12 and 35 : 42

    c. 12 : 14 and 30 : 42 d. 12 : 26 and 30 : 65

11. Which of the following is not an equivalent ratio of 6 : 9 : 12?

    a. 4 : 6 : 8 b. 2 : 3 : 4

    c. 1 : 3 : 2 d. 8 : 12 : 16

12. Which of the following is not an equivalent ratio of 16 : 24 : 12?

    a. 20 : 30 : 15 b. 8 : 12 : 6

    c. 28 : 42 : 21 d. 24 : 36 : 18

13. Find the ratio of the following:

    a. 9 months to 2 years

    b. 30 minutes to 1 hour and 15 minutes

    c. 750 g to 3 kg

14. Find the ratio of the following:

    a. 3 weeks to 126 days

    b. 55 minutes to 2 hours and 45 minutes

    c. 120 g to 2 kg

For Problems 15 to 22, find the unit rate.

15. 525 km in 7 hours = ? km/hr
16. 680 km in 8 hours = ? km/hr
17. 154 km to 14 litres = ? km/L
18. 228 km to 19 litres = ? km/L
19. 450 words typed in 6 minutes = ? words/minute
20. 496 words typed in 8 minutes = ? words/minute
21. 261 pages in 9 minutes = ? pages/minute
22. 192 pages in 9 minutes = ? pages/minute

For Problems 23 to 30, identify the option that is less expensive based on unit rate.

23. A 240 gram box of cereal at $3.69, or a 360 gram box of cereal at $4.89.
24. A 600 gram of spread at $3.72, or a 400 gram of spread at $2.80.
25. 2 kg of flour at $3.30, or 5 kg of flour at $8.40.
26. 3 kg of sugar at $3.90, or 5 kg of sugar at $6.25.
27. 12 pencils at $4.44, or 8 pencils at $2.88.
28. 6 litres of paint at $45.60, or 5 litres of paint at $37.25.

29. 1.2 litres of juice at $2.16, or 0.8 litres of juice at $1.40.
30. 2.2 kg of jam at $11.00, or 1.5 kg of jam at $7.20.
31. What is the ratio of a Canadian quarter (25¢) to a Canadian $5 bill, reduced to its lowest terms?
32. What is the ratio of 12 minutes to 2 hours, reduced to its lowest terms?
33. In a race, participants are required to complete two successive events, swimming and bicycling, without stopping. If they have to swim 3,850 metres and bike 7 kilometres, calculate the ratio of the distance covered by swimming to biking, in its lowest terms.
34. Adam, a hardware engineer, wants to install a microchip that is 38.2 mm in length into his laptop. The length of the installation space provided in his laptop is 4.8 cm. Calculate the ratio of the length of the microchip to the installation space, in its lowest terms.
35. Emily was planning to make an authentic Indian dish for her guests. She planned to use 36 eggs, 6 litres of water, 3 tablespoons of chilli powder, and 12 tomatoes.
    a. What is the ratio of the ingredients in her recipe?
    b. If she decides to reduce the quantity of chilli powder to $1\frac{1}{2}$ tablespoons, calculate the new ratio of the ingredients in her recipe.
36. In Murphy's battery manufacturing company, 600 kg of lead, 45 kg of carbon, 30 litres of battery acid, and 120 kg of rubber are used per day to make batteries.
    a. What is the ratio of the raw materials used to make batteries per day?
    b. If they alter the quantity of carbon used in the batteries and utilize 30 kg of carbon per day, calculate the new ratio of raw materials used per day.
37. An aircraft travels a distance of 3,105 km in 5 hours and 45 minutes. Calculate the ratio of the distance traveled to the time taken, reduced to a rate of kilometres per hour.
38. Speed is defined as the ratio of the distance travelled to the time taken. If Mary, who lives in Toronto, took 6 hours and 15 minutes to reach her parent's home in Montreal, which is 575 km away, calculate the speed at which she was travelling.
39. A TV cable bill of $90 is shared between two house-mates, Mike and Sarah, in the ratio of $2 : 2\frac{1}{2}$. How much would each person pay?
40. Alexander and Alyssa invested a total of $10,000 in a web-design business. If the ratio of their investments is 3 : 5, what are their investments?
41. Amy and 2 of her friends received the first prize for a marketing case competition. They received an amount of $7,500; however, they decided to share the prize in the ratio of the amount of time each of them spent on the marketing case. If Amy spent 5 hours, Gary spent 8 hours, and Andrew spent 2 hours, what would be each person's share of the prize?
42. Three friends, Andy, Berry, and Cassandra, *A*, *B*, and *C*, jointly insured a commercial property in the ratio of 10 : 9 : 6, respectively. How will an annual premium of $8,000 be distributed among the three of them?
43. Three friends, Alex, Brooks, and Charlie, have decided to invest $4,000, $6,000, and $2,000, respectively, to start a software development business. If Charlie decided to leave the business, how much would Alex and Brooks have to pay for Charlie's share if they want to maintain their initial investment ratio?

44. Chuck decided to build a yacht with his two friends Rob and Bob and they invested $9,000, $11,000, and $6,500, respectively. After the yacht was built, Bob decided to sell his share of the investment to Chuck and Rob. How much would each of them have to pay if they want to maintain the same ratio of their investments in the yacht?
45. If A earns $196 for working 8 hours and B earns $98 for working 5 hours, whose average hourly rate is higher?
46. If Amanda travelled 325 km in 4 hours and 15 minutes and Ashton travelled 290 km in 3 hours and 30 minutes, whose average speed was greater?
47. Abey and Baxter invested equal amounts of money in a business. A year later, Abey withdrew $7,500 making the ratio of their investments 5 : 9. How much money did each of them invest in the beginning?
48. Jessica and Russel invested equal amounts to start a business. Two months later, Jessica invested an additional $3,000 in the business, making the ratio of their investments 11 : 5. How much money did each of them invest in the beginning?
49. If $A : B = 4 : 3$ and $B : C = 6 : 5$, find $A : B : C$.
50. If $X : Y = 5 : 2$ and $Y : Z = 7 : 6$, find $X : Y : Z$.
51. Kate earned $210 for 7.5 hours of work and Susan earned $249.75 for 9 hours of work.
    a. Calculate their hourly rate.
    b. Whose hourly rate was higher and by how much?
52. Jack's monthly pay is $4,200. Steve's weekly pay is $975.
    a. Calculate their annual salary. (1 year = 12 months = 52 weeks)
    b. Whose annual salary is more and by how much?
53. A 500 km trip by car took 6 hours and 45 minutes. Calculate the speed of the car in km/hr.
54. The average speed of a car is 75 km/hour. At this speed, how many hours will it take to travel 700 km.

4.2 | Proportions

Proportions

When two sets of ratios are equal, we say that they are proportionate to each other. In the proportion equation, the ratio on the left side of the equation is equal to the ratio on the right side of the equation.

Consider an example where $A : B$ is 50 :100 and $C : D$ is 30 : 60.

Reducing the ratio to its lowest terms, we obtain the ratio of $A : B$ as 1 : 2 and the ratio of $C : D$ as 1 : 2.

Since these ratios are equal, they are equally proportionate to each other and their proportion equation is,

$$\boldsymbol{A : B = C : D}$$

If two sets of fractions are equal, then the product obtained by cross-multiplying the fractions will be equal.

The proportion equation can also be formed by representing the ratios as fractions.

Equating the fraction obtained by dividing the 1st term by the 2nd term on the left side, to the one obtained by dividing the 1st term by the 2nd term on the right side we get,

$$\frac{A}{B} = \frac{C}{D}$$

This proportion equation can be simplified by multiplying both sides of the equation by the product of both denominators, which is $B \times D$.

$\frac{A}{B} = \frac{C}{D}$ Multiplying both sides by $(B \times D)$,

$\frac{A}{B}(B \times D) = \frac{C}{D}(B \times D)$ Simplifying,

$AD = BC$

The same result could be obtained by equating the product of the numerator of the 1st ratio and the denominator of the 2nd ratio with the product of the denominator of the 1st ratio and the numerator of the 2nd ratio. This is referred to as cross-multiplication and is shown below:

Cross-multiplying, $\frac{A}{B} \times \frac{C}{D}$

$$AD = BC$$

If 3 terms of the proportion equation are known, the 4th term can be calculated.

Therefore, $A : B = C : D$ is equivalent to $\frac{A}{B} = \frac{C}{D}$.

If $A : B : C = D : E : F$

then,

$\frac{A}{B} = \frac{D}{E}, \frac{B}{C} = \frac{E}{F}, \frac{A}{C} = \frac{D}{F}$

or,

$\frac{A}{D} = \frac{B}{E} = \frac{C}{F}$

Proportion Equation With Sets of Ratios Having More Than Two Terms

For example,

If $A : B : C = D : E : F$,

Then this ratio can be expressed as $\frac{A}{B} = \frac{D}{E}$, $\frac{B}{C} = \frac{E}{F}$, and $\frac{A}{C} = \frac{D}{F}$.

Cross multiplying,

$AE = BD$, $BF = CE$, and $AF = CD$

The given ratio can also be expressed as, $\frac{A}{D} = \frac{B}{E} = \frac{C}{F}$.

In both cases, cross-multiplying leads to the same result.

Therefore, $AE = BD$, $BF = CE$, and $AF = CD$.

Example 4.2-a **Solving for the Unknown Quantity in Proportions**

Find the missing term in the following proportions:

(i) $4 : 5 = 8 : x$

(ii) $6 : x = 10 : 25$

(iii) $x : 1.9 = 2.6 : 9.88$

(iv) $3 : 3\frac{3}{4} = x : 5\frac{1}{4}$

Solution

(i) $4 : 5 = 8 : x$

In fractional form,	$\frac{4}{5} = \frac{8}{x}$	or,	$\frac{4}{8} = \frac{5}{x}$
Cross-multiplying,	$4x = 40$		
Simplifying,	$x = \frac{40}{4}$		
Therefore,	$x = 10$		

(ii) $6 : x = 10 : 25$

In fractional form,	$\frac{6}{x} = \frac{10}{25}$	or,	$\frac{6}{10} = \frac{x}{25}$
Cross-multiplying,	$150 = 10x$		
Simplifying,	$x = \frac{150}{10}$		
Therefore,	$x = 15$		

(iii) $x : 1.9 = 2.6 : 9.88$

In fractional form,	$\frac{x}{1.9} = \frac{2.6}{9.88}$	or,	$\frac{1.90}{9.88} = \frac{x}{2.6}$
Cross-multiplying,	$9.88x = 4.94$		
Simplifying,	$x = \frac{4.94}{9.88}$		
Therefore,	$x = 0.5$		

(iv) $3 : 3\frac{3}{4} = x : 5\frac{1}{4}$

Rewriting in improper fractional form,	$3 : \frac{15}{4} = x : \frac{21}{4}$		
Multiply both sides by 4,	$12 : 15 = 4x : 21$		
In fractional form,	$\frac{12}{15} = \frac{4x}{21}$	or,	$\frac{4x}{21} = \frac{12}{15}$
Cross-multiplying,	$60x = 252$		
Simplifying,	$x = \frac{252}{60}$		
Therefore,	$x = 4.2$		

Example 4.2-b Solving Word Problems Using Proportions

Ben can walk a distance of 9 km in 2 hours. Calculate:

(i) The distance (in km) that Ben can walk in $3\frac{1}{2}$ hours.

(ii) How long (in hours) will it take him to walk 15 km?

Solution

(i) Calculating the distance in (km):

hr : km = hr : km

$2 : 9 = 3\frac{1}{2} : x$ Using fractional notation,

$$\frac{2}{9} = \frac{\frac{7}{2}}{x}$$

$\frac{2}{9} = \frac{7}{2x}$ Cross-multiplying,

$4x = 63$ Dividing both sides by 4,

$x = \frac{63}{4}$ Dividing,

$x = 15.75$

Therefore, Ben can walk a distance of 15.75 km in $3\frac{1}{2}$ hours.

(ii) Calculating the time it will take him to walk 15km:

hr : km = hr : km

$2 : 9 = x : 15$ Using fractional notation,

$\frac{2}{9} = \frac{x}{15}$ Cross-multiplying,

$30 = 9x$

$9x = 30$ Dividing both sides by 9,

$x = \frac{30}{9}$ Dividing,

$= 3.333333... = 3.33$

Therefore, Ben can walk 15 km in 3.33 hours.

Example 4.2-c Sharing, Using Proportions

Andrew (A), Brandon (B), and Chris (C) decide to form a partnership to start a snow removal business together. A invests \$31,500, B invests \$42,000, and C invests \$73,500. They agree to share the profits in the same ratio as their investments.

(i) What is the ratio of their investments?

(ii) In the first year of running the business, A's profit was \$27,000. What were B's and C's profits?

(iii) In the second year, their total profit was \$70,000. How much would each of them receive from this total profit?

Solution

(i) Ratio of their inv0estments:

$A : B : C$

31,5070 : 42,000 : 73,500 Dividing each term by the common factor of 100,

315 : 420 : 735 Dividing each term by the common factor of 5,

63 : 84 : 147 Dividing each term by the common factor of 7,

9 : 12 : 21 Dividing each term by the common factor of 3,

3 : 4 : 7

Therefore, the ratio of their investments is 3 : 4 : 7.

(ii) A's profit was \$27,000. What were B's and C's profits?

Method 1:

Ratio of Investment = Ratio of Profit

$A : B : C = A : B : C$

Substituting terms, $3 : 4 : 7 = 27{,}000 : x : y$

In fractional form, $\frac{3}{4} = \frac{27{,}000}{x}$ and $\frac{3}{7} = \frac{27{,}000}{y}$

Cross-multiplying, $3x = 108{,}000$ $3y = 189{,}000$

Simplifying, $x = \$36{,}000.00$ $y = \$63{,}000.00$

Therefore, B's profit is \$36,000.00. Therefore, C's profit is \$63,000.00.

Method 2:

Ratio of Investment = Ratio of Profit

$A : B : C = A : B : C$

Substituting terms, $3 : 4 : 7 = 27{,}000 : x : y$

$$\frac{3}{27{,}000} = \frac{4}{x} = \frac{7}{y}$$

Hence, $\frac{3}{27{,}000} = \frac{4}{x}$ and $\frac{3}{27{,}000} = \frac{7}{y}$

Cross-multiplying, $3x = 108{,}000$ $3y = 189{,}000$

$x = \$36{,}000.00$ $y = \$63{,}000.00$

Therefore, B's profit is \$36,000.00. Therefore, C's profit is \$63,000.00.

Solution
continued

(iii) In the second year, their total profit was $70,000. How much would each of them receive from this total profit?

Method 1:

Since A, B, and C agreed to share profits in the same ratio as their investments, $70,000 must be shared in the ratio, 3 : 4 : 7.

By adding the ratio of their investments (3 + 4 + 7), we know that the total profit of $70,000 should be distributed over 14 units. Therefore,

$$A:B:C:\text{Total} \quad = \quad A:B:C:\text{Total}$$

Substituting terms, $3:4:7:14 \quad = \quad A:B:C:70{,}000$

This means, $\dfrac{3}{14}=\dfrac{A}{70{,}000},\ \dfrac{4}{14}=\dfrac{B}{70{,}000},\ \dfrac{7}{14}=\dfrac{C}{70{,}000}$

Cross-multiplying, $14A = 210{,}000 \quad 14B = 280{,}000, \quad 14C = 490{,}000$

$$A = \$15{,}000.00, \quad B = \$20{,}000.00, \quad C = \$35{,}000.00$$

Therefore, A, B, and C will receive profits of $15,000.00, $20,000.00, and $35,000.00, repsectively.

Method 2:

$$\text{Ratio of Investment} \quad = \quad \text{Ratio of Profit}$$

$$A:B:C:\text{Total} \quad = \quad A:B:C:\text{Total}$$

Substituting terms, $3:4:7:14 \quad = \quad A:B:C:70{,}000$

This means, $\dfrac{3}{A}=\dfrac{4}{B}=\dfrac{7}{C}=\dfrac{14}{70{,}000}$

$$\frac{3}{A}=\frac{14}{70{,}000}, \quad \frac{4}{B}=\frac{14}{70{,}000}, \quad \frac{7}{C}=\frac{14}{70{,}000}$$

Cross-multiplying, $14A = 3 \times 70{,}000, 14B = 4 \times 70{,}000, 14C = 7 \times 70{,}000$

$$A=\frac{3\times 70{,}000}{14} \quad B=\frac{4\times 70{,}000}{14} \quad C=\frac{7\times 70{,}000}{14}$$

Simplifying, $A = \$15{,}000.00, \quad B = \$20{,}000.00, \quad C = 35{,}000.00$

Therefore, A, B, and C will receive profits of $15,000.00, $20,000.00, and $35,000.00, respectively.

Pro-rations

Pro-ration is defined as sharing or allocating the quantities, usually the amounts, on a proportionate basis.

Consider an example where Sarah paid $690 for a math course but decided to withdraw from the course after attending half the course. As she attended only half the course, the college decided to refund half her tuition fee, ($\dfrac{\$690}{2} = \$345$).

As the college calculated the refund amount proportionate to the time she attended the course, we say that the college refunded her tuition fee on a **pro-rata basis.**

A few examples where pro-rated calculations are used:

- When a propery is sold, the property tax paid in advance will be refunded on a pro-rata basis.
- When an insurance is cancelled before the end of the period for which the premiums were paid, the amount refunded is calculated on a pro-rata basis.
- Employees' overtime pay, part-time pay, and vacation times are calculated on a pro-rata basis.

Example 4.2-d

Calculating the Pro-rated Amount of a Payment

Find the pro-rated insurance premium for seven months if the annual premium paid for car insurance is $2,250.

Solution

Ratio of their investments:

$$\text{Premium (\$)} : \text{time (months)} = \text{Premium (\$)} : \text{time (months)}$$

$$2{,}250 : 12 = x : 7$$

Expressed in fractional form, $\dfrac{2{,}250}{12} = \dfrac{x}{7}$

$$12x = 15{,}750$$

$$x = \$1{,}312.50$$

Therefore, the pro-rated premium for seven months is $1,312.50.

Example 4.2-e

Calculating the Pro-rated Amount of a Refund

Johnson paid $350 for a 2-year weekly subscription of a health journal. After receiving 18 issues of the journal in his second year, he decided to cancel his subscription. What should be the amount of his refund? Assume 1 year = 52 weeks.

Solution

Paid for 104 issues (2×52) and received 70 issues (52+18); therefore, he should be refunded for 34 issues ($104 - 70$).

$$\text{Issues (\#)} : \text{Cost (\$)} = \text{Issues (\#)} : \text{Cost (\$)}$$

Substituting values, $104 : 350 = 34 : x$

Solving for x, $\dfrac{104}{350} = \dfrac{34}{x}$

$$104x = 34 \times 350$$

$$x = 114.423077...$$

$$= \$114.42$$

Therefore, his refund should be $114.42.

4.2 | Exercises

Answers to all problems are available online.

1. Determine which of the following pairs of ratios are in proportion:

   a. 6 : 9 and 14 : 21 b. 5 : 15 and 2 : 8

   c. 18 : 24 and 12 : 16 d. 12 : 60 and 6 : 24

2. Determine which of the following pairs of ratios are in proportion:

   a. 9 : 12 and 4 : 3 b. 10 : 30 and 8 : 24

   c. 14 : 20 and 28 : 42 d. 15 : 12 and 24 : 30

3. Solve the following proportions for the unknown value:

   a. $1 : 2 = 5 : x$ b. $x : 1.2 = 3.4 : 5.8$

   c. $1 : 4\frac{1}{2} = x : 2\frac{3}{4}$ d. $2.25 : 1\frac{1}{2} = x : 1\frac{3}{4}$

4. Solve the following proportions for the unknown value:

   a. $5 : 9 = x : 3$ b. $12.34 : 1.8 = x : 2.2$

   c. $11\frac{3}{4} : 8 = 18\frac{1}{4} : x$ d. $4.75 : x = 6\frac{3}{4} : 3.28$

5. A truck requires 96 litres of gas to cover 800 km. How many litres of gas will it require to cover 1,500 km?

6. Based on Alvin's past experience, it would take his team 5 months to complete two projects. How long would his team take to complete 8 similar projects?

7. Eric paid a property tax of $3,600 for his land that measures 330 square metres. What would his neighbour's property tax be if the size of the house is 210 square metres and is taxed at the same rate?

8. The city of Brampton charges $1,750 in taxes per year for a 2,000 square metre farm. How much would Maple Farms have to pay in taxes if they had a 12,275 square metre farm in the same area?

9. On a map, 4 cm represents 5.0 km. If the distance between town *A* and town *B* on the map is 9.3 cm, how many kilometres apart are these towns?

10. On a house plan, 1.25 cm represents 3 metres. If the actual length of a room is 5.4 metres, how many centimetres would represent this length in the plan?

11. Steve invested his savings in a GIC, mutual funds, and a fixed deposit in the ratio of 5 : 4 : 3, respectively. If he invested $10,900 in mutual funds, calculate his investments in the GIC and the fixed deposit.

12. The ratio of the distance from Ann's house to Mark, Jeff, and Justin's houses is 3 : 5.25 : 2, respectively. If the distance from Ann's house to Mark's is 9.50 km, calculate the distance from Ann's house to Justin's and Ann's house to Jeff's.

13. A, B, and C, started a business with investments in the ratio of 5 : 4 : 3, respectively. A invested $25,000, and all three of them agreed to share profits in the ratio of their investments.

    a. Calculate C's investment.

    b. If A's profit was $30,000 in the first year, calculate B and C's profits.

    c. How much would each of them receive if in the second year, the total profit was $135,000?

14. A, B, and C formed a partnership and invested in the ratio of 7 : 9 : 5, respectively. They agreed to share the profit in the ratio of their investments. A invested $350,000.

    a. Calculate B and C's investments in the business.

    b. If the business made a profit of $126,000 in the first year, calculate each partner's share of the profit.

    c. In the second year, if A made $38,500 in profit from the partnership, how much did B and C make?

15. A student pays $620 for a course that has 25 classes. Find the pro-rated refund she would receive if she only attends 5 classes before withdrawing from the course.

16. Megan joined a driving school that charges $375 for 12 classes. After attending 7 classes, she decided that she did not like the training and wanted to cancel the remaining classes. Calculate the pro-rated refund she should receive.

17. Frank bought a brand new car on August 01, 2012 and obtained pre-paid insurance of $1,058 for the period of August 01, 2012 to July 31, 2013. After 2 months of using the car, he sold it and cancelled his insurance. Calculate the pro-rated refund he should receive from the insurance company.

18. The owner of a new gaming business decided to insure his servers and computers. His insurance company charged him a premium of $2,000 per quarter, starting January 01. If the insurance started on February 01, how much pro-rated insurance premium did he have to pay for the rest of the first quarter? (Hint: Quarter of a year is 3 months).

19. Chris, Diane, and David invested a total of $520,000 in the ratio of 3 : 4 : 6, respectively to start a business. Two months later, each of them invested an additional $25,000 into the business. Calculate their new investment ratio after the additional investments.

20. Michael and his two sisters purchased an office for $720,000. Their individual investments in the office were in the ratio of 5 : 4 : 3, respectively. After the purchase, they decided to renovate the building and purchase furniture, so each of them invested an additional $60,000. Calculate their new investment ratio after the additional investments.

21. If the annual salary of an employee is $45,000, calculate his bi-weekly salary using pro-ration. Assume that there are 52 weeks in a year and 26 bi-weekly payments.

22. Ashley received a job offer at a company that would pay her $2,800, bi-weekly. What would her annual salary be, assuming that she would receive 26 payments in a year?

23. Charles set up a new charity fund to support children in need. For every $10 collected by the charity, the Government donated an additional grant of $5 to the charity. At the end of 3 months, if his charity fund had a total of $135,000, including the Government grant, calculate the amount the charity received from the Government.

24. The tax on education materials sold in Ontario is such that for every $1.00 worth of a material sold, the buyer would have to pay an additional $0.05 in taxes. If $25,000 worth of textbooks were sold at a bookstore before taxes, calculate the total amount of tax to be paid by the purchasers.

25. A, B, and C invested $35,000, $42,000, and $28,000, respectively, to start an e-learning business. They realized that they required an additional $45,000 for operating the business. How much did each of them have to individually invest to maintain their original investment ratio?

26. Three wealthy business partners decided to invest \$150,000, \$375,000, and \$225,000, respectively, to purchase an industrial plot in the outskirts of the city. They required an additional \$90,000 to build an industrial shed on the land. How much did each of them have to individually invest to maintain their original investment ratio?
27. A first semester class in a college has 6 more girls than boys and the ratio of the number of girls to boys in the class is 8 : 5.
    a. How many students are there in the class?
    b. If 4 girls and 3 boys joined the class, find the new ratio of girls to boys in the class.
28. The advisory board of a public sector company has 10 more men than women and the ratio of the number of men to women is 8 : 3.
    a. How many people are there on the board?
    b. If 4 men and 4 women joined the board, calculate the new ratio of men to women.
29. To estimate the number of tigers in a forest, a team of researchers tagged 84 tigers and released them into the forest. Six months later, 30 tigers were spotted, out of which 7 had tags. How many tigers are estimated to be in the forest?
30. Researchers were conducting a study to estimate the number of frogs in a pond. They put a bright yellow band on the legs of 60 frogs and released them into the pond. A few days later, 15 frogs were spotted, out of which 5 had bands. How many frogs are estimated to be in the pond?

4 | Review Exercises

Answers to odd-numbered problems are available online.

1. Solve the following proportions for the unknown value:
    a. $\frac{x}{26} = \frac{9}{39}$
    b. $\frac{16}{12} = \frac{24}{x}$
    c. $\frac{x}{0.16} = \frac{0.45}{1.20}$
2. Solve the following proportions for the unknown value:
    a. $\frac{x}{24} = \frac{15}{36}$
    b. $\frac{8}{x} = \frac{14}{35}$
    c. $\frac{12.5}{x} = \frac{70}{1.4}$
3. Which of the following ratios are equal:
    a. 6 : 8 and 18 : 24
    b. 30 : 25 and 36 : 48
    c. 10 : 35 and 14 : 49
    d. 24 : 30 and 12 : 18
4. Which of the following ratios are equal:
    a. 16 : 20 and 18 : 30
    b. 4 : 10 and 10 : 24
    c. 35 : 50 and 21 : 36
    d. 20 : 16 and 30 : 24
5. If Christina, a graphic designer, receives an annual salary of \$55,000, calculate her weekly salary using pro-rations. Assume that there are 52 weeks in a year.

6. As the CFO of a technology company, every year, Tyler would receive 26 bi-weekly payments of $6,000 each. Calculate his monthly salary.

7. Which is the better buy based on their unit price: 360 grams at $2.99 or 480 grams at $3.75?

8. Which is the better buy based on their unit price: 125 grams at $4.75 or 175 grams at $5.95?

9. A 450 gram loaf of bread costs $3.15 and has 15 slices.

   a. Find the cost per 100 grams of bread

   b. Find the cost per slice of bread

10. 250 grams of sliced cheese costs $4.50 and has 6 slices.

    a. Find the cost per 100 grams of cheese.

    b. Find the cost per slice of cheese.

11. Ali can run 12 km in 20 minutes.

    a. Calculate his speed in km/hour.

    b. At this speed, how far can he run in 1.5 hours?

12. A car can travel 486 km using 45 litres of gas.

    a. Calculate the fuel efficency of the car in km/litre.

    b. At this rate, how many litres of gas is required for a trip of 810 km?

13. If the ratio of sugar to flour in a pie is 3 : 5 and that of flour to eggs is 3 : 1, calculate the ratio of sugar : flour : eggs in the pie.

14. If the ratio of sales people to marketing people in an organization is 5 : 4 and the ratio of marketing people to finance people is 5 : 2, what is the ratio of sales people : marketing people : finance people in the organization?

15. Calculate the unit price for each of the following offers and identify which offer is the best, based on the unit price:

    a. 3 kg of oranges for $7.99

    b. 4 kg of oranges for $9.99

    c. 5 kg of oranges for $11.99

16. Calculate the unit price for each of the following offers and identify which offer is the best, based on the unit price:

    a. 5 kg of rice for $4.99

    b. 8 kg of rice for $7.99

    c. 10 kg of rice for $9.49

17. Alexander, an investment banker, invests all his yearly earnings in stocks of high-tech, mining, and real-estate in the ratio of 4 : 5 : 3, respectively. Calculate his investment in mining stocks if his investment in high-tech stocks was $10,900.

18. The ratio of the driving distance from London to Hamilton, Mississauga, and Toronto is 3 : 4 : 5, respectively. If the distance from London to Hamilton is 125 km, calculate the distance from London to Mississauga and from London to Toronto.

19. Three college classmates, Khan, Thomas, and Lee decided to start a small business and invested $1,000, $2,500, and $3,500, respectively. If Lee decided to leave the business, how much would Khan and Thomas have to pay for Lee's shares if they wanted to maintain their initial investment ratio?

20. Calvin decided to build a shopping complex with his two brothers, Kevin and Alex. They invested $200,000, $350,000, and $450,000, respectively. After the complex was built, Kevin decided to sell his share of the investment to Calvin and Alex. How much would each of them have to pay if they wanted to maintain the same ratio of their investments in the complex?

21. A, B, and C invested a total of $900 in the ratio of 3 : 4 : 5 , respectively, to purchase a billiards table for their club house. After the table was delivered, each invested an additional $200 to purchase balls and cue sticks. Calculate their new investment ratio after their additional investments.

22. Samuel, his wife, and his mother jointly purchased an estate for $1,350,000. Their individual investments in the estate were in the ratio of 5:3:1, respectively. Each of them decided to invest an additional $250,000 to develop the estate into a small family resort. Calculate their new investment ratio after the additional investments.

For Problems 23 to 26, find the most economic price of the following items by comparing their unit prices.

23. Jeffrey and Gina were classmates who graduated together from college. Jeffrey found a job as a banker that pays him $189 for 9 hours and Gina found a job as a freelance artist that pays her $174 for 8 hours of work. Who is being paid a higher hourly rate and by how much?

24. Gregory purchased a racing motorbike and Chris purchased a cruising motorbike. Jeffery travelled 765 km from Toronto to New York City and covered this journey in 8 hours and 20 minutes. Chris travelled for 165 km from Toronto to Buffalo in 2 hours and 10 minutes. Based on this information, whose average speed was greater and by how much was it greater (in km/hr)?

25. Anton, Cheryl, and Ellen invested $4,000, $7,500, and $6,000, respectively, to start a video production studio. The company did very well in the first year and they wanted to invest an additional $5,250 to expand their business. How much would each of them have to individually invest to maintain their original investment ratio?

26. Russel, an investment banker, invested $8,000, $12,000, and $4,000 in stocks of three different companies. The market showed potential to grow so he decided to invest an additional $1,500 in stocks of the same companies. How did he invest this amount into stocks of the three companies to maintain the original investment ratio?

4 | Self-Test Exercises

Answers to all problems are available online.

1. Solve for the unknown quantity:

   a. $\frac{35}{60} = \frac{7}{x}$ b. $\frac{45}{70} = \frac{x}{63}$

2. Solve for the unknown quantity:

   a. $\frac{2.5}{x} = \frac{9}{2.7}$ b. $\frac{x}{2\frac{1}{4}} = \frac{8}{2\frac{1}{2}}$

3. The scale on a map is 3 cm = 50 km. Calculate the actual distance between the two cities that are 12.75 cm apart on a map.

4. The property tax on a property assessed at $430,000 is $4,235.50. Calculate the property tax on a similar property assessed at $612,750.

5. An investment of $1,500 earned $820 in interest in one year. What amount should be invested at this rate to earn $1,459 in interest?

6. Nabil and Mohammad invested a total of \$100,000 in the ratio of 3 : 5, respectively. After one year, both of them withdrew \$10,000 from the invesment. Calculate the ratio of their investments after the withdrawal.

7. Profits are distributed to the 3 partners, Alice, Bill and Carol, based on their investments of \$60,000, \$40,000 and \$96,000, respectively. If the profit last year was \$58,800, calculate their share of the profits.

8. Georgia paid a yearly subscription amount of \$250 to receive a business magazine monthly. After receiving two issues, she cancelled her subscription. Calculate the pro-rated refund she should receive from the magazine company.

9. For every \$25 that a not-for-profit foundation transferred to a relief fund, the Government donated \$10 towards the same cause. After 2 months of fund raising, the foundation had a total of \$9,450, including the Government's contribution. Calculate the amount donated by the Government.

10. A car travelled 250 km. If the fuel efficency of the car is 9 litres per 100 km, calculate the amount of gas used for the trip.

11. Which offer is best based on the unit price?

    a. 75 grams of chocolate for \$1.49

    b. 100 grams of choclate for \$1.99

    c. 125 grams of chocolate for \$2.25

12. Andrew's earnings to Bill's was in the ratio of 3 : 5 and Bill's to Cathy's was in the ratio of 4 : 6. What was the ratio of the earnings of Andrew : Bill : Cathy?

Chapter 5
Percents and Percent Changes

Learning Outcomes

- Convert percents to equivalent fractions and decimal numbers.
- Solve percent problems using different methods.
- Compute bases, rates, or portions of quantities, expressed in percents.
- Identify the terminology used in percent change.
- Use percents to measure percent increase and decrease.

Chapter Outline

5.1 Percents

5.2 Percent Changes

Percents and percent changes make comparisons easy and are used very often in our daily lives in making business decisions. Due to the simplicity of expressions in day-to-day business statements, percents have turned out to be a widely accepted measure of expressing fractions or decimal numbers. Some examples of the use of percents include interest rate charged by banks on loans, discounts offered at stores, sales tax charged on items purchased, commissions recieved by sales representatives, etc.

5.1 | Percents

Percent is the number of parts per hundred,

$C\% = \frac{C}{100} = 0.01C$

Introduction

In Chapter 2, you learned that 'fractions' and 'decimal numbers' are used to represent portions (part) of a whole number or quantity. In this chapter, you will learn about '**percent**' as another **form** of representing portions of a whole quantity.

'**Percent**' (per cent or per hundred in the literal meaning) is used to express a quantity out of 100 units and is represented by the symbol '%'.

For example, 5% means 5 **per** hundred, or 5 out of 100, or $\frac{5}{100}$, or 5 hundredths, or 0.05.

100% means 100 out of 100 (i.e, the whole quantity)

75% means 75 out of 100 (i.e., $\frac{75}{100} = \frac{3}{4}$ or 0.75)

50% means 50 out of 100 (i.e., $\frac{50}{100} = \frac{1}{2}$ or 0.50)

25% means 25 out of 100 (i.e., $\frac{25}{100} = \frac{1}{4}$ or 0.25)

Note: 200% means 2 times (or double or twice) the whole quantity. It it not meaningful to say 200 out of 100. Similarily 350% means $3\frac{1}{2}$ times the whole quantity.

Relationship Among Percents, Fractions, and Decimal Numbers

Fractions and decimal numbers can be converted to percent and vice-versa. For example, 3 parts out of 4 equal parts of a quantity can be represented as a fraction, decimal number, or in percent form, as follows:

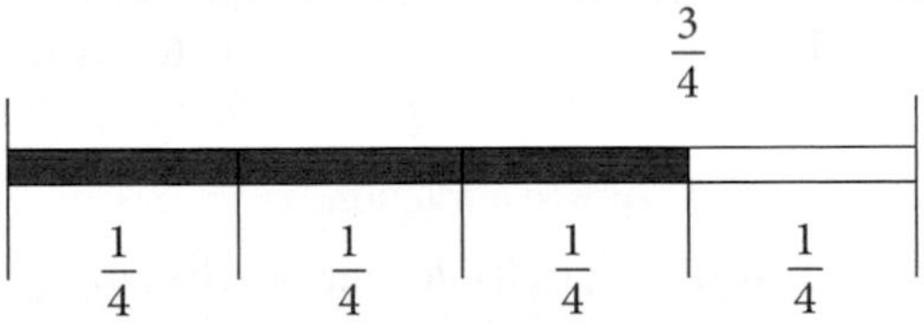

As a fraction, it is $\frac{3}{4}$.

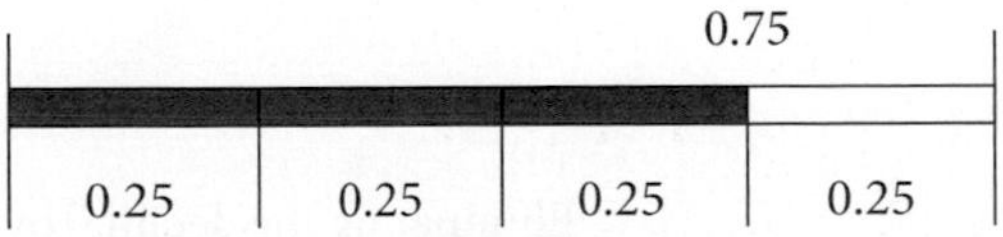

As a decimal, it is 0.75.

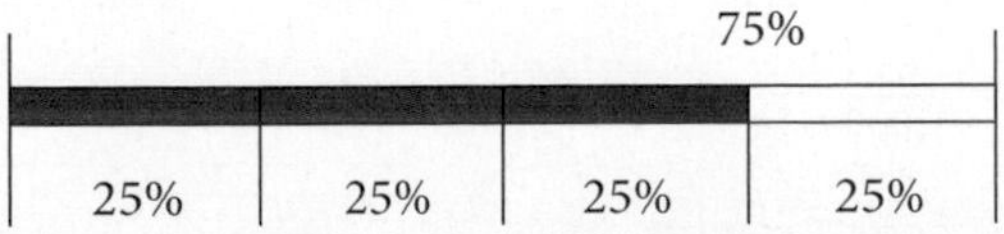

As a percent, it is 75%.

In day-to-day business, '**percent**' is commonly used in interest rates, sales discounts, commissions, comparison of changes in quantity, etc. However, in actual calculations, fractions (ratios) or decimal equivalents are used. Therefore, it is necessary to know the method of converting from one form to the other.

Converting Percents to Fractions

- **If the percent is a whole number,** remove the percent sign, divide by 100 (or multiply by $\frac{1}{100}$), and reduce to its lowest terms.

For example, to convert 60% to a fraction in its lowest terms:

Using the definition of percent,

$$60\% = \frac{60}{100}$$ Reducing this to the lowest terms,

$$= \frac{3}{5}$$

Therefore, $60\% = \frac{3}{5}$.

- **If the percent includes a decimal number**, remove the percent sign, divide by 100, change it to its fractional equivalent by eliminating the decimal in the numerator, and reduce to its lowest terms.

For example, to convert 42.5% to a fraction:

Using the definition of percent,

$$42.5\% = \frac{42.5}{100}$$ Eliminating the decimal in the numerator by multiplying both the numerator and the denominator by 10,

$$= \frac{425}{1{,}000}$$ Reducing this to the lowest terms,

$$= \frac{17}{40}$$

Therefore, $42.5\% = \frac{17}{40}$.

- **If the percent is a fraction or a mixed number** (combination of a whole number and a fraction), either convert it to its decimal equivalent or convert it to an improper fraction and follow the steps below.

For example, to convert $6\frac{1}{2}\%$ to a fraction:

Method 1: By converting it to its decimal equivalent

Using the definition of percent,

$$6\tfrac{1}{2}\% = \frac{6\frac{1}{2}}{100}$$ Rewriting the numerator in decimal form,

$$= \frac{6.5}{100}$$ Eliminating the decimal by multiplying both the numerator and denominator by 10,

$$= \frac{65}{1{,}000}$$ Reducing this to the lowest terms,

$$= \frac{13}{200}$$

Method 2: By converting it to its fractional equivalent

Using the definition of percent,

$6\frac{1}{2}\% = \frac{6\frac{1}{2}}{100} = 6\frac{1}{2} \div 100$ Converting the mixed number to an improper fraction,

$= \frac{13}{2} \div 100$

$= \frac{13}{2} \times \frac{1}{100}$ Simplifying,

$= \frac{13}{200}$

Therefore, $6\frac{1}{2}\% = \frac{13}{200}$

Example 5.1-a

Converting Percents to Fractions

Convert each percent to its equivalent fraction or mixed number and simplify to its lowest term.

(i) 45% (ii) $8\frac{1}{3}\%$ (iii) 6.25%

(iv) 175% (v) $\frac{1}{5}\%$

Solution

(i) $45\% = \frac{45}{100} = \frac{9}{20}$

(ii) $8\frac{1}{3}\% = 8\frac{1}{3} \div 100 = \frac{25}{3} \times \frac{1}{100} = \frac{1}{12}$

(iii) $6.25\% = \frac{6.25}{100} = \frac{6.25}{100} \times \frac{100}{100} = \frac{625}{10{,}000} = \frac{1}{16}$

(iv) $175\% = \frac{175}{100} = \frac{7}{4} = 1\frac{3}{4}$

(v) $\frac{1}{5}\% = \frac{\left(\frac{1}{5}\right)}{100} = \frac{1}{5} \div 100 = \frac{1}{5} \times \frac{1}{100} = \frac{1}{500}$

Converting Percents to Decimal Numbers

- **If the percent is a whole number or a decimal number,** remove the '%' sign and move the decimal point 2 places to the left. (This is the same as dividing the number by 100 and dropping the '%' sign.)

For example,

(i) To convert 45% to a decimal number,

45% = 45.0% Removing the % sign and moving the decimal point 2 places to the left,

= 0.45

Therefore 45% = 0.45 (this is the same as $\frac{45}{100}$ = 0.45).

(ii) To convert 0.38% to a decimal number,

0.38% = 0.38% — Removing the % sign and moving the decimal point 2 places to the left,

= 0.0038

Therefore 0.38% = 0.0038 (this is the same as $= \frac{0.38}{100} = 0.0038$).

- **If the percent is a fraction or a mixed number** (combination of a whole number with a fraction), change it to its decimal equivalent and follow the steps as shown above.

For example, to convert $2\frac{1}{2}$% to a decimal number,

$2\frac{1}{2}$% = 2.5% — Converting the fractional portion to a decimal number,

$2\frac{1}{2}$% = 2.5% — Removing the % sign and moving the decimal point 2 places to the left,

= 0.025

Therefore, $2\frac{1}{2}$% = 0.025 (this is the same as $\frac{2.5}{100} = 0.025$).

Example 5.1-b

Converting Percents to Decimal Numbers

Convert each percent to its equivalent decimal number.

(i) 85% (ii) $5\frac{1}{4}$% (iii) 20.75%

(iv) 225% (v) $\frac{2}{3}$%

Solution

(i) 85% = 85.0% = 85.0% = 0.85

(ii) $5\frac{1}{4}$ = 5.25% = 5.25% = 0.0525

(iii) 20.75% = 20.75% = 0.2075

(iv) 225% = 225.0% = 2.250 = 2.25

(v) $\frac{2}{3}$ = 0.666666...% = 0.666666...% = 0.006666... = $0.00\overline{6}$

Converting Decimal Numbers to Percents

To convert a decimal number or a whole number to a percent, move the decimal point 2 places to the right and insert the '%' sign. This is the same as multiplying the number by 100 and inserting the '%' sign.

For example,

(i) To convert 0.35 to a percent

0.35 = 0.35 — Moving the decimal point 2 places to the right and inserting the % sign,

= 35% — This is the same as 0.35 × 100% = 35%

Therefore 0.35 = 35% .

(ii) To convert 5 to a percent

5 = 5.00 — Moving the decimal point 2 places to the right and inserting the % sign,

= 500% — This is the same as 5 × 100% = 500%

Therefore, 5 = 500%.

Example 5.1-c

Converting Decimal Numbers to Percents

Convert each of the following decimal numbers to its equivalent percent.

(i) 5.25 (ii) 0.45

(iii) 0.03 (iv) 0.002

Solution

(i) 5.25 = 5.25 = 525%

(ii) 0.45 = 0.45 = 45%

(iii) 0.03 = 0.03 = 3%

(iv) 0.002 = 0.002 = 0.2%

Example 5.1-d

Percent Application

If Alexander earns 3 times the amount that Emma earns, what percent is Alexander's earnings compared to Ema's earnings?

Solution

Here, '3 times' when converted to a percent = 3 × (100%) = 300%.

Therefore, Alexander's earnings are 300% of Emma's.

Note: This also means that Alexander earns 300% − 100% = 200% more than Emma.

Converting Fractions or Mixed Numbers to Percents

To convert a fraction or a mixed number to a percent, first convert the fraction or the mixed number to a decimal. Then, convert the decimal to a percent.

For example,

(i) To convert $\frac{3}{8}$ to a percent:

$\frac{3}{8}$ = 0.375 — Converting the fraction to its decimal equivalent and then the decimal to percent,

= 37.50% — This is the same as 0.375 × 100% = 37.50%

Therefore $\frac{3}{8}$ = 37.50%.

(ii) To convert $5\frac{1}{2}$ to a percent:

$5\frac{1}{2} = 5.50$	Moving the decimal point 2 places to the right and placing the % sign,
$= 550\%$	This is the same as $5.50 \times 100\% = 550\%$

Therefore $5\frac{1}{2} = 550\%$.

Example 5.1-e

Converting Fractions or Mixed Numbers to Percents

Convert each of the following fractions to its equivalent percent.

(i) $\frac{3}{25}$ (ii) $5\frac{1}{4}$

(iii) 2 (iv) $\frac{1}{200}$

Solution

(i) $\frac{3}{25} = 0.12 = 0.12 = 12\%$

(ii) $5\frac{1}{4} = 5.25 = 5.25 = 525\%$

(iii) $\frac{18}{5} = 3\frac{3}{5} = 3.60 = 360\%$

(iv) $\frac{1}{200} = \frac{1}{2 \times 100} = \frac{1}{2} \times \frac{1}{100} = 0.5 \times \frac{1}{100} = 0.005 = 0.5\%$

Example 5.1-f

Application Problem

Peter and Angela are two students studying Business Mathematics, but at different colleges. Peter managed to secure a score of 46 out of 60 on his final exam, while Angela scored 63 out of 75 on her exam. Who scored better?

Solution

By observation, it is not possible to answer the question because Peter's score is expressed on a base of 60, while Angela's score is on a base of 75. To compare their scores, we need to convert them to their percent equivalents, as shown below:

Peter's score: $\frac{46}{60} = 0.766666... = 76.67\%$

Angela's score: $\frac{63}{75} = 0.84 = 84.00\%$

Therefore, Angela scored better than Peter on the exam.

Solving Percent Problems

There are many methods used in solving percent problems. Described below are three common methods:

Method 1: Formula Method

Every percent problem will contain three variables: B, P, and R.

Base (B): Whole quantity or value (100%). It is usually followed by the word 'of', or 'percent of'.

Portion (P): Portion of the whole quantity or value (portion of the base).

Rate (R): Percent relationship between base and portion. It usually carries the percent sign (%) or the word '**percent**'. Every percent statement can be expressed as: ***P* is *R*% of *B*.** The value of R is used as a decimal or fractional equivalent in calculations.

Based on the above explanation, it is easy to identify the variables '***B***' and '***R***'. Once identified, the third variable will be '***P***'.

The relationship between these variables can be expressed as follows:

$$\textit{Portion} = \textit{Rate} \times \textit{Base}$$

This is given by the formula,

Formula 5.1

Portion

$$P = R \times B$$

Rearranging, $R = \dfrac{P}{B}$ and $B = \dfrac{P}{R}$.

Therefore, if any two of these quantities are known, then the third quantity can be calculated.

P, R, B Triangle

Here is a triangle that can be used to help in rearranging the formula $P = R \times B$ to find R *or* B.

Variables beside each other at the bottom are multiplied ($R \times B$, as shown).

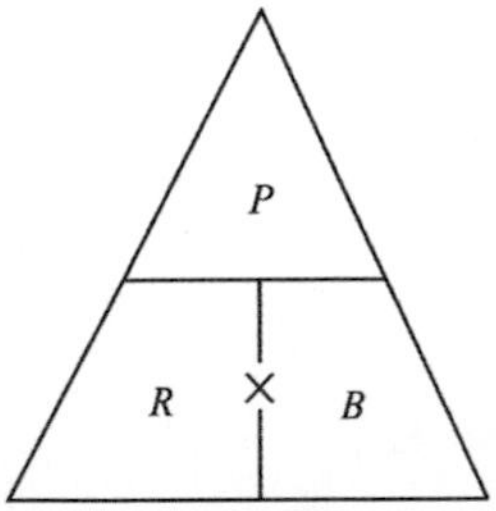

The variables at the bottom are divided by the variable on top: P.

Cover the variable that you want to rearrange to see the new formula.

For example, if you want to solve for 'R', the formula can be found by covering 'R' and reading the remaining variables in the above triangle, to get $R = \dfrac{P}{B}$.

Method 2: Algebraic Method

Solving problems using algebraic methods involve forming an equation for an unknown 'x' and then solving for 'x'. In this method, we assume that the unknown is 'x'.

Method 3: Ratio-Proportion Method

The whole amount or quantity is represented by 100% and is known as the **base (*B*)**. The **portion (*P*)** is a part of the base and it forms a **percent (*R*%)** of the base. Thus, in the ratio-proportion method, we first identify the base and portion in the problem, then using the proportion equation we solve for the unknown.

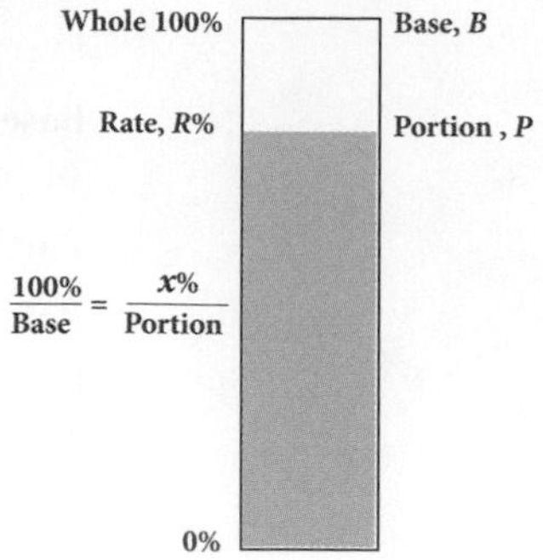

Portion : Base = Rate % : 100%

$$P : B = R\% : 100\%$$

$$\frac{P}{B} = \frac{R\%}{100\%}$$

$$\frac{P}{B} = \frac{R}{100}$$

Example 5.1-g — **Calculating the Portion of a Whole Quantity**

What is 75% of $250? (Or, 75% of $250 is how much?)

Solution

Method 1: Using the Formula Method

$R\% = 75\%$ (value with % sign); i.e., $R = 0.75$

$B = \$250.00$ (value after the word 'of')

$$P = R \times B$$

$$P = 0.75 \times 250$$

$$= \$187.50$$

Therefore, 75% of $250 is $187.50.

Method 2: Using the Algebraic Method

This can be re-written as '*x*' is 75% of $250.

We need to find '*x*'.

$$x = 75\% \times 250$$

Expressing the percent as a fraction,

$$x = \left(\frac{75}{100}\right) \times 250$$

$$= 0.75 \times 250$$

$$= \$187.50$$

Clues to remember some arithmetic operations used in problems:

Addition (+):
Add, sum, plus, more than, increased by, appreciate, rise

Subtraction (−):
Subtract, difference, minus, less than, decreased by, depreciate, fall

Multiplication (×):
multiply, product, times, of

Division (÷ or /):
divide, ratio, divided by, quotient

Equal (=):
is, was, gives, given by

Unknown value:
What, how much, (usually denoted by some letter, such as '*x*')

Solution continued

Method 3: Using the Ratio-Proportion Method

Here, the whole amount of $250 is the base and is represented by 100%. 75% is a portion of the base, as illustrated:

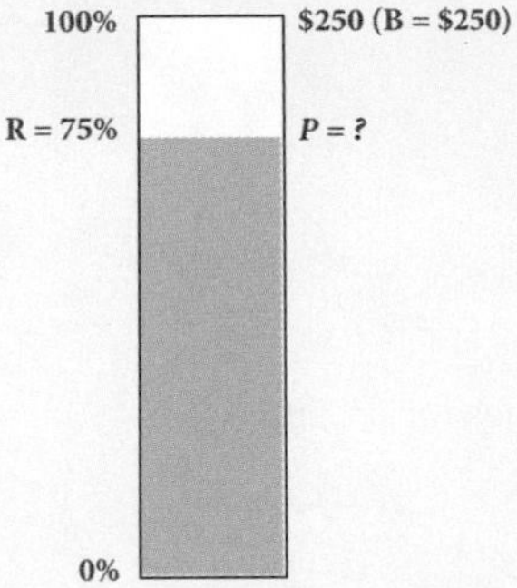

Portion : Base = Rate : 100%

$P : B = R\% : 100\%$

$P : 250 = 75\% : 100\%$

$$\frac{P}{250} = \frac{75\%}{100\%}$$

$$\frac{P}{250} = \frac{75}{100}$$ Cross-multiplying,

$$P = \frac{250 \times 75}{100} = \$187.50$$

Therefore, 75% of $250 is $187.50.

The following examples use the formula method; however, you can solve them using any of the three methods described earlier.

Example 5.1-h **Calculating Rate When Portion and Base are Known**

What percent of $775 is $1,250? (Or, $1,250 is what percent of $775?)

Solution

B = $775.00 (value after the word 'of')

P = $1,250.00 (the other value)

R = ? (value for the word percent)

Using Formula, $P = R \times B$ Rearranging,

$$R = \frac{P}{B}$$ Substituting values for 'P' and 'B',

$$R = \frac{1,250}{775}$$

$$R\% = \frac{1,250}{775} \times 100\% = 161.290322...\%$$

Therefore, 161.29% of $775.00 is $1,250.00.

Example 5.1-i

Calculating Base When Portion and Rate are Known

50% of what number is 200?

Solution

$R\%$ = 50% (value with '%' sign) = 0.50

P = 200 (the other value)

B = ? (value after the word 'of')

Using Formula, P = R × B — Rearranging,

$$B = \frac{P}{R}$$ Substituting values for 'P' and 'R',

$$B = \frac{200}{0.5} = 400$$

Therefore, 50% of 400 is 200.

Example 5.1-j

Calculating Portion When Rate is More Than 100%

What is 150% of 200?

Solution

$R\%$ = 150% (value with '%' sign)

= 1.50

B = 200 (value after the word 'of')

P = ? (other value)

Using, $P = R \times B$

$= 1.50 \times 200 = 300$

Therefore, 150% of 200 is 300.

Example 5.1-k

Application Problem Based on Repeating Decimals

Sandra owns $25\frac{1}{3}\%$ of a web development company. If the company is valued at $180,000 what is the value of Sandra's ownership in the company?

Solution

Do not round intermediary steps in calculations. Store the intermediary step value in your calculator and recall it for later calculations.

Identify the base, portion, and rate:

B = $180,000 (whole value)

$R\%$ = $25\frac{1}{3}\%$ (the value with % sign)

= 25.333333...%

= 0.253333... (Store this value in the calculator's memory and recall when multiplying later)

Solution
continued

$P = R \times B$

$= 0.253333... \times 180{,}000$

$= \$45{,}600.00$

Alternatively, this can be solved by converting the mixed fraction to a proper fraction:

$R\% = 25\tfrac{1}{3}\%$ — Converting the mixed number to an improper fraction,

$= \frac{76}{3}\%$ — Expressing the percent as a fraction,

$= \frac{76}{3} \times \frac{1}{100} = \frac{76}{300}$

$P = R \times B$

$= \frac{76}{300} \times 180{,}000$

$= \$45{,}600.00$

Therefore, the value of Sandra's ownership in the company is \$45,600.00.

5.1 | Exercises

Answers to odd-numbered problems are available online.

For Problems 1 to 10, convert each percent to its equivalent (i) fraction (or mixed number) in its lowest terms and (ii) decimal.

1. a. 75% b. 5%
2. a. 50% b. 2%
3. a. 12.5% b. 0.6%
4. a. 7.5% b. 0.8%
5. a. 150% b. 4.8%
6. a. 225% b. 3.6%
7. a. 0.05% b. $\frac{3}{5}\%$
8. a. 0.08% b. $\frac{3}{8}\%$
9. a. $1\frac{1}{4}\%$ b. $6\frac{1}{2}\%$
10. a. $2\frac{3}{4}\%$ b. $10\frac{3}{5}\%$

For Problems 11 to 20, convert each fraction (or mixed number) to its equivalent (i) decimal and (ii) percent.

11. a. $\frac{1}{4}$ b. $\frac{3}{5}$
12. a. $\frac{1}{5}$ b. $\frac{3}{8}$
13. a. $\frac{9}{2}$ b. $\frac{23}{5}$
14. a. $\frac{15}{4}$ b. $\frac{18}{15}$
15. a. $\frac{12}{25}$ b. $\frac{3}{80}$
16. a. $\frac{7}{20}$ b. $\frac{22}{75}$
17. a. $\frac{1}{400}$ b. $1\frac{1}{8}$
18. a. $\frac{1}{250}$ b. $2\frac{3}{8}$

19. a. $1\frac{3}{50}$ b. $\frac{52}{325}$

20. a. $2\frac{4}{25}$ b. $\frac{65}{260}$

For Problems 21 to 30, convert each decimal to its equivalent (i) fraction (or mixed number) in its lowest terms and (ii) percent.

21. a. 0.30 b. 0.02
22. a. 0.70 b. 0.08
23. a. 0.45 b. 0.064
24. a. 0.65 b. 0.085
25. a. 0.025 b. 0.175
26. a. 0.075 b. 0.225
27. a. 1.08 b. 2.025
28. a. 2.04 b. 1.075
29. a. 0.05 b. 0.005
30. a. 0.03 b. 0.003

Calculate the following (round your answer to two decimal places, where applicable):

31. a. 20% of 350 b. 12.5% of 800
32. a. 45% of 180 b. 2.5% of 960
33. a. 0.25% of 75 b. $\frac{1}{4}$% of 200 km
34. a. 0.755% of 120 b. $\frac{1}{8}$% of 450 km
35. a. 130% of 40 b. $5\frac{1}{2}$% of $1,000
36. a. 285% of 110 b. $12\frac{3}{4}$% of $1,260

Calculate the following (round your answer to two decimal places, where applicable):

37. What is 2.5% of 80?
38. What is 40% of 160?
39. $8\frac{1}{4}$% of $200 is how much?
40. $25\frac{3}{4}$% of $2,680 is how much?
41. How much is $\frac{1}{4}$% of $108?
42. How much is $\frac{3}{4}$% of 350 kg?

Calculate the following (round your answer to two decimal places, where applicable):

43. 12 is what percent of 30?
44. 18 is what percent of 40?
45. What percent of 4 is 16?
46. What percent of 9 is 45?
47. What percent of 220 is 100?
48. What percent of 22.10 is 110.50?
49. What percent of $90 is $100?
50. What percent of $275 is $110?

Calculate the following (round your answer to two decimal places, where applicable):

51. 280 metres is what percent of a km?
52. 180 g is what percent of 3 kg?
53. 400 is 50% of what number?
54. 225 is 25% of what number?
55. 15% of what amount is $27.90?
56. 30% of what amount is 708?
57. 120% of what amount is 156?
58. 215% of what amount is 258?
59. What number is 125% of 6?
60. What number is 250% of 12?
61. $16.50 is 0.75% of what amount?
62. $16.40 is 0.5% of what amount?
63. 98% of what number is 49?
64. 42% of what number is 162?
65. A table costs $250. The tax is 13%. How much is the tax?
66. The monthly salary of an employee is $6,250. 26% of the salary was deducted for taxes. How much money was deducted for taxes?

67. 5% of commission on sales was $1,250. How much was the sales amount?

68. 3% interest on a loan was $210. How much was the loan?

69. In a survey of 450 people, 117 responded 'yes'. What percent of the people surveyed responded 'no'?

70. 144 out of 600 students took Business Mathematics. What percent of students did not take the course?

71. A company that makes games sets sales targets of $280,000 per year for each of their sales people. If Amanda, an excellent salesperson, achieved 250% of her target this year, calculate the amount of sales she made.

72. If the population of Canada was estimated to be 33,930,830 on January 2010, and the population of Ontario was estimated to be $37\frac{2}{3}$% of Canada's population, calculate the population of Ontario, rounded up to the nearest whole number.

73. When there was a boom in the real-estate market, Lucy sold her property for $410,440, which was 130% of the amount she paid for it originally. Calculate the amount she paid for the property originally.

74. Ronald, an investment banker sold his shares for $18,568.50 when there was a boom in the stock market. Calculate the amount he paid for the shares if his selling price was 180.65% of the amount he paid for the shares originally.

75. Evan, a business development representative of a leading pharmaceutical firm, took his client out for a dinner that cost $180.75 before taxes. If the tax was $23.50, calculate the tax rate.

76. A leading information technology company donated $87,790 out of its 2010 fiscal revenue of $17,558,643 towards socially-responsible causes. What percent of their revenue did they contribute towards these causes?

77. Neel Plastics Manufacturing Corporation targets to obtain $120,000 of funding from their investors to purchase new machinery. If they could only obtain 25.5% of their total target, calculate the amount of money that is yet to be received.

78. Pamela and Martha run a business that made a profit of $12,750. As Pamela invested a higher amount in the business, she received 57.5% of the profits and Martha received the rest. Calculate Martha's share of the profit, in dollars.

79. Dawson purchased a pair of shoes on boxing-day that was discounted by 10% from the original price of $50. Calculate the amount he paid for the pair of shoes.

80. Jamie went to the mall during the holiday season to purchase a wall painting for his mother. He liked a picture that was selling for $199.99 and which had a seasonal discount of 18% on its selling price. How much would this picture cost Jamie after the discount?

81. The Ministry of Transportation was upset that they overshot their construction budget for a local highway. If their total expenditure was $1,280,000 for the highway, which was 111% of their budgeted amount, calculate the amount budgeted to build the highway.

82. If Henry's business expenditures were $14,480 in March and $14,806.50 in April, which were 112% and 122% of his budgeted expenditure for March and April respectively, calculate his total budgeted expenditure for the two months.

83. Assume that of the 300,000 people who immigrated to Canada in 2010, 12.25% were from China, 9.75% were from the Philippines, and the rest were from other countries.
    a. Calculate the number of people who immigrated to Canada from China.
    b. If the combined number of immigrants from China and the Philippines constituted 0.195% of the population of Canada, calculate the population of Canada in 2010. (Round your answer up to the nearest whole number.)
84. A dinner at a restaurant cost you $27.80 and you tipped the waiter 15% of the cost.
    a. What was the value of the tip?
    b. If the tip that you gave the waiter was 2% of all the money he made from tips that night, calculate the amount that the waiter earned from tips that night.
85. The labour cost for manufacturing a $30,000 car increased by 5%. If the cost of labour was 30% of the total cost for manufacturing the car, by what amount did the cost of the car increase?
86. The material cost for manufacturing a $2,000 TV decreased by 10%. If the cost of material was 40% of the total cost for manufacturing the TV, by what amount did the cost of the TV decrease?
87. Tudor and Rani, two sales representatives in a company, were earning $2,815 per month and $2,875 per month, respectively. After a yearly appraisal, if Tudor's salary increased by 14% and Rani's increased by 11%, who had the higher salary?
88. Reggie's annual salary increased from $42,000 to $46,830 this year and his colleague Gerald's annual salary increased from $39,500 to $44,437.50. Who received a higher rate of increase this year?

5.2 | Percent Changes

Introduction

In business, percent changes are often used to express the amount of change to the initial (original) value; i.e., the amount of change (increase or decrease) is calculated as a **percent change** (*%C*) of its initial value.

$$\textit{Amount of Change} = \%C \times \textit{Initial Value}$$

The amount of change is the difference between the final value (V_f) and the initial value (V_i); i.e., the amount can also be calculated by subtracting the initial value from the final value.

$$\textit{Amount of Change} = \textit{Final Value} - \textit{Initial Value}$$

Therefore, $\%C \times \textit{Initial Value} = \textit{Final Value} - \textit{Initial Value}$

$$\%C = \frac{(\textit{Final Value} - \textit{Initial Value})}{\textit{Initial Value}}$$

Percent Change → $\%C = \dfrac{(V_f - V_i)}{V_i}$ ← Amount of Change (numerator); ← Initial Value (denominator)

Percent change is calculated as a ratio of the amount of change to the initial value. This ratio is converted to its percent equivalent by multiplying it by 100 and inserting a '%' sign.

Formula 5.2-a

Percent Change

To find a percent increase or decrease, find the amount of increase or decrease and then determine its percent value compared to the initial value.

$$\%C = \frac{(V_f - V_i)}{V_i}$$

$$= \frac{(V_f - V_i)}{V_i} \times 100\%$$

Final Value = Initial Value + Amount of Change

$$V_f = V_i + \%C \times V_i$$

Formula 5.2-b

Final Value

$$V_f = V_i\,(1 + \%C)$$

Using Formula 5.2-a for percent change, we can derive the equation used to calculate the initial value (V_i) as follows,

$$\%C = \frac{(V_f - V_i)}{V_i} \quad \text{Cross-multiplying,}$$

$$\%C(V_i) = V_f - V_i \quad \text{Rearranging,}$$

$$V_i + \%C\,(V_i) = V_f \quad \text{Factoring by the common factor } V_i,$$

$$V_i\,(1 + \%C) = V_f$$

$$V_i = \frac{V_f}{1 + \%C}$$

- If the final value is greater than the initial value, then a percent change is a percent increase, which will be a positive value ($\%C$).
- If the final value is smaller than the initial value, then a percent change is a percent decrease, which will be a negative value ($-\%C$).
- Percent change is measured either as a percent increase (profit, rise, appreciate, etc) or as a percent decrease (loss, fall, depreciate,etc).

Example 5.2-a

Calculating the Amount of Increase and Final Value

The price of an item that originally sells at $150 is increased by 20%. Calculate the dollar amount of the increase and the price after the increase.

Solution

Amount of Change $= \%\,C \times$ *Initial Value*

$$= 20\% \times 150$$

$$= 0.2 \times 150$$

Solution
continued

$= \$30.00$ (increase)

Therefore, the dollar amount of the increase is \$30.00.

Using Formula 5.2-b, $V_f = V_i (1 + \%C)$

$= 150 (1 + 20\%)$

$= 150 (1 + 0.20)$

$= 150 (1.2)$

$= \$180.00$

Therefore, the price after the increase is \$180.00.

This is the same as *Initial Value* (\$150) + *Amount of Increase* (\$30) = \$180.00.

Example 5.2-b **Calculating the Amount of Decrease and Final Value**

An item normally sells at \$400 and is discounted (reduced in price) by 15% during a sale. Calculate the dollar amount of discount and the price after the discount.

Solution

Amount of Change $= \%C \times$ *Initial Value*

$= -15\% \times 400$

$= -0.15 \times 400$

$= -\$60.00$ (decrease)

Therefore, the dollar amount of discount is \$60.00.

Using Formula 5.2-b, $V_f = V_i (1 + \%C)$

$= 400 (1 - 15\%)$

$= 400 (1 - 0.15)$

$= 400 (0.85)$

$= \$340.00$

Therefore, the price after the discount is \$340.00.

This is the same as *Initial Value* (\$400) – *Amount of discount* (\$60) = \$340.00

Example 5.2-c

Calculating Percent Increase

A store had sales of $50,000 in July and $80,000 in August. Calculate the percent change from July to August.

Solution

Final Value, V_f = $80,000

Initial Value, V_i = $50,000

Using Formula 5.2-a, $\%C = \frac{(V_f - V_i)}{V_i} \times 100\%$

$= \frac{80{,}000 - 50{,}000}{50{,}000} \times 100\%$

$= \frac{30{,}000}{50{,}000} \times 100\%$

= 60% (which is an increase)

Therefore, the percent change from July to August is an increase of 60%.

Example 5.2-d

Calculating Percent Decrease

The total expenses in September were $2,400 and those in October were $1,800. Calculate the percent change in expenses from September to October.

Solution

Final Value, V_f = $1,800

Initial Value, V_i = $2,400

Using Formula 5.2-a, $\%C = \frac{(V_f - V_i)}{V_i} \times 100\%$

$= \frac{1{,}800 - 2{,}400}{2{,}400} \times 100\%$

$= \frac{-6{,}000}{2{,}400} \times 100\%$

= −25% (which is a decrease)

Therefore, the percent change from September to October is a decrease of 25%.

Example 5.2-e

Calculating Initial Value When the Percent Change is Positive

The value of a stock increased by 35% since it was purchased. If the stock is now selling at $81.00, calculate its value when it was purchased.

Solution

$\%C$ = 35% (increase)

V_f = $81.00

Solution
continued

Using Formula 5.2-b, $V_i = \frac{V_f}{1 + \%C}$

$$= \frac{81}{1 + 35\%}$$

$$= \frac{81}{1 + 0.35}$$

$$= \frac{81}{1.35}$$

$$= \$60.00$$

Therefore, the the value of the stock when it was purchased was $60.00.

Example 5.2-f

Calculating Initial Value When the Percent Change is Negative

After a discount of 25%, an item was sold at $450. Calculate the price before the discount.

Solution

$\%C = -25\%$ (discount)

$V_f = \$450.00$

Using Formula 5.2-b, $V_i = \frac{V_f}{1 + \%C}$

$$= \frac{450}{1 - 25\%}$$

$$= \frac{450}{1 - 0.25}$$

$$= \frac{450}{0.75}$$

$$= \$600.00$$

Therefore, the the price before the discount was $600.00.

Example 5.2-g

Understanding Relative Percent Change Applications

Company A's profit increased from $165,000 to $170,000 last year. Company B's profit increased from $122,000 to $126,000 in the same year. Which company showed a better relative change in profit?

Solution

At first instinct, you may think you need to only calculate the difference in profits and compare them to arrive at the answer. That is, Company A's profit for the year increased by 170,000 – 165,000 = $5,000. Company B's profit for the year increased by 126,000 – 122,000 = $4,000. Therefore, you might say that Company A has grown more than Company B. However, this comparison is **incorrect** because you need to determine which company had a better **relative** change in profit.

Solution
continued

To compare the relative change in profits, you have to calculate the 'percent change' in profits of companies A and B last year.

Using Formula 5.2-b, $\%C = \frac{(V_f - V_i)}{V_i} \times 100\%$

> In financial applications, it would be more important to calculate percent changes and associated values instead of relying on a mere difference between two values.

Company A's Percent Change in Profit:

$$\%C_{\text{Company A}} = \frac{170{,}000 - 165{,}000}{165{,}000} \times 100\%$$

$$= \frac{5{,}000}{165{,}000} \times 100\%$$

$$= 3.030303... = 3.03\%$$

Company B's Percent Change in Profit:

$$\%C_{\text{Company B}} = \frac{126{,}000 - 122{,}000}{122{,}000} \times 100\%$$

$$= \frac{4{,}000}{122{,}000} \times 100\%$$

$$= 3.278688... = 3.28\%$$

Therefore, even though Company B had a smaller increase in profit than Company A during the year, Company B had a better relative growth (3.28%) compared to Company A (3.03%).

There are many methods used in solving percent change calculations. Described in the following example are four common methods used to solve a percent change problem:

Example 5.2-h **Calculating Final Value When Percent Change is Positive Using Different Methods**

If a $20 hourly rate of pay is increased by 10%, find the new hourly rate.

Solution

Method 1: Using the Algebraic Method

$\%C = +10\% = +0.1, \quad V_i = \$20, \quad V_f = ?$

Initial Value + Amount of Increase = Final Value

$$V_i + \%C \times V_i = V_f$$

Substituting values,

$$20 + 0.1\,(20) = V_f$$

$$20 + 2 = V_f$$

$$V_f = \$22.00$$

Therefore, the new hourly rate is $22.00.

> When there is an increase in initial value, %C will be positive and the final value will be greater than the initial value.

Method 2: Using the Formula Method

$V_i = \$20, \quad \%C = 10\%, \quad V_f = ?$

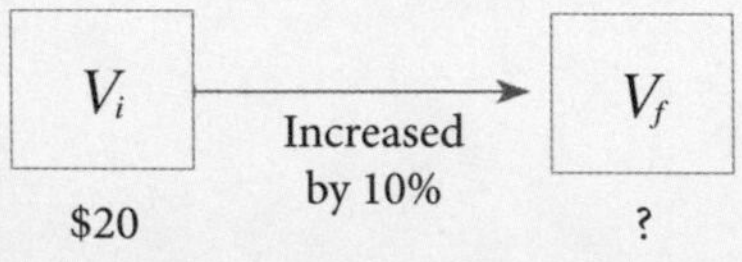

Using Formula 5.2-a,

Solution
continued

$$\%C = \frac{(V_f - V_i)}{V_i} \times 100\%$$ Substituting values,

$$10\% = \frac{V_f - 20}{20} \times 100\%$$ Eliminating the percent,
(Note: 10% = 0.10 and 100% = 1)

$$0.1 = \frac{V_f - 20}{20}$$ Cross-multiplying,

$$20(0.1) = V_f - 20$$ Simplyfying,

$$2 = V_f - 20$$

$$V_f = \$22.00$$

Helpful Check:
If the percent change is positive, then the final value must be greater than the initial value.

Therefore, the new hourly rate is $22.00.

Method 3: Using the Ratio-Proportion Method

In this method, we compare the original value and final value using ratios and proportions to find the unknown.

The original value of $20 represents 100%. This is increased by 10% to a final value of 110%, as illustrated:

Original value	Final value
20	x
100%	110%

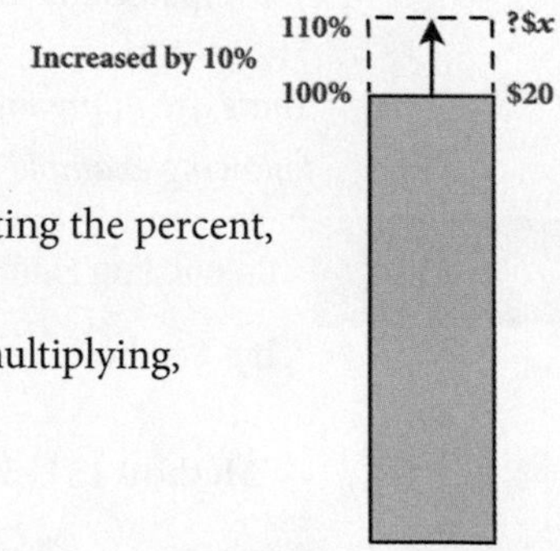

$$\frac{20}{100\%} = \frac{x}{110\%}$$ Eliminating the percent,

$$\frac{20}{1} = \frac{x}{1.1}$$ Cross-multiplying,

$$1(x) = 1.1 \times 20$$

$$x = \$22.00$$

Therefore, $20.00 increased by 10% is $22.00.

Method 4: Using the Texas Instruments BA II Plus Calculator

The Texas Instruments BAII Plus has a percent change worksheet that can be used for solving percent change problems, as shown:

Solution
continued

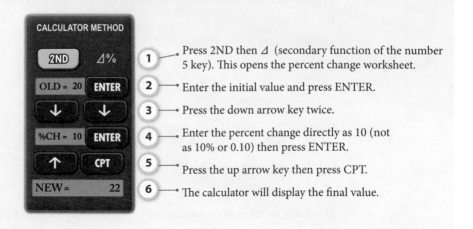

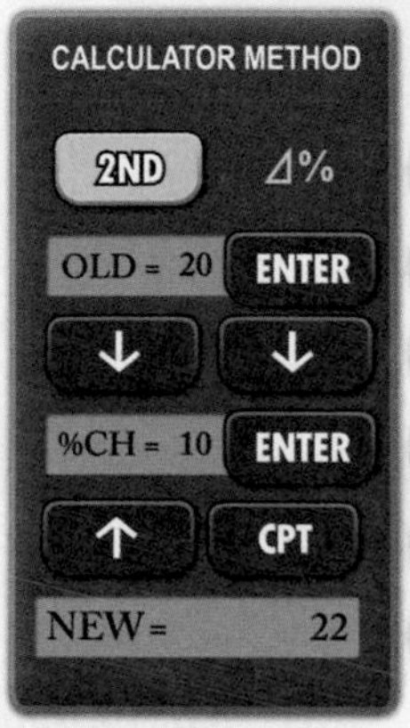

1. Press 2ND then Δ (secondary function of the number 5 key). This opens the percent change worksheet.
2. Enter the initial value and press ENTER.
3. Press the down arrow key twice.
4. Enter the percent change directly as 10 (not as 10% or 0.10) then press ENTER.
5. Press the up arrow key then press CPT.
6. The calculator will display the final value.

The examples that follow use the formula method and the calculator method. However, you can solve them using any of the methods described in Example 5.2-h.

Example 5.2-i **Calculating Percent Change When Initial and Final Values are Given as a Percent**

If the Bank of Canada increases its prime lending rate from 2.25% to 3.35%, calculate the percent increase in the prime rate.

Solution

$V_i = 2.25\%$, $V_f = 3.35\%$, $\%C = ?$

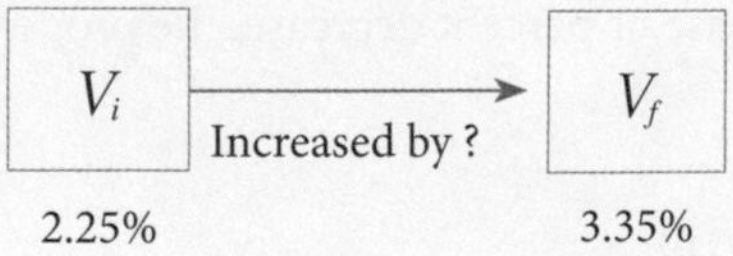

Using Formula 5.2-b, $\%C = \dfrac{(V_f - V_i)}{V_i} \times 100\%$

Substituting the values, $\%C = \dfrac{3.35\% - 2.25\%}{2.25\%} \times 100\%$

$= \dfrac{3.35 - 2.25}{2.25} \times 100\%$

$= \dfrac{1.10}{2.25} \times 100\%$

$= 0.488888... \times 100\% = 48.89\%$

Therefore, the percent increase in prime rate is 48.89%.

Percent increase cannot be reversed by the same percent decrease.

For example,

\$100 increased by 10% results in \$110.

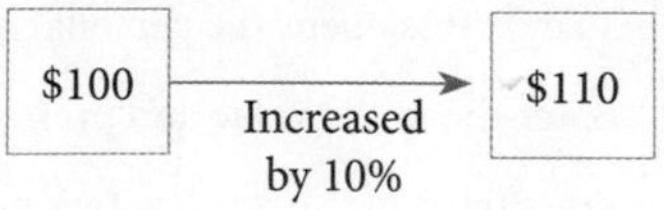

$$= 100 + 10\% \text{ of } 100$$
$$= 100 + 10$$
$$= \$110$$

But \$110 decreased by 10% results in \$99.

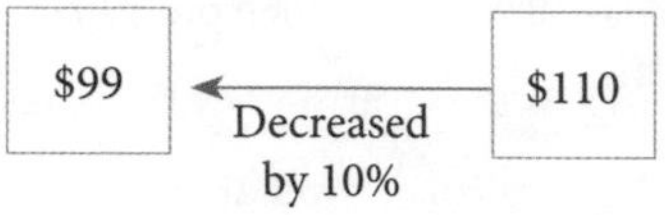

$$= 110 - 10\% \text{ of } 110$$
$$= 110 - 11$$
$$= \$99$$

Similarly, percent decrease cannot be reversed by the same percent increase.

For example, \$100 decreased by 10% results in \$90.

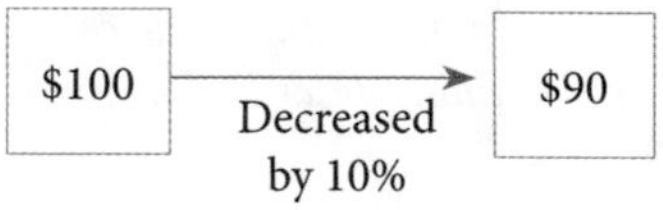

$$= 100 - 10\% \text{ of } 100$$
$$= 100 - 10$$
$$= \$90$$

But \$90 increased by 10% results in \$99.

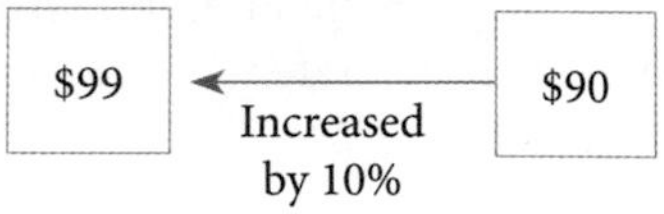

$$= 90 + 10\% \text{ of } 90$$
$$= 90 + 9$$
$$= \$99$$

To reverse a percent increase or percent decrease, the proper method should be used, as shown below.

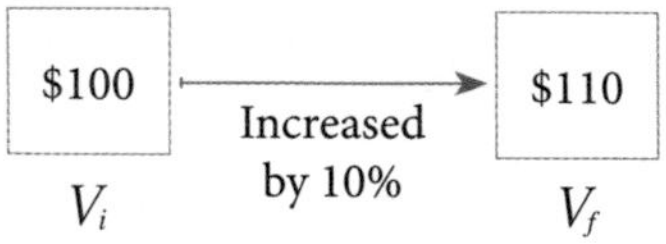

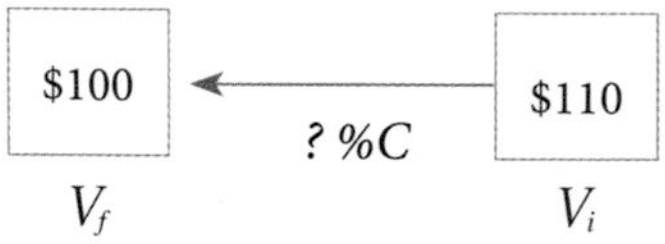

$$\%C = \frac{(V_f - V_i)}{V_i} \times 100\% = \frac{100 - 110}{110} \times 100\%$$
$$= -9.090909... = -9.09\%$$

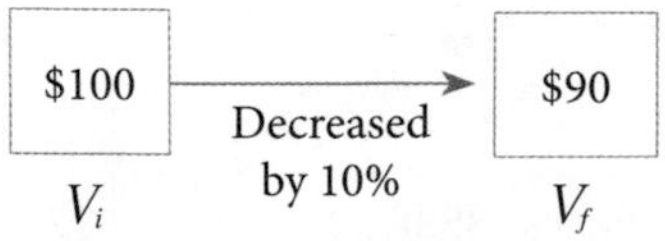

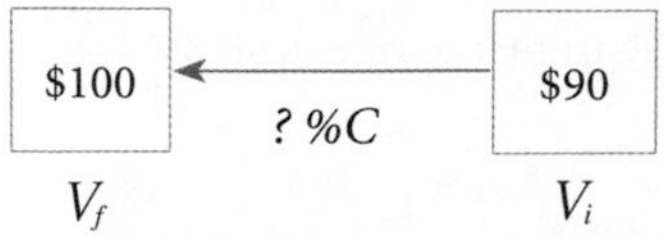

$$\%C = \frac{100 - 90}{90} \times 100\% = \frac{10}{90} \times 100\%$$
$$= 11.111111... = 11.11\% \text{ (Increase)}$$

Example 5.2-j

Calculating Percent Change When the Statement is Reversed

If Ali earns 25% more than Brian, then Brian earns what percent less than Ali?

Solution

Method 1: Using the Algebraic Method

Let Ali's earnings be A and Brian's earnings be B.

$A = B + 25\%$ of B (or $A = 125\%$ of B)

$A = 1.25B$ Expressing B as a fraction of A,

$$B = \frac{1}{1.25}A$$

$$B = 0.80A$$

That is, B is 80% of A (which is the same as B is 20% less than A).

Therefore, if Ali earns 25% more than Brian, then Brian earns 20% less than Ali.

Method 2: Using the Algebraic Method, Assuming a Value for B

Given: $A = B + 25\%$ of B

$A = 1.25B$

Assume $B = \$1{,}000$, then A earns \$1,250

To find: B earns what % less than A,

i.e., \$1,000 is what % less than \$1,250

$1{,}000 = 1{,}250 - x\,\%$ of $1{,}250$

$x\,\%$ of $1250 = 1{,}250 - 1{,}000 = 250$

$$x\,\% = \frac{250}{1250} = \frac{1}{5} = \left(\frac{1}{5}\right) \times 100\% = 20\%$$

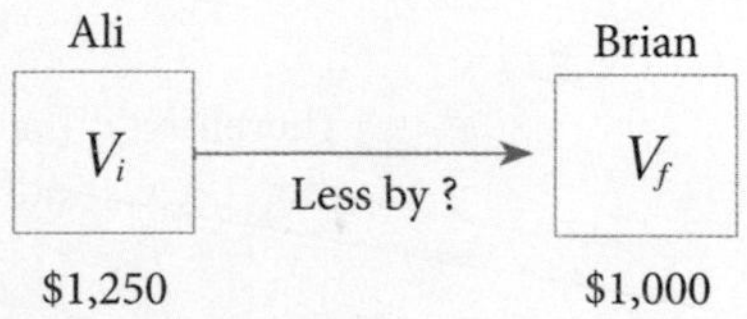

Therefore, if Ali earns 25% more than Brian, then Brian earns 20% less than Ali.

Method 3: Using a Financial Calculator, Assuming a Value for Brian's Earnings

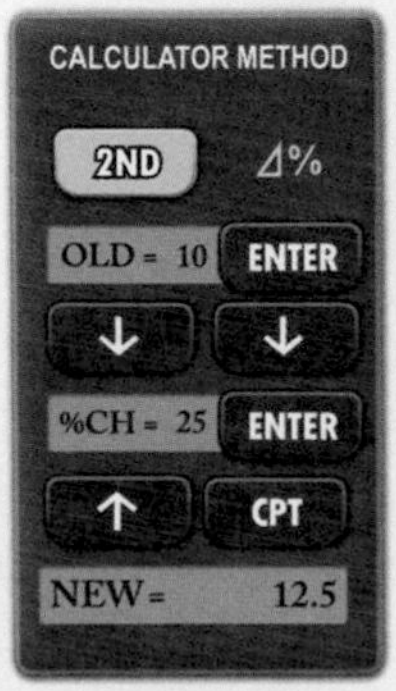

Assuming Brian earns \$10 per hour

Ali earns 25% more

Ali earns \$12.50 per hour

Ali earns \$12.50 per hour

Brian earns \$10 per hour

Thus, Brian earns 20% less than Ali

Example 5.2-k

Calculating Percent Change When the Value of a Currency Increases (Appreciates) or Decreases (Depreciates) Against Another Currency

If the US dollar appreciated by 10% relative to the Canadian dollar, by what percent has the Canadian dollar depreciated relative to the US dollar?

Solution

Assume US$1 = C$$x$

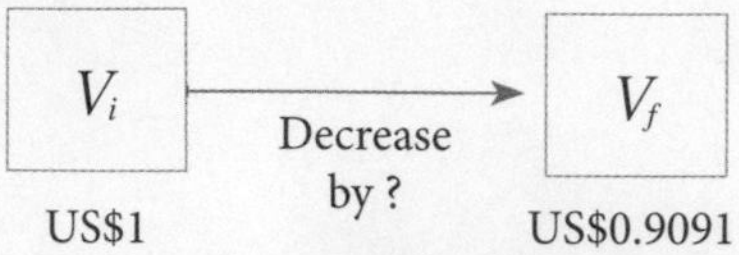

If the US dollar appreciated by 10%, then,

$$\text{US\$1} = \text{C\$}1.10x$$

Dividing both sides by 1.10, $\text{US\$}\dfrac{1}{1.10} = \text{C\$}x$

$$\text{US\$}0.909090... = \text{C\$}x$$

Therefore, V_i = US$1, and V_f = US$0.909090...

Using Formula 5.2-b, $\%C = \dfrac{(V_f - V_i)}{V_i} \times 100\%$

Substituting the values, $\%C = \dfrac{\text{US\$}0.909090... - \text{US\$}1}{\text{US\$}1}$

$$= -\ 0.090909... = -\ 9.09\%$$

Therefore, if the US dollar appreciated by 10% relative to the Canadian dollar, then the Canadian dollar depreciated by 9.09% relative to the US dollar.

The absolute value of a number 'a' written as |a| will always be a positive number (regardless of the sign for 'a').

For example, |-5| = 5 and |5| = 5.

Percent Change When the Initial Value (V_i) is Negative

In the algebraic equation $V_i + \textit{Amount of Increase} = V_f$,

where, $\textit{Amount of Increase} = \%C \times V_i$

When V_i is increased by an amount, regardless of the value or sign for V_i, add the amount of increase to find V_f; i.e., the 'quantity' added to V_i should be positive.

$$V_i + \textit{Amount of Increase} = V_f$$

When V_i is decreased by an amount, regardless of the value or sign for V_i, subtract the amount of decrease to find V_f; i.e., the 'quantity' that is subtracted from V_i should be positive.

$$V_i - \text{Amount of Decrease} = V_f$$

Therefore, the 'quantity' that is added or subtracted should always be a positive quantity. The sign in the formula will determine the increase or decrease.

When the original quantity (V_i) is negative, use the absolute sign for V_i to calculate the amout of increase or decrease. This ensures that the amount of increase or decrease will be a positive answer.

Therefore, when V_i is negative,

$$\textit{Amount of Increase or Decrease} = \%C \times \textit{Absolute value of } V_i$$
$$= \%C|V_i|$$

If the final value is greater than the initial value,

$$\textit{Initial Value} + \textit{Amount of Increase} = \textit{Final Value}$$
$$V_i + \%C|V_i| = V_f$$
$$\%C = \frac{(V_f - V_i)}{|V_i|}$$

If the final value is smaller than the initial value,

$$\textit{Initial Value} - \textit{Amount of Decrease} = \textit{Final Value}$$
$$V_i - \%C\ |V_i| = V_f$$
$$\%C = -\ \frac{(V_f - V_i)}{|V_i|}$$

Therefore, the value of $\%C$ will be negative.

Example 5.2-I

Percent Change When V_i is a Negative Value

The average temperature in Toronto last winter was -4°C. If the average temperature this winter increased by 1.15°C, calculate the percent change in temperature this winter from last year's winter.

Solution

Method 1: Since V_i is negative, $\textit{Amount of Increase} = \%C|\ V_i|$

$$1.15 = \%C\,|-4|$$
$$1.15 = \%C\ (4)$$

Cross-multiplying,

$$\%C = \frac{1.15}{4} \times 100\%$$
$$= 28.75\% \text{ increase}$$

Therefore, the temperature increased by 28.75% this winter from last year's winter.

Solution
continued

Method 2:

$V_f = -4 + 1.15 = -2.85$

Last year: V_i = −4 → %C = ? → This year: V_f = −2.85

Using Formula 5.2-b, $\%C = \frac{(V_f - V_i)}{|V_i|} \times 100\%$

Substituting values, $\%C = \frac{-2.85 - (-4)}{|-4|} \times 100\%$

$= \frac{-2.85 + 4}{4} \times 100\%$

$= \frac{1.15}{4} \times 100\%$

$= 28.75\%$ increase

Therefore, the temperature increased by 28.75% this winter from last year's winter.

Example 5.2-m

Percent Change Comparing Unit Quantities

A jeweler made and sold 500 g of silver chains for \$90. If he reduced the weight of the silver in the chain to 450 g and reduced the price to \$85.50, by what percent did the unit rate change?

Solution

Unit price of the 500 g silver chain: $\frac{90}{500} = \$0.18$ per gram of silver

Unit price of the 450 g silver chain: $\frac{85.50}{450} = \$0.19$ per gram of silver

There is an increase in the unit price of the chain.

V_i = 0.18 → %C = ? → V_f = 0.19

Using Formula 5.2-a, $\%C = \frac{(V_f - V_i)}{|V_i|}$

Substituing values, $\%C = \frac{0.19 - 0.18}{0.18} \times 100\%$

$= 0.055555... \times 100\% = 5.56\%$ increase

Therefore, the unit rate increased by 5.56%.

5.2 | Exercises

Answers to odd-numbered problems are available online.

For Problems 1 to 24, find the missing values (round your answer to 2 decimal places, where applicable).

	Initial Value	Percent Increase	Final Value
1.	270	45%	?
2.	250	35%	?
3.	4,500	137.5%	?
4.	3,500	112.5%	?
5.	?	25%	600
6.	?	40%	800
7..	?	262.5%	2,250
8..	?	187.5%	6,950
9.	150	?	225
10.	170	?	204
11.	3,400	?	9,200
12..	7,500	?	24,500

	Initial Value	Percent Decrease	Final Value
13.	145	45%	?
14.	525	35%	?
15.	1,275	112.5%	?
16.	6,800	137.5%	?
17.	?	25%	412.5
18.	?	40%	525
19..	?	23.75%	3,400
20..	?	18.75%	4,800
21.	740	?	400
22.	222	?	120
23.	5,200	?	1,600
24..	8,125	?	2,500

25. If Harley's salary of $2,000 per month is increased by 5.5%, what is his new salary?
26. Revenues of Python Graphics Corporation rose by 280% from last year. If their revenue last year was $860,760, calculate their revenue this year.
27. After a discount of $12\frac{1}{2}\%$, a publishing company purchased an offset printing press for $245,000. Calculate the original price of the machine.
28. A clothing retail outlet purchased clothes in bulk from a wholesaler for $86,394. This was after a discount of $10\frac{3}{4}\%$ on the purchase. Calculate the original price of the clothes.
29. A sales tax of 13% increased the cost of a meal at a restaurant to $34.50. What was the cost of the meal before taxes?
30. After paying income taxes of 45%, Carla's take-home annual income was $45,000. Calculate her income before deducting income taxes.
31. If calculators that sell in stores for $30 each are being offered online for $24 each, calculate the percent discount offered online.
32. If Lilo's student loan of $12,000 will increase to $12,860 by the end of the year, calculate the percent increase of her debt.
33. The average daytime summer temperature in Calgary increased by 3.0°C this year. If the average daytime summer temperature last year was 29°C, calculate the percent change in the average daytime summer temperature this year.
34. The average yearly snowfall in Vancouver increased by 3 cm this year. If the average yearly snowfall last year was 47.5 cm, calculate the percent change in average yearly snowfall this year.

35. The average winter temperature in Toronto increased by 2.0°C this year. If the average winter temperature last year was -15°C, calculate the percent change in average winter temperature this year.

36. The average winter temperature in Montreal increased by 1.15°C this year. If the average winter temperature last year was -10°C, calculate the percent change in the average winter temperature this year.

37. Gabrielle's portfolio of shares comprised of investments of $8600 and $12,400 in the telecommunication and information technology industries, respectively. If the market price of her telecommunication shares dropped by 65% and that of information technology grew by 25%, by what percent did the total value of her investments change?

38. Kemi had her money invested in two types of mutual funds: $2800 in low-risk funds and $700 in high-risk funds. If the value of her high-risk funds grew by 30% and that of the low-risk funds dropped by 10%, by what percent did the total value of her investments change?

39. If the current fixed mortgage rate of 5.4% rises to 6.6%, calculate the percent increase in the mortgage rate.

40. If the prime rate of 3.5% increased to 4.2%, calculate the percent increase in the prime rate.

41. The price of a telecommunication share dropped by $2.50 at the end of the first year and dropped by a further $3.45 at the end of the second year. If the price of the share at the end of the second year was $12.55, calculate the percent change in the price of the share at the end of each year from its price at the beginning of each year. What was the percent drop in the price over the two-year period?

42. Amtex Computers Inc. sells refurbished laptops online. They were selling a particular model at $400 at the beginning of the year and reduced the price by $80 at the end of the first year. At the end of the second year, they increased the price by $64. Calculate the percent change in the price of this model at the end of each year from its price at the beginning of each year. Calculate the percent discount offered in the second year from the original price of $400.

43. If Roger scored 20% more than Judie, by what percent is Judie's score less than Roger's?

44. If Harry earns 15% more than Beary per hour, by what percent is Beary's earning less than Harry's?

45. If the Canadian dollar appreciated by 5% relative to the British pound, by what percent has the British pound depreciated relative to the Canadian dollar?

46. If the Australian dollar appreciated by 15% relative to the British pound, by what percent has the British pound depreciated relative to the Australian dollar?

47. Sandra posted an advertisement on an auction site to sell her phone for 50% more than what she had paid for it. Since it did not sell within a month, she decreased the advertised price by 50% and it sold immediately. By what percent, more or less than her purchase price, did she sell the phone?

48. If the temperature rose by 12% from the average temperature, then fell by 12%, by what percent did the final temperature increase or decrease from the average temperature?

49. Last month, a 750g box of cereal was sold at a grocery store for $3.00. However, this month, the cereal manufacturer launched the same cereal in a 600g box, which is being sold at $2.50. By what percent did the unit rate change?

50. A 450 g pack of butter was sold for $3.50. If the manufacturer reduced the size of the pack to 250g and sold it at a reduced price of $2.00, by what percent did the unit rate change?

51. The overall increase in the price of a house from 2008 to 2010 was 4%. If the price increased by 5% from 2008 to 2009 and its value in 2009 was $472,500, calculate the value of the house in 2010.

52. The price of a share dropped by 3% from February to March, down to $4.25 in March. If the overall price fell by 5% between February and April, calculate its price in April.

5 | Review Exercises

Answers to odd-numbered problems are available online.

Compute the missing values in Problems 1 and 2:

1.

	Percentage	Decimal	Fraction in lowest terms
a.	80%	?	?
b.	?	0.25	?
c.	?	?	$\frac{3}{2}$
d.	$6\frac{1}{2}\%$	?	?
c.	?	0.048	?
f.	?	?	$\frac{2}{25}$
g.	$10\frac{3}{5}\%$	?	?
h.	?	2.25	?
i.	?	?	$\frac{1}{400}$

2.

	Percentage	Decimal	Fraction in lowest terms
a.	2%	?	?
b.	?	0.245	?
c.	?	?	$\frac{5}{12}$
d.	$\frac{1}{2}\%$	?	?
e.	?	0.002	?
f.	?	?	$\frac{97}{365}$
g.	$12\frac{2}{5}\%$	?	?
h.	?	1.075	?
i.	?	?	$\frac{3}{80}$

3. Answer the following (round your answers to two decimal places):
   a. 125% of what number is 45?
   b. What % of $180 is $36?
   c. How much is $\frac{3}{8}\%$ of $60?

4. Answer the following (round your answers to two decimal places):
   a. 225% of what number is 180?
   b. What % of $750 is $300?
   c. How much is $\frac{2}{5}\%$ of $30?

5. Paul sold a property for $575,000, which was 125% of the purchased price. Calculate the purchased price.

6. Peter sold his shares for $14,437.50. Calculate the amount he paid for the shares if his selling price was 275% of the amount he paid for the shares.

7. Lian scored 45 out of 60 on a math test. What was his percent grade on the test?

8. There were 48 questions in a test. Ann answered 40 questions correctly. What percent of the questions did she answer correctly?
9. Answer the following problems, rounding your answers to two decimal places:
   a. What is 180 increased by 70%?
   b. $90 decreased by 90% is how much?
   c. How much is $4,500 increased by 150%?
   d. What amount increased by 25.75% is 855.10 kg?
10. Answer the following problems, rounding your answers to two decimal places:
    a. What is 2,680 increased by 85%?
    b. $880.45 decreased by 85% is how much?
    c. How much is $1,850.50 increased by 300%?
    d. What amount increased by $90\frac{1}{2}\%$ is 110.49 kg?
11. Answer the following problems, rounding your answers to two decimal places:
    a. What amount decreased by 10% is $477?
    b. What amount increased by 180% is 20.65?
    c. $1,200 decreased by what percent is $300?
    d. 750 kg is what percent less than 1,000 kg?
12. Answer the following problems, rounding your answers to two decimal places:
    a. What amount increased by 28% is 231.75?
    b. What amount increased by 600% is 24.92?
    c. $800 increased by what percent is $1,800?
    d. 102 km is what percent more than 85 km?
13. The sales tax of 13% increased the cost of a dinner at a restaurant to $55.37. What was the cost of dinner before taxes?
14. After paying income taxes of 32%, Sally's annual pay was $35,600. Calculate Sally's income before deducting income taxes.
15. If toner cartridges that sell in stores for $45 each are being offered online for $36 each, calculate the percent discount offered online.
16. A college tuition fee of $4,500 increases to $4,900. Calculate the percent increase of the fee.
17. The average summer temperature in Toronto increased by 3.5°C this year. If the average daytime temperature last year was 28°C, calculate the percent change in the average summer temperature this year.
18. The average winter snowfall in Montreal increased by 2.5 cm this year. If the average winter snowfall last year was 50 cm, calculate the percent change in average winter snowfall this year.
19. The selling price of an apartment was $335,000. This is 34% more than the purchased price. Calculate the original purchase price.
20. The selling price of a home was $663,000. This is 23.5% more than the purchased price. Calculate the original purchase price.
21. A car dealer reduced the price of a car by 8.75%. The current price of the car is $38,000. What was the price of the car before the reduction in price?
22. A property developer reduced the price of a house by 6.25%. The current price of the house is $703,125. What was the price of the house before the reduction in price?
23. The marketing department's expenses rose by 30% from last year. If this year's expenses are $234,260, calculate last year's expenses.

24. A manufacturing company paid $56,400 (after a discount) for a heavy-duty packing machine from Japan. If they received a discount of 21%, calculate the original price of the machine.

25. Katelyn's financial manager invested her savings in a portfolio of shares that comprised of investments of $2,000, $1,800, and $3,100 in the infrastructure, hi-tech, and garment industries, respectively. Towards the end of 2011, if the value of her shares in the infrastructure industry rose by 20% while the rest remained the same, calculate the percent change in the value of her total investments.

26. Preston's website company invests their annual savings in different mutual funds. In 2010, they invested $12,500 in high-growth funds, $5,000 in medium-growth funds, and $2,000 in low-growth funds. If the value of their low-growth funds dropped by 10% this year while the rest stayed the same, by what percent did the total value of their investments change?

27. On a mathematics quiz, Chelsea scored 15% more than Zane. By what percent is Zane's score less than Chelsea's?

28. If Sabrina's annual salary is 10% more than Christina's, by what percent is Christina's annual earning less than Sabrina's?

29. Holistic Energy Ltd. spends $1,200, $1,400, $800, and $1,700 on average on replacing printer cartridges for their black & white inkjet printers, colour inkjet printers, black & white laser printers, and colour laser printers, respectively, every month.

    a. What percent of the total expenditure on printer cartridges do they spend on colour laser printers every month?

    b. If they decide to reduce the expense on both colour inkjet printers and colour laser printers by 50%, what percent of the total expenditure would they spend on black & white laser printers?

30. A manufacturing company has 280 production people, 21 quality inspectors, 15 sales people, 6 marketing people, and 15 people in other departments such as HR, Finance, etc.

    a. What percent of the total employees are quality inspectors?

    b. If 15% of the production people quit their jobs, what percent of the total remaining employees are quality inspectors?

5 | Self-Test Exercises

Answers to all problems are available online.

1. Colton's store expenses for the month of July and August were $33,480 and $36,580, which were 110% and 90% of the budgeted expenditure for the months of July and August, respectively. Calculate the total budgeted expenses for the two months.
2. Sandra lives in a condominium in downtown Toronto and works for a leading telecommunications company as a multimedia specialist. She earns an annual take-home salary of $60,000, and every month she spends $1,400 on rent, $600 on car expenses, $200 on a line-of-credit interest payment, $800 on miscellaneous expenses, and saves $2,000.
   a. What percent of her annual take-home salary are her annual expenses?
   b. Her bank manager advised her to invest 10% of her annual take-home salary in a medium-risk mutual fund. What would this amount be every month and what percent of her current savings would this amount be?
3. Calculate the original price for a pair of shoes if Ruby paid $140 for it after receiving a discount of 7%.
4. Lindsey invested her savings in shares of her brother's engineering company. The value of the shares, which she owned, dropped by $1.25 at the end of the first year, and a further $2.50 at the end of the second year. If the price of the share at the end of the second year was $12.55, calculate:
   a. The percent change in the price of the share each year.
   b. The percent drop in the price over the two-year period.
5. The value of a currency appreciated by 20% of its value last month and then depreciated by 20% this month. By what percent did the currency appreciate or depreciate over the 2-month period?
6. What amount when reduced by 13% results in $198.36?
7. What amount when increased by 5% results in $236.25?
8. Calculate the percent decrease if the initial value of 20 decreased to 17.
9. What is the amount of decrease if the initial value was 75 and the percent decrease is 28%?
10. What is the percent increase if the original value was 20 and the final value is 37?
11. A car dealer is giving a 12% discount on a car that was priced at $31,800. Calculate the price of the car after the discount.
12. If a discount of $51.00 is equivalent to a 60% decrease from the initial value, calculate the initial value.
13. During 2010, a stock lost 60% of its value. During 2011, the stock's value increased by 80%. Calculate the percent change in the stock's value over the two-year period.
14. The share price of a stock purchased for $20 a share increased by 30% during the first year and decreased by 30% during the second year. Calculate the percent change in the share price over the two-year period and the value of the stock at the end of the two years.

15. Prior to July 01, 2010, first-time buyers of new homes in Ontario had to pay only 5% in federal sales taxes. However, since July 01, 2010, they have to pay 13% in harmonized sales taxes to the Federal Government when purchasing new homes worth more than $400,000. What is the percent increase in sales taxes to a first-time home buyer of a new house worth $500,000?

Chapter 6
Basic Business Applications

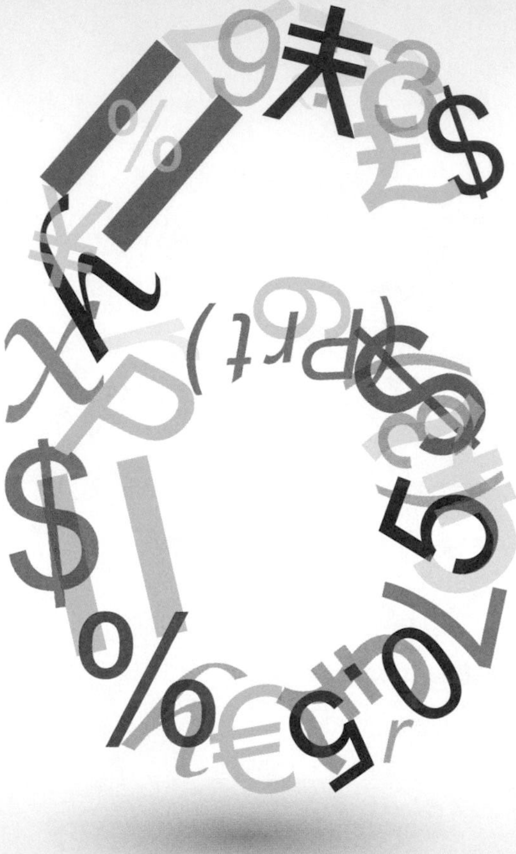

Learning Outcomes

- Calculate the amount and rate of markup.
- Calculate the amount and rate of markdown.
- Calculate the amount and rate of simple interest, principal, time period, and maturity value of investments and loans.
- Calculate gross pay based on annual salary, sales commissions, and hourly rate.
- Convert currencies between countries using exchange rates.
- Determine index numbers and their applications.

Chapter Outline

6.1 Markup and Markdown
6.2 Simple Interest
6.3 Payroll
6.4 Currency Conversion
6.5 Index Numbers

Have you ever wondered how businesses decide the selling price of a product, how your money grows; when it is in a savings account of a bank; how to calculate your hourly wage when you know your annual salary; why you lose money when you covert it to US dollars; or how the stock market performs? As you will learn in this chapter, by using your knowledge on percentages, ratios, and proportions, you will be able to solve basic business questions like these.

6.1 | Markup and Markdown

Markup

Markup is the amount that a business adds to the cost of the product to arrive at the selling price of the product.

Cost + Markup = Selling price

Therefore, ***Markup = Selling price – Cost***

The amount of markup includes the business' overhead expenses, such as rent, utilities, insurance, advertising, etc., that are necessary to operate the business and the desired operating profit of the business.

Markup is usually expressed as a percentage of cost, known as the rate of markup.

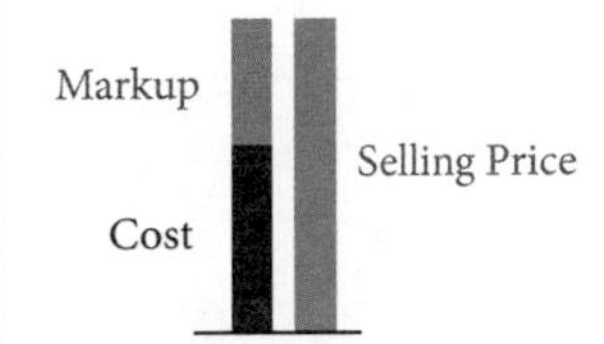

Exhibit 6.1-a Relationship among Markup, Cost, and Selling Price

Markup = Rate of markup × Cost

Therefore, $\textbf{\textit{Rate of markup}} = \dfrac{\textbf{\textit{Markup}}}{\textbf{\textit{Cost}}} \times \mathbf{100\%}$

Example 6.1-a

Calculating Selling Price and Rate of Markup

A store purchases printers for \$800 each. If the markup on each printer is \$600, calculate:

(i) Selling price.

(ii) Rate of markup.

Solution

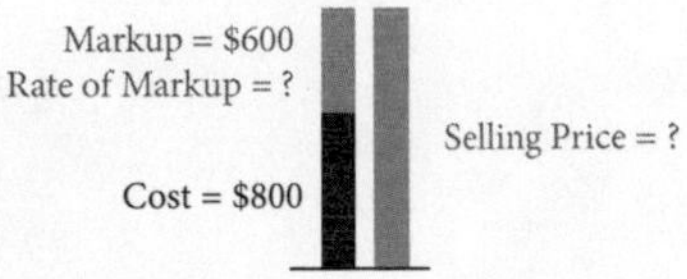

(i) $\textit{Selling price} = \textit{Cost} + \textit{Markup}$

$= 800.00 + 600.00$

$= \$1{,}400.00$

Therefore, the selling price of each printer is \$1,400.00.

(ii) $\textit{Rate of markup} = \left(\dfrac{\textit{Markup}}{\textit{Cost}}\right) \times 100\%$

$= \left(\dfrac{600.00}{800.00}\right) \times 100\%$

$= 75.00\%$

Therefore, the rate of markup is 75.00%.

Example 6.1-b

Calculating Cost and Rate of Markup

A retailer sells a handbag for \$87.75. If the markup on each handbag is \$22.75, calculate:

(i) Cost of each handbag.

(ii) Rate of markup on each handbag.

Solution

(i) $\textit{Cost} + \textit{Markup} = \textit{Selling price}$

$$\textit{Cost} = \textit{Selling price} - \textit{Markup}$$

$$\textit{Cost} = 87.75 - 22.75$$

$$= \$65.00$$

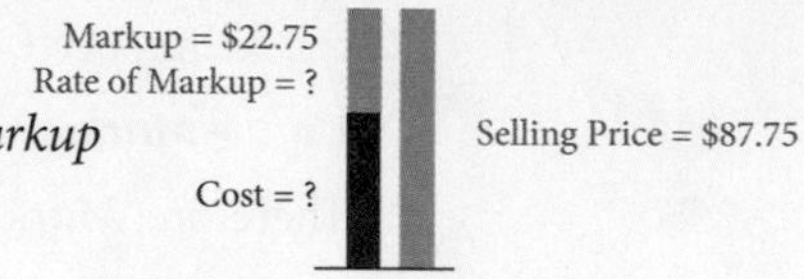

Therefore, the cost of the handbag is \$65.00.

(ii) $\textit{Rate of markup} = \left(\dfrac{\textit{Markup}}{\textit{Cost}}\right) \times 100\%$

$$= \left(\frac{22.75}{65.00}\right) \times 100\%$$

$$= 35.00\%$$

Therefore, the rate of markup is 35.00%.

Example 6.1-c

Calculating Markup and Rate of Markup

A wholesaler purchases cell phones for \$65.60 each and sells them for \$82.00 each. Calculate:

(i) Markup on each cell phone.

(ii) Rate of markup.

Solution

(i) $\textit{Markup} = \textit{Selling price} - \textit{Cost}$

$$= 82.00 - 65.60$$

$$= \$16.40$$

Therefore, the markup on each cell phone is \$16.40.

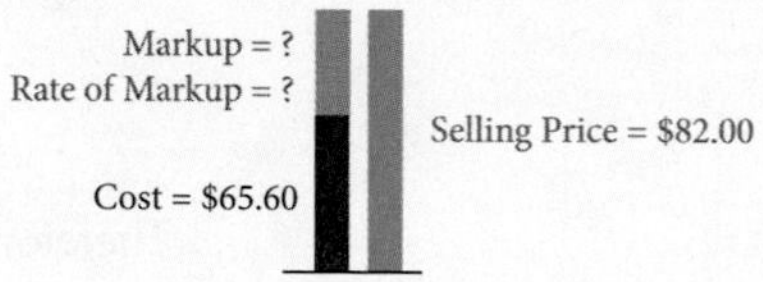

(ii) $\textit{Rate of markup} = \left(\dfrac{\textit{Markup}}{\textit{Cost}}\right) \times 100\%$

$$= \left(\frac{16.40}{65.60}\right) \times 100\%$$

$$= 25.00\%$$

Therefore, the rate of markup on each cell phone is 25.00%.

Example 6.1-d Calculating Markup and Selling Price

A wholesaler purchases a product for $2,000. If he has a markup of 40% on the cost of the product, calculate:

(i) Markup.

(ii) Selling price of the product.

Solution

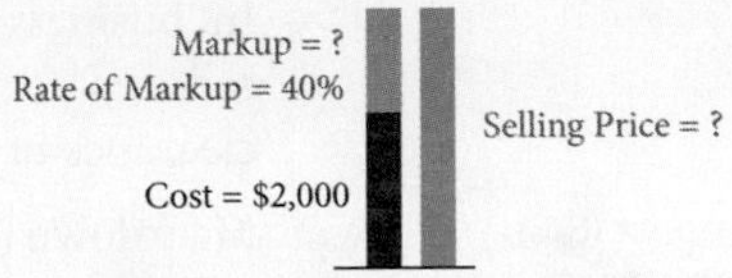

(i) $Markup = Rate\ of\ markup \times Cost$

$= 0.40 \times 2{,}000.00$

$= \$800.00$

Therefore, the markup is $800.00.

(ii) $Selling\ price = Cost + Markup$

$= 2{,}000.00 + 800.00$

$= \$2{,}800.00$

Therefore, the selling price is $2,800.00.

Example 6.1-e Calculating Cost and Selling Price

A car dealership sells used cars with a 20% markup on cost. The markup on a used car sold was $2,950. Calculate:

(i) Cost of the car to the dealer.

(ii) Selling price.

Solution

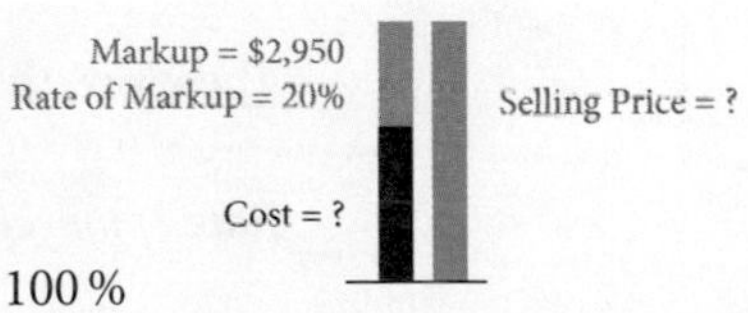

(i) $$Rate\ of\ markup = \left(\frac{Markup}{Cost}\right) \times 100\%$$

$$Cost = \left(\frac{\text{Markup}}{Rate\ of\ markup}\right) \times 100\,\%$$

$$Cost = \left(\frac{2{,}950.00}{20\%}\right) \times 100\%$$

$$Cost = \$14{,}750.00$$

Therefore, the cost of the car is $14,750.00.

(ii) $Selling\ price = Cost + Markup$

$= 14{,}750.00 + 2{,}950.00$

$= \$17{,}700.00$

Therefore, the selling price is $17,700.00.

Markdown

The selling price (S) of an item refers to the regular (or normal) selling price. i.e., the price before markdown (D).

The sale price (S_{Red}) of an item refers to the reduced (or discounted) selling price. i.e., the price after markdown (D).

Markdown is the amount by which the selling price of a product is reduced in determining the sale price.

Selling price – Markdown = Sale price

Therefore, ***Markdown = Selling price – Sale price***

In business, the selling price of an item is often reduced for various reasons, such as competition, clearance of seasonal items, etc.

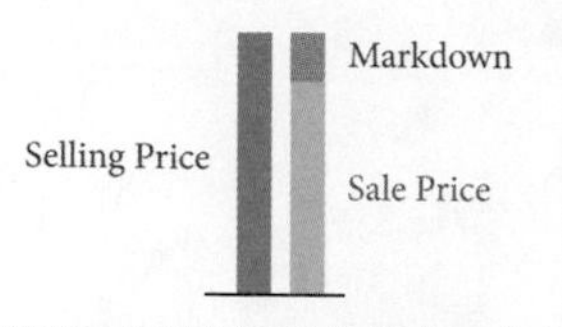

Exhibit 6.1-b Relationship among Selling Price, Markdown, and Sale Price

Markdown is usually expressed as a percentage of the selling price, known as the rate of markdown.

Markdown = Rate of markdown × Selling price

$$\text{Therefore, } \textbf{\textit{Rate of markdown}} = \left(\frac{\textbf{\textit{Markdown}}}{\textbf{\textit{Selling price}}}\right) \times \mathbf{100\%}$$

Example 6.1-f

Calculating Sale Price (Reduced Selling Price) and Rate of Markdown

Calculate the sale price and rate of markdown of an item that regularly sells for $680, but which is now being marked down by $204.

Solution

Selling price – Markdown = Sale price

Sale price = Selling price – Markdown

Sale price = 680.00 – 204.00

= $476.00

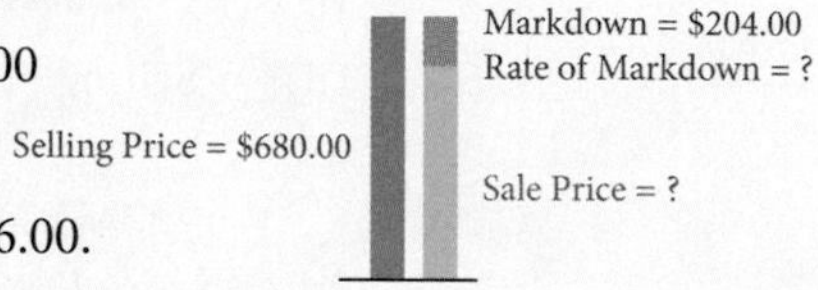

Therefore, the sale price of the item is $476.00.

$$\textit{Rate of markdown} = \left(\frac{\textit{Markdown}}{\textit{Selling price}}\right) \times 100\%$$

$$= \left(\frac{204.00}{680.00}\right) \times 100\%$$

$$= 30.00\%$$

Therefore, the rate of markdown is 30.00%.

Example 6.1-g

Calculating Markdown and Sale Price (Reduced Selling Price)

An item was marked down by 20% from the regular selling price of $1,250. Calculate:

(i) Markdown.

(ii) Sale price.

Solution

(i) $Markdown = Rate\ of\ markdown \times Selling\ price$

$= 0.20 \times 1{,}250.00$

$= \$250.00$

Therefore, the markdown was $250.00.

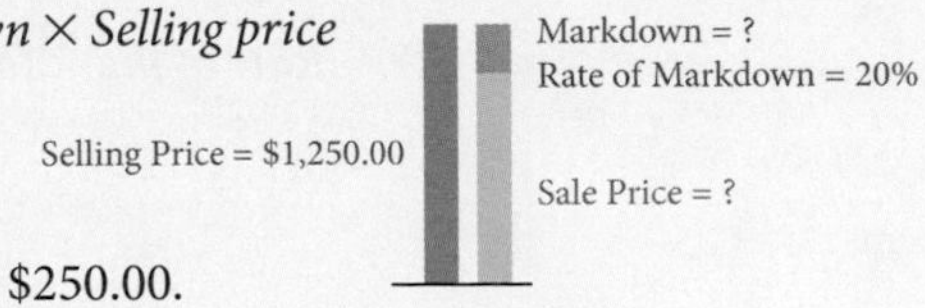

(ii) $Sale\ price = Selling\ price - Markdown$

$= 1{,}250.00 - 250.00$

$= \$1{,}000.00$

Therefore, the sale price was $1,000.00.

Example 6.1-h Calculating the Selling Price and Rate of Markdown

After a markdown of $276.50, an item was sold for $513.50. Calculate:

(i) Regular selling price.

(ii) Rate of markdown.

Solution

(i) $Selling\ price = Sale\ price + Markdown$

$Selling\ price = 513.50 + 276.50$

$= \$790.00$

Therefore, the regular selling price was $790.00.

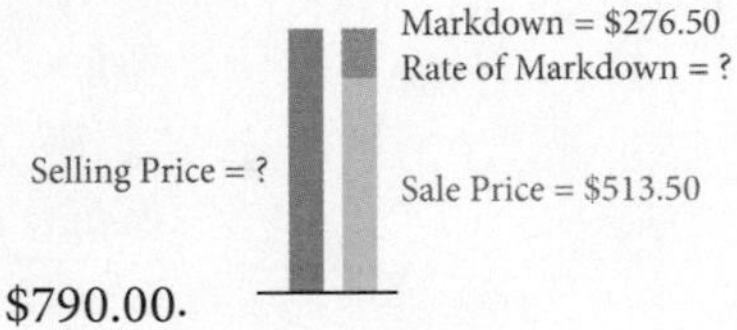

(ii) $$Rate\ of\ markdown = \left(\frac{Markdown}{Selling\ price}\right) \times 100\%$$

$$= \left(\frac{276.50}{790.00}\right) \times 100\%$$

$$= 0.35 \times 100\% = 35.00\%$$

Therefore, the rate of markdown was 35.00%.

Example 6.1-i Calculating Markdown and Rate of Markdown

During a sale, a shirt that was regularly priced at $49, sold for $41.65. Calculate:

(i) Markdown.

(ii) Rate of markdown.

Solution

(i) $Sale\ price = Selling\ price - Markdown$

$Markdown = Selling\ price - Sale\ price$

$Markdown = 49.00 - 41.65$

$= \$7.35$

Therefore, the markdown was $7.35.

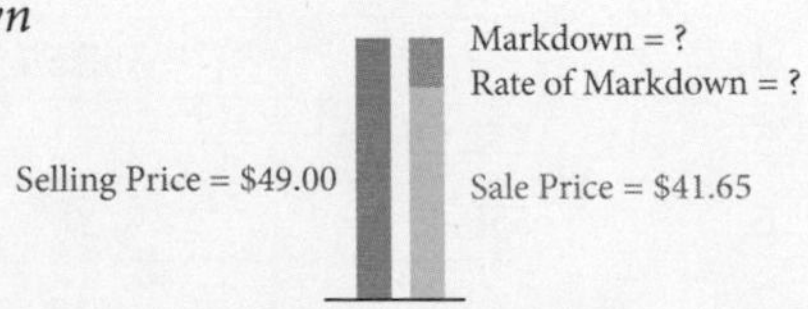

Solution
continued

(ii) $$\text{Rate of markdown} = \left(\frac{\text{Markdown}}{\text{Selling price}}\right) \times 100\%$$

$$= \left(\frac{7.35}{49.00}\right) \times 100\%$$

$$= 0.15 \times 100\%$$

$$= 15.00\%$$

Therefore, the rate of markdown was 15.00%.

Example 6.1-j

Calculating Selling Price and Sale Price (Reduced Selling Price)

During a sale, an item was sold for $150 after a markdown of 20%. Calculate,

(i) Regular selling price.

(ii) Sale price.

Solution

(i) $$\text{Markdown} = \text{Rate of markdown} \times \text{Selling price}$$

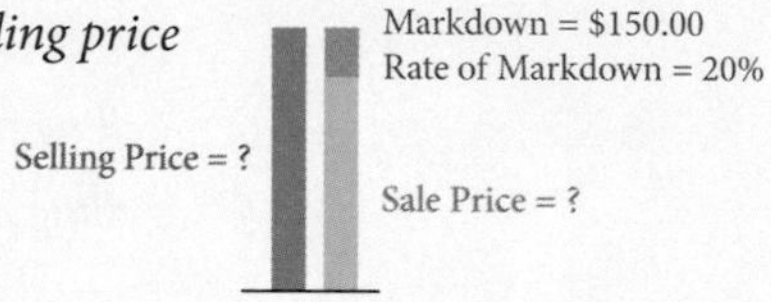

$$\text{Selling price} = \frac{\text{Markdown}}{\text{Rate of markdown}}$$

$$\text{Selling price} = \frac{150.00}{0.20}$$

$$= \$750.00$$

Therefore, the regular selling price was $750.00.

(ii) $$\text{Sale price} = \text{Selling price} - \text{Markdown}$$

$$= \$750.00 - \$150.00$$

$$= \$600.00$$

Therefore, the sale price was $600.00.

6.1 | Exercises

Answers to odd-numbered problems are available online.

	Cost ($)	Markup ($)	Selling Price ($)	Rate of Markup (%)
1.	$99.00	$24.75	?	?
2.	$37.50	$15.00	?	?
3.	?	$52.50	$490.00	?
4.	?	$67.50	$517.50	?
5.	$52.00	?	$97.50	?
6.	$50.40	?	$63.00	?
7.	$252.00	?	?	35.00%

	Cost ($)	Markup ($)	Selling Price ($)	Rate of Markup (%)
8.	$210.00	?	?	90.00%
9.	?	$175.00	?	12.50%
10.	?	$62.90	?	40.00%

11. A store sells a camera that costs $270 for $430. Find the amount of markup and the rate of markup.
12. A bicycle costs a store $64.50. If the store sells the bicycle for $93.15, calculate the amount of markup and the rate of markup.
13. A furniture shop purchased a certain mattress for $625, and marked it up by $325. Calculate the selling price and the rate of markup.
14. A store purchases monitors for $86.25 each. The store's markup is $31.50. Calculate the selling price and the rate of markup.
15. A computer store used a markup rate of 40%. Find the amount of markup and the selling price of a computer software DVD that the store bought for $38.75.
16. I purchased a laptop for $187.50 for the purpose of reselling it later. If my rate of markup was 90% of the cost, what was the amount of markup and the selling price?
17. The selling price of an item is $540. If the markup is $108, calculate the cost and rate of markup of the item.
18. A DVD player is sold for $124 after a markup of $27. Calculate the cost and rate of markup of the item.
19. A bookstore uses a 40% markup on calculators and the amount of markup of a particular calculator was $24. Calculate the bookstore's purchase price of the calculator and its selling price.
20. If a $96 markup of an item represents an 80% rate of markup on cost, calculate the cost and the selling price of that item.

For Problems 21 to 30, find the missing values (round your answer to 2 decimal places, where applicable).

	Selling Price ($)	Markdown ($)	Sale Price ($)	Rate of Markdown (%)
21.	$94.75	$74.50	?	?
22.	$90.40	$22.60	?	?
23.	$136.00	?	?	22.50%
24.	$72.90	?	?	40.00%
25.	?	$34.00	$46.00	?
26.	?	$36.75	$173.25	?
27.	$25.00	?	$17.50	?
28.	$58.50	?	$29.25	?
29.	?	$31.71	?	25.00%
30.	?	$150.00	?	37.50%

31. During a sale, a sofa that regularly sells for $250 is marked down by $75. Calculate the sale price and the rate of markdown.

32. A scanner that regularly sells for \$99 was sold after a markdown of \$29. Calculate the sale price and the rate of markdown.
33. A treadmill with a regular selling price of \$190 is on sale for 15% off the original price. Calculate the amount of markdown and the sale price.
34. The regular selling price of a rocking chair is \$139. During a sale, it was sold after a markdown of 25%. Find the amount of markdown and sale price.
35. A store offers an \$18 discount on a bookcase and it was sold for \$30. Calculate the regular selling price of the bookcase and the rate of discount offered.
36. Calculate the regular selling price and the rate of markdown of an item sold for \$27.30 after a markdown of \$18.20 during a sale.
37. A fax machine that regularly sells for \$127.50 is marked down to \$86.70 during a special sale. Find the percent markdown and the amount of markdown during the sale.
38. A camcorder regularly selling for \$299 was marked down to sell for \$233.22. Find the percent markdown and the amount of markdown.
39. During a sale, a furniture store marked down all the items by 35%. The amount of markdown on a bed was \$166.25. Find the regular selling price and the sale price.
40. A winter jacket was sold after a markdown of \$16.25. If this represents a markdown rate of 13%, find the regular selling price and the sale price of the winter jacket.

6.2 | Simple Interest

Interest is a fee that borrowers pay to lenders for using their money temporarily for a period of time. For example, when we invest money, the financial institution uses our money and therefore, pays us interest for the time period it has been invested. Similarly, when we borrow money from a financial institution, we pay interest to them for the time period borrowed.

Usually, the unit of 't' is converted to match the unit of 'r' using 1 year = 12 months or 1 year = 365 days.

In simple interest calculations, **Interest (*I*)** is calculated as a **percentage (%)** of the initial amount of money invested or borrowed, known as the **Principal (*P*)**.

This interest percentage (%) is the product of the **interest rate (*r*)** and the **time.** Therefore, **interest percentage** = $r \times t$.

For example,

If '*r*' is expressed as per annum (*r*% p.a.), then '*t*' should be in years.

If '*r*' is expressed as per month (*r*% p.m.), then '*t*' should be in months.

In calculations, 'r' is used as the decimal or fractional equivalent of the percentage rate.

Interest = Principal × interest percentage

Interest = Principal × interest rate × time

$I = P \times r \times t$

This can be re-arranged to solve for the variables ***P***, ***r***, and ***t*** as follows:

$$P = \frac{I}{r \times t} \qquad r = \frac{I}{P \times t} \qquad t = \frac{I}{P \times r}$$

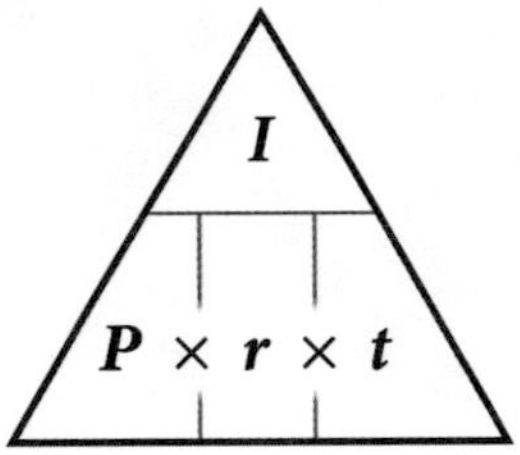

P, r, t triangle

Here is a triangle that can be used to help in re-arranging the formula $I = Prt$ to find the variable P, r, or t.

Variables beside each other at the bottom are multiplied ($P \times r \times t$, as shown).

Variables at the bottom are divided by the variable on top: I.

Cover the variable that you want to solve to see the new formula.

For example, if you want to solve for 'P', the formula can be found by covering 'P' and reading the remaining variables in the above triangle to obtain, $P = \dfrac{I}{rt}$

Interest rate is usually expressed as percentage per annum (r% p.a.) or percentage per month (r% p.m.) and time (t) is expressed in days or months or years.

In this section, we will use annual interest rates (r% p.a.) and time periods (t) expressed in years (or converted to years) when calculating the amount of interest.

For example,

$$4 \text{ months} = \frac{4}{12} \text{ year.}$$

$$1 \text{ year } 3 \text{ months} = 15 \text{ months} = \frac{15}{12} \text{ years.}$$

$$125 \text{ days} = \frac{125}{365} \text{ year.}$$

As time goes by, the value of money increases by the amount of interest earned for that period. Therefore, when money is returned after a period of time, interest is added to the principal and the accumulated value is known as the **Maturity value (S).**

Maturity value = Principal + Interest

$$S = P + I$$

This can be re-arranged to solve for the variables I and P, as follows:

$$I = S - P$$

$$P = S - I$$

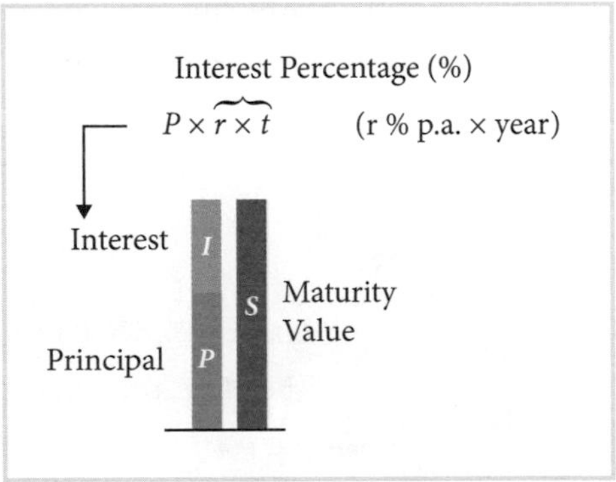

Example 6.2-a

Calculating the Interest

Calculate the amount of interest earned from an investment of $2,250 for 6 months at an interest rate of 4.2% p.a.

Solution

$r = 4.2\%$ p.a.

$t = 6 \text{ months} = \frac{6}{12} \text{ year}$

$I = P \times r \times t$

$I = 2{,}250.00 \times 0.042 \times \frac{6}{12} = \$47.25$

Therefore, the amount of interest earned is $47.25.

Example 6.2-b

Calculating Principal

Calculate the amount of money that should be invested now at an annual interest rate of 6% for 3 years to earn interest of $675.

Solution

$r = 6\%$ p.a.

$t = 3$ years

$$P = \frac{I}{r \times t}$$

$$= \frac{675.00}{(0.06 \times 3)} = \$3{,}750.00$$

Therefore, $3,750.00 should be invested now.

Example 6.2-c

Calculating Interest and Maturity Value

Tony invested $7,500 for 2 years at an annual interest rate of 4.8%. Calculate:

(i) Amount of interest earned from this investment.

(ii) Maturity value at the end of 2 years.

Solution

(i) $r = 4.8\%$ p.a.

$t = 2$ years

$I = P \times r \times t$

$Interest = 7{,}500.00 \times 0.048 \times 2 = \$720.00$

Therefore, the amount of interest earned in 2 years is $720.00.

(ii) $S = P + I$

$S = 7{,}500.00 + 720.00 = \$8{,}220.00$

Therefore, the maturity value at the end of 2 years is $8,220.00.

Example 6.2-d **Calculating Interest and Rate of Interest**

An investment of $4,500 results in a maturity value of $4,938.75 after 18 months. Calculate:

(i) Amount of interest earned.

(ii) Annual rate of interest.

Solution

(i) $I = S - P$

$I = 4{,}938.75 - 4{,}500.00 = \$438.75$

Therefore, the amount of interest earned in 18 months is $438.75.

(ii) $t = 18 \text{ months} = \frac{18}{12} \text{ years}$

$$r = \frac{I}{P \times t}$$

$$r = \frac{438.75}{4{,}500 \times \frac{18}{12}} \times 100\% = 6.50\% \text{ p.a.}$$

Therefore, the annual interest rate is 6.50%.

6.2 | Exercises

Answers to odd-numbered problems are available online.

Calculate the Interest (I) and the Maturity Value (S) for Problems 1 to 6.

	Principal (***P***)	Rate (***r***)	Time (***t***)	Interest (***I***)	Maturity Value (***S***)
1.	$900.00	5% p.a.	3 years	?	?
2.	$6,250.00	4% p.a.	2 years	?	?
3.	$1,480.00	2.5% p.a.	18 months	?	?
4.	$2,500.00	3.5% p.a.	15 months	?	?
5.	$5,840.00	2% p.a.	75 days	?	?
6.	$7,300.00	3% p.a.	250 days	?	?

7. Calculate the interest due on a $2,600 investment made for 2 years at 3.5% p.a.
8. Calculate the interest due on a loan of $1,250 borrowed for 4 years at 4.25% p.a.
9. How much interest is owed on a loan of $1,500 borrowed for 1 year 9 months at 4.8% p.a.?
10. How much interest is earned from an investment of $2,400 made for 2 years 3 months at 3.6% p.a.?
11. Khan borrowed $1,460 at 5% p.a. for 200 days. Calculate the interest due on the loan and the maturity value of the loan.
12. Ann invested $4,380 for 100 days in an account that pays 3% p.a. Calculate the interest earned and the maturity value of the investment.

Calculate the missing values for Problems 13 to 22.

	Principal (*P*)	Rate (*r*)	Time (*t*)	Interest (*I*)	Maturity Value (*S*)
13.	$750.00	?	3 years	?	$930.00
14.	$1,300.00	?	2 years	?	$1,404.00
15.	$5,000.00	2.5% p.a.	?	$500.00	?
16.	$8,000.00	3.5% p.a.	?	$1,120.00	?
17.	?	?	9 months	$60.00	$2,600.00
18.	?	?	15 months	$120.00	$1,720.00
19.	$1,600.00	4% p.a.	?	?	$1,792.00
20.	$950.00	3% p.a.	?	?	$1,000.00
21.	?	6% p.a.	120 days	$36.00	?
22.	?	5% p.a.	180 days	$63.00	?

23. At what rate (% p.a.) will a $6,000.00 investment result in a maturity value of $6,600.00 in 2 years?
24. At what rate (% p.a.) will a $1,250.00 investment result in a maturity value of $1,625.00 in 5 years?
25. In how many years will $3,000.00 invested at 3% p.a. result in a maturity value of $3,360.00?
26. How many years will it take for a deposit of $5,000.00 earning at 6% p.a. to reach $6,500.00?
27. What amount invested at 4% p.a. for 4 years gives an interest of $400.00?
28. The interest on a loan for 3 years at 6% p.a. is $810.00. Calculate the amount of the loan.
29. A loan of $4,800.00 was paid off at the end of 5 months with a payment of $4,940.00. Calculate the interest rate (% p.a.) charged on the loan.
30. John deposited $3,600.00 in a savings account. The balance in this account after 9 months was $3,681.00. Calculate the interest rate (% p.a.) used.

6.3 | Payroll

Payroll

Employees of an organization receive payment from their employers for their services. In this section, we will calculate (or use) the gross pay given to employees based on an annual salary, hourly rate of pay, or commission.

Annual Salary

Annual salary employees are usually supervisory, managerial, or professional employees who work on an annual basis and are not paid an hourly rate. If you are employed by an organization paying you an annual salary, this is the amount that you will be paid for your service over a period of one year.

Pay Period

Pay period refers to the frequency of payments (how often payments are being made). The most common pay periods are:

- Monthly (once a month): 12 payments throughout the year (1 year = 12 months)
- Weekly (once a week): 52 payments throughout the year (1 year = 52 weeks)
- Bi-weekly (every two weeks): 26 payments throughout the year. (Once in two weeks, $\frac{52}{2} = 26$ bi-weekly pay periods)

Note: In the examples and exercises in this section, we will be using 52 weekly pay periods or 26 bi-weekly pay periods. However, it is possible to have 53 weekly pay periods or 27 bi-weekly pay periods depending on the year and the payment days.

$$\textit{Pay for a pay period} = \frac{\textit{Annual salary}}{\textit{Number of pay periods}}$$

Therefore,

$$\textit{Annual salary} = \textit{Pay for a pay period} \times \textit{Number of pay periods}$$

Example 6.3-a **Calculating Payment for a Pay Period, Given the Annual Salary**

Ann works for a publishing company and receives an annual salary of \$62,400.00. Calculate her gross pay for a pay period, if paid,

(i) monthly.

(ii) weekly.

(iii) bi-weekly.

Solution

$$\textit{Pay for a pay period} = \frac{\textit{Annual salary}}{\textit{Number of pay periods}}$$

(i) $\textit{Monthly pay} = \frac{62{,}400.00}{12} = \$5{,}200.00$

Therefore, if paid monthly, her pay would be \$5,200.00.

(ii) $\textit{Weekly pay} = \frac{62{,}400.00}{52} = \$1{,}200.00$

Therefore, if paid weekly, her pay would be \$1,200.00.

(iii) $\textit{Bi-weekly pay} = \frac{62{,}400.00}{26} = \$2{,}400.00$

Therefore, if paid bi-weekly, her pay would be \$2,400.00

Example 6.3-b **Calculating Annual Salary and the Equivalent Monthly Pay, Given the Weekly Pay**

Sam is paid $1,500.00 weekly. Calculate:

(i) Annual salary.

(ii) Equivalent monthly pay.

Solution

(i) $Annual\ salary = Pay\ for\ a\ pay\ period \times Number\ of\ pay\ periods$

$= 1{,}500.00 \times 52$

$= \$78{,}000.00$

Therefore, the annual salary is $78,000.00.

(ii) $$Pay\ for\ a\ pay\ period = \frac{Annual\ salary}{Number\ of\ pay\ periods}$$

$$Monthly\ pay = \frac{78{,}000.00}{12}$$

$= \$6{,}500.00$

Therefore, the equivalent monthly pay is $6,500.00.

Hourly Rate of Pay

Hourly rate of pay employees usually have a variable and unpredictable workload. They receive payment based on an hourly rate of pay for the number of hours worked during the pay period.

Depending on the type of profession/job, the number of working hours per week (workweek) may vary. The most common workweeks are: 40 hours, 37.5 hours, 35 hours, and 32.5 hours.

By knowing the hourly rate of pay and the number of hours one has worked during a pay period, you can calculate the total gross pay for that pay period.

$$\boldsymbol{Pay\ for\ a\ pay\ period = Hourly\ Rate \times Number\ of\ Hours\ Worked}$$

$$\boldsymbol{Weekly\ Pay = Hourly\ Rate \times Workweek}$$

$$\boldsymbol{Hourly\ rate = \frac{Weekly\ pay}{Workweek}}$$

Example 6.3-c **Calculating Bi-Weekly Pay, Given the Hourly Rate and the Workweek**

Aran is paid bi-weekly. His workweek is 35 hours and his hourly rate is $29.50. Calculate his bi-weekly pay.

Solution

$Number\ of\ working\ hours\ for\ 2\ weeks = 2 \times 35$

$= 70$ hours

Solution *continued*

$$\textit{Total Pay} = \textit{Hourly Rate} \times \textit{Number of Hours Worked}$$
$$= 29.50 \times 70$$
$$= \$2{,}065.00$$

Therefore, his bi-weekly pay is $2,065.00.

Example 6.3-d **Calculating Weekly Pay and Hourly Rate, Given the Annual Pay and the Workweek**

Mythili is being paid $39,000 per annum. Her workweek is 40 hours. Calculate:

(i) Her weekly pay.

(ii) Her hourly rate of pay.

Solution

(i) $$\textit{Weekly pay} = \frac{\textit{Annual salary}}{52}$$
$$= \frac{39{,}000.00}{52}$$
$$= \$750.00$$

Therefore, her weekly pay is $750.00.

(ii) $$\text{Hourly rate} = \frac{\textit{Weekly pay}}{\textit{Workweek}}$$
$$= \frac{750.00}{40}$$
$$= \$18.75$$

Therefore, her hourly rate is $18.75.

Example 6.3-e **Calculating Workweek and Annual Salary, Given the Bi-Weekly Pay and the Hourly Rate**

Albert is paid $1,687.50 bi-weekly. His hourly rate of pay is $22.50. Calculate:

(i) His regular workweek.

(ii) His equivalent annual salary.

Solution

(i) $$\textit{Total pay} = \textit{Hourly rate} \times \textit{Number of hours worked}$$
$$1687.50 = 22.50 \times \textit{Number of hours worked bi-weekly}$$
$$\textit{Number of hours worked bi-weekly} = \frac{1{,}687.50}{22.50}$$
$$= 75 \text{ hours}$$
$$\textit{Number of hours worked per week} = \frac{75}{2}$$
$$= 37.5 \text{ hours}$$

Therefore, his regular workweek is 37.5 hours.

Solution
continued

(ii) $\textit{Annual salary} = \textit{Pay for a pay period} \times \textit{Number of pay periods}$

$= 1{,}687.50 \times 26$

$= \$43{,}875.00$

Therefore, his annual salary is $43,875.00.

Overtime Rate of Pay

If you work more than the specified number of hours per week (workweek), you will be eligible for overtime payment for the additional hours worked. This extra payment is calculated using an overtime rate. The overtime rate of pay is usually more than one and one-half (1.5) times the regular rate of pay. This factor (1.5 times or 2 times) that employers use to calculate the overtime rate is called the overtime factor.

$$\textbf{\textit{Overtime Rate}} = \textbf{\textit{Overtime factor}} \times \textbf{\textit{Hourly rate}}$$

$$\textbf{\textit{Overtime Pay}} = \textbf{\textit{Overtime rate}} \times \textbf{\textit{Number of hours worked overtime}}$$

Example 6.3-f

Calculating Regular Rate of Pay and Overtime Rate of Pay, Given Annual Salary, Workweek, and Overtime Factor

Cindy earns $46,800.00 per year. Her workweek is 40 hours and her overtime factor is 1.5. Calculate:

(i) Her regular rate of pay.

(ii) Her overtime rate of pay.

Solution

(i) $$\textit{Pay for a pay period} = \frac{\textit{Annual salary}}{\textit{Number of pay periods}}$$

$$\textit{Weekly pay} = \frac{46{,}800.00}{52}$$

$$= \$900.00$$

$$\textit{Hourly rate} = \frac{\textit{Weekly pay}}{\textit{Workweek}}$$

$$= \frac{900.00}{40}$$

$$= \$22.50 \text{ per hour}$$

Therefore, her regular rate of pay is $22.50 per hour.

(ii) $\textit{Overtime rate} = \textit{Overtime factor} \times \textit{Hourly rate}$

$= 1.5 \times 22.50$

$= \$33.75$

Therefore, her overtime rate of pay is $33.75 per hour.

Example 6.3-g

Calculating Pay for a Pay Period Including Overtime Pay

Fred earns $58,500.00 annually and he is paid bi-weekly. His regular workweek is 37.5 hours. Overtime is paid at 1.5 times the regular rate. Calculate his pay for the last pay period in which he worked 85 hours.

Solution

$$\textit{Pay for a pay period} = \frac{\textit{Annual salary}}{\textit{Number of pay periods}}$$

$$\textit{Bi-weekly pay} = \frac{58{,}500.00}{26}$$

$$= \$2{,}250.00$$

$$\textit{Weekly pay} = \frac{\textit{Bi-weekly pay}}{2} = \frac{2{,}250.00}{2} = \$1{,}125.00$$

$$\textit{Hourly rate} = \frac{\textit{Weekly pay}}{\textit{Workweek}}$$

$$= \frac{1{,}125.00}{37.50}$$

$$= \$30.00 \text{ per hour}$$

$$\textit{Overtime factor} = 1.5$$

$$\textit{Overtime rate} = \$30.00 \times 1.5$$

$$= \$45.00 \text{ per hour}$$

$$\textit{Overtime hours during a two-week pay period} = 85 - 37.5 \times 2$$

$$= 85 - 75$$

$$= 10 \text{ hours}$$

$$\textit{Overtime Pay} = \textit{Overtime rate} \times \textit{Number of hours worked overtime}$$

$$= 45.00 \times 10$$

$$= \$450.00$$

Therefore, Fred's pay for the last pay period = $2,250.00 + $450.00 = $2,700.00

Commissions

Sales commissions are usually given to sales people to encourage them to sell more, because the more they sell, the more they will earn. If the employment is based on commission, then the gross pay for a given pay period is calculated based on a percentage of sales, known as the commission rate.

In this section we will use only a straight (single) commission rate in calculating the gross pay for a pay period.

$$\textbf{\textit{Commission}} = \textbf{\textit{Commission rate}} \times \textbf{\textit{Amount of sales}}$$

Example 6.3-h **Calculating Salary Based on a Straight (Single) Commission Rate**

David's salary is 5% of the sales that he makes for the month. If the sales he makes for the month are $50,000.00, then what is David's salary for that month?

Solution

$$Commission = Commission\ rate \times Amount\ of\ sales$$
$$= 0.05 \times 50{,}000.00$$
$$= \$2{,}500.00$$

Therefore, David's salary for the month is $2,500.00.

Example 6.3-i **Calculating Amount of Sales, Given the Commission and the Rate of Commission**

Mercy is paid 4.5% sales commission. She earned $2,025.00 in commission last month. Calculate her sales for last month.

Solution

$$Commission = Commission\ rate \times Amount\ of\ sales$$
$$Sales\ amount = \frac{Commission}{Commission\ rate}$$
$$= \frac{2{,}025.00}{0.045}$$
$$= \$45{,}000.00$$

Therefore, Mercy's sales for last month were $45,000.00.

Example 6.3-j **Calculating Rate of Commission, Given the Commission and the Amount of Sales**

Carol earned a commission of $11,375.00 from the sale of a house sold for $650,000. Calculate the rate of commission she charged for the sale of the house.

Solution

$$Commission = Commission\ rate \times Amount\ of\ sales$$
$$Commission\ rate = \frac{Commission}{Amount\ of\ sales}$$
$$Commission\ rate = \frac{11{,}375.00}{650{,}000}$$
$$= 0.0175$$
$$= 1.75\%$$

Therefore, she charged a rate of commission of 1.75%.

6.3 | Exercises

Answers to odd-numbered problems are available online.

For Problems 1 to 8, find the missing values (round your answer to 2 decimal places, where applicable).

	Annual Salary($)	Monthly Pay ($)	Bi-Weekly Pay ($)	Weekly Pay ($)
1.	$48,750.00	?	?	?
2.	$32,760.00	?	?	?
3.	?	$3,380.00	?	?
4.	?	$4,550.00	?	?
5.	?	?	$1,350.00	?
6.	?	?	$1,540.50	?
7.	?	?	?	$673.50
8.	?	?	?	$864.00

9. Scott is paid an annual salary of $36,400.00. Calculate his bi-weekly pay and the equivalent monthly pay.
10. Judy receives an annual salary of $45,000.00. Calculate her weekly pay and the equivalent monthly pay.
11. Floyd's bi-weekly pay is $1,912.50. Calculate his annual salary and the equivalent monthly pay.
12. Barb receives a weekly pay of $936.00. Calculate her annual salary and the equivalent monthly pay.
13. Joyce receives a monthly pay of $4,143.75. Calculate her annual salary and the equivalent weekly pay.
14. Chris receives a monthly pay of $2,625.00. Calculate his annual salary and the equivalent bi-weekly pay.

For Problems 15 to 22, find the missing values (round your answer to 2 decimal places, where applicable).

	Annual Salary($)	Weekly Pay ($)	Workweek (Hrs/Week)	Hourly Rate ($/hr)	Overtime Factor	Overtime Rate ($/hr)
15.	$57,200.00	?	40.0	?	1.50	?
16.	$47,775.00	?	47.5	?	2.00	?
17.	?	$747.50	32.5	?	?	$34.50
18.	?	$938.00	35.0	?	?	$40.20
19.	?	$513.50	?	$15.75	1.50	?
20.	?	$890.00	?	$22.25	2.00	?
21.	?	?	37.5	$17.20	2.25	?
22.	?	?	32.5	$24.00	1.75	?

23. Susan's annual salary of $68,000.00 is based on a 35-hour workweek and she is paid weekly. Calculate her weekly pay and her hourly rate of pay.
24. James receives an annual salary of $46,800.00. His workweek is 37.5 hours. Calculate his weekly pay and his hourly rate of pay.

25. For Problem 23, calculate the overtime rate of pay at 1.5 times the regular rate of pay and the gross pay for a week in which she worked 6 overtime hours.
26. For Problem 24, calculate the overtime rate of pay at 2 times the regular rate of pay and the gross pay for a week in which he worked 9 overtime hours.
27. Terry receives a weekly pay of $1,267.50. He has a 32.5-hour workweek. Calculate his hourly rate of pay and his annual salary.
28. Ron's weekly pay of $918.75 is based on a 37.5 -hour workweek. Calculate his hourly rate of pay and his annual salary.
29. Alex earns an hourly rate of pay of $23.70 for a 35-hour workweek. Calculate his weekly pay and his annual salary.
30. Tom earns $25.00 per hour and his workweek is 40 hours. Calculate his weekly pay and his annual salary.

For Problems 31 to 36, find the missing values (round your answer to 2 decimal places, where applicable).

	Sales ($)	Commission Rate (%)	Commission ($)
31.	$45,500.00	4.50%	?
32.	$21,375.00	7.50%	?
33.	?	5.00%	$2,925.00
34.	?	7.00%	$1,775.00
35.	$46,500.00	?	$1,395.00
36.	$35,000.00	?	$1,925.00

37. Tracy is paid a fixed commission of 5.5% on her sales in a month. What will she be paid for a month in which her sales are $47,500.00?
38. Nancy is paid a fixed commission of 3.75% on all sales during the month. Sales for last month were $38,550.00. What were her gross earnings for last month?
39. Dianne is paid a commission of 4.5% on all sales in a month. Determine her sales for the month in which she earned $2,317.50 in commission.
40. Joana receives a commission of 6.5% on all sales during that period. Last week she earned $1,935.05. What were her sales for last week?
41. Bill is paid on a fixed commission rate basis and his gross pay in September was $2,730.00 on sales totalling $42,000.00. Calculate his rate of commission.
42. Jennifer is paid on a fixed commission rate based on her sales. Calculate the rate of commission if she earned $3,696.00 in a month when her sales were $67,200.00.

6.4 | Currency Conversion

Exchange rates are used to convert currencies between countries.

Currency Conversion

The exchange rate, also called the foreign exchange rate or forex rate, is used for converting currencies between countries. The exchange rate allows you to calculate the amount of a currency required to purchase one unit of another currency.

For example, to convert Canadian currency to US currency, it is important to know how many Canadian dollars are equivalent to one US dollar, or vice versa.

The value of a currency may fluctuate constantly during the day and the exchange rate may vary accordingly. For example, on Oct. 25, 2012, US$1 was equal to C$0.9940 and C$1 was equal to US$1.0060 at noon EST. Thus, the exchange rate on that date and time was US$1 = C$0.9940 and C$1 = US$1.0060.

Currency Cross-Rate Table

Currency exchange rates are generally displayed in a table called the currency cross-rate table for quick reference. Exchange rates presented in the currency cross-rate table below are from Oct. 25, 2012.

Table 6.4

Currency Cross-Rate Table

Currency	Symbol	C$	US$	€	£	A$
Canadian dollar	C$	1	0.9940	1.2868	1.6027	1.0295
US dollar	US$	1.0060	1	1.2946	1.6124	1.0359
Euro	€	0.7770	0.7724	1	1.2455	0.8002
British Pound	£	0.6240	0.6202	0.8028	1	0.6423
Australian dollar	A$	0.9711	0.9654	1.2497	1.5565	1

The vertical columns of the table represent one unit of the currency to be converted and the horizontal rows represent the equivalent value of it in another currency.

For example, £1 = US$1.6124, and US$1 = A$0.9654.

For calculations involving conversion from one currency to another, we will either use the cross-rate table or the exchange rates provided in the question. We will be using the method of proportions to solve examples that follow.

Example 6.4-a Converting Currency from Canadian Dollar (C$) to US$

Based on the exchange rates provided in Table 6.4 (Currency Cross-Rate Table), how many US dollars would you receive when you convert C$400?

Solution

From the cross-rate table, US$1 = C$0.9940

$$\text{US\$: C\$ = US\$: C\$}$$

$$1 : 0.9940 = x : 400$$

$$\frac{1}{0.9940} = \frac{x}{400.00}$$

$$x = \frac{400.00}{0.9940} = 402.414486... = \text{US\$}402.41$$

Therefore, you would receive US$402.41 when you convert C$400.00.

Example 6.4-b Converting Currency from C$ to US$ and from US$ to C$

If US$1 = C$0.9940, calculate:

(i) The amount you will receive if you convert US$1,000 to Canadian dollars.

(ii) The amount you will receive if you convert C$1,000 to US dollars.

Solution

(i) $$\text{US\$: C\$ = US\$: C\$}$$

$$1 : 0.9940 = 1{,}000 : x$$

$$\frac{1}{0.9940} = \frac{1{,}000.00}{x}$$ Cross-multiplying and solving for x,

$$x = \text{C\$}994.00$$

Therefore, you will receive C$994.00 when you convert US$1,000.00.

(ii) $$\text{US\$: C\$ = US\$: C\$}$$

$$1 : 0.9940 = x : 1{,}000$$

$$\frac{1}{0.9940} = \frac{x}{1{,}000.00}$$ Cross-multiplying and solving for x,

$$x = 1006.036217... = \text{US\$}1{,}006.04$$

Therefore, you will receive US$1,006.04 when you convert C$1,000.00.

Example 6.4-c Converting from One Currency to Another Currency, Given Exchange Rates

Samantha is travelling from Canada to London on vacation. If £1 = C$1.6027, how much would she receive if she converted C$1,000 to British pounds?

Solution

$$\text{£ : C\$ = £ : C\$}$$

$$1 : 1.6027 = x : 1{,}000$$

Solution *continued*

$$\frac{1}{1.6027} = \frac{x}{1{,}000.00}$$ Cross-multiplying and solving for x,

$$x = 623.947089... = £623.95$$

Therefore, she would receive £623.95 when she converts C$1,000.00.

Example 6.4-d

Series of Currency Conversions

If US$1 = C$0.9940 and C$1 = A$0.9711, calculate the amount of US dollars you would receive with 100 Australian dollars.

Solution

First, find out how many Canadian dollars you would receive with A$100.

$$C\$: A\$ = C\$: A\$$$

$$1 : 0.9711 = x : 100$$

$$\frac{1}{0.9711} = \frac{x}{1{,}00.00}$$ Cross-multiplying and solving for x,

$$x = C\$102.976006...$$

Now, determine how many US dollars you would receive with C$102.976006...

$$US\$: C\$ = US\$: C\$$$

$$1 : 0.9940 = x : 102.976006...$$

$$\frac{1}{0.9940} = \frac{x}{102.976006...}$$ Cross-multiplying and solving for x,

$$x = 103.597592... = US\$103.60$$

Therefore, you would receive US$103.60 when you convert A$100.00.

Buying and Selling Currencies

If you would like to convert currencies, you should go to a bank or other financial institution that is authorized to purchase and sell currencies. These financial institutions usually have different exchange rates for buying and selling currencies, which they call their buying rate and selling rate. They use the actual currency exchange rates and their rate of commission to create their own buying and selling rates for each currency. Commission is charged for their services on these transactions.

Example 6.4-e

Currency Conversion Including Commission in Buying or Selling Currencies

Sarah plans to travel to the US from Canada and approaches a local bank to purchase US$1,000. Assume US$1 = C$0.9940 and that the bank charges a commission of 0.75% to sell or buy US dollars. Calculate:

(i) The amount in Canadian dollars that Sarah would have to pay for US$1,000.

(ii) If Sarah changes her plan and wishes to convert US$1,000 back to Canadian dollars, how much will she receive from the same bank, assuming the same exchange rate and the same commission rate?

Solution

When calculating the buying or selling rate, it does not matter if you calculate the commission first and then convert the value, or vice-versa. You will always obtain the same answer.

When you buy currencies, you will pay the converted amount and the financial institution's commission.

When you sell currencies, you will receive the converted currency less the financial institution's commission.

(i) US$: C$ = US$: C$

$1 : 0.9940 = 1{,}000 : x$

$\frac{1}{0.9940} = \frac{1{,}000}{x}$ Cross-multiplying and solving for x,

x = C$994.00 Amount in C$ before the bank's commission

Bank's commission:

0.0075 × 994.00 = – C$7.455 Adding the bank's 0.75% commission,

Total = C$1,001.46 Amount that Sarah will pay the bank

Or

994.00 (1 + 0.0075) = 1,001.455 = C$1,001.46

Therefore, Sarah would have to pay C$1,001.46 for US$1,000.00.

(ii) US$1,000 = C$994.00 As calculated in (i)

0.0075 × 994.00 = – C$7.455 Subtracting the bank's 0.75% commission,

Total = C$986.545 Amount the bank will pay Sarah

Or

C$996.00 (1 – 0.0075) = 986.545 = C$986.55

Therefore, Sarah will receive C$986.55 from the bank.

6.4 | Exercises

Answers to odd-numbered problems are available online.

Based on the following exchange rates, answer Problems 1 to 4:

£1 = A$1.5565, US$1 = C$0.9940, €1 = US$1.2946, C$1 = £0.6240

1. Convert A$200 to British pounds (£).
2. Convert C$3,000 to US dollars (US$).
3. Convert US$5,000 to Euros (€).
4. Convert £10 to Canadian dollars (C$).

Based on the following exchange rates, answer Problems 5 to 8:

€1 = C$1.2868, A$1 = US$1.0359, US$1 = £0.6202, C$1 = A$0.971

5. Convert C$2,500 to Euros (€).
6. Convert US$2,850 to Australian dollars (A$).
7. Convert £18 to US dollars (US$).
8. Convert A$300 to Canadian dollars (C$).
9. A bank in Ottawa charges 2.5% commission to buy and sell currencies. Assume the exchange rate is US$1 = C$0.9940.

   a. How much commission in Canadian dollars (C$) would you pay the bank for the above transaction?

   b. How many Canadian dollars would you have to pay to purchase US$1,500?
10. A bank in Montreal charges 2.25% commission to buy and sell currencies. Assume the exchange rate is US$1 = C$0.9940.

    a. How many Canadian dollars would you receive from the bank if you sell US$1,375?

    b. How much commission would you pay the bank for this transaction?
11. Mark converted US$4,500 into Canadian dollars at a bank that charged him a commission of 0.25%. How much did he receive from the bank? Assume that the exchange rate was C$1 = US$1.0060.
12. Carmin converted £2,000 into Canadian dollars. If the commission the bank was charging was 0.90%, calculate how many Canadian dollars she received. Assume that the exchange rate was C$1 = £0.6240.
13. If C$1 = A$0.9711 and A$1 = US$1.0359, how many Canadian dollars would you receive with US$1,000?
14. If C$1 = £0.6240 and £1 = US$1.6124, how many Canadian dollars would you receive with US$1,000?
15. David planned to travel to Australia from Canada and purchased 5,000 Australian dollars. A week later, he decided to cancel his trip and wanted to convert his Australian dollars back into Canadian dollars at the same bank. How much money did he lose or gain? Assume that the bank charged a commission of 0.5% to buy and sell currencies. Assume that the exchange rate was C$1 = A$0.9711.
16. Lisa purchased US$10,000 from a bank in America, which charged her a commission of 0.80%, and sold the US dollars to a bank in Canada, which charged her 0.80% commission. How much money did she lose or gain? Assume that the exchange rate was C$1 = US$0.9711.
17. Dell left Canada for the UK with C$8,000. When he reached the UK, he converted all his cash into British pounds. The conversion rate was £1 = C$1.6350. After spending £1,000 in the UK, he returned to Canada. Calculate the number of Canadian dollars he received when he converted the remaining British pounds into Canadian dollars at an exchange rate of C$1 = £0.6500.
18. Jason travelled from Toronto to Australia, where he converted C$3,000 to Australian dollars at an exchange rate of C$1 = A$0.9750. He spent A$2,000 in Australia before returning to Toronto. How many Canadian dollars did he receive when he converted the remaining Australian dollars into Canadian dollars at an exchange rate of C$1 = A$0.9650?

19. A bank in London, Ontario has a selling rate of £1 = C$1.6544. If the exchange rate is £1 = C$1.5756, calculate the rate of commission that the bank charges.
20. A bank in London, Ontario has a buying rate of A$1 = C$1.0206. If the exchange rate is A$1 = C$1.0468, calculate the rate of commission that the bank charges.

6.5 | Index Numbers

The Index Number is used to express the relative value of an item compared to a base value.

Index Numbers

The price of many items constantly fluctuates at different points in time. You may have noticed that the cost of transportation, entertainment, education, housing, etc., have constantly been on the rise. Index Numbers are used to quantify such economic changes over time.

An index number is a comparison of the value of an item on a selected date to the value of the same item on a designated date, known as the base date. That is, if the index number is lower than the base value, the value of that item has gone down since the base date; if the index number is higher than the base value, the value of that item has gone up since the base date.

For example, the index number of 120.5 for an item on a selected date indicates that the value of that item is 20.5% above the base period price of 100 for the same item.

The index number is calculated as follows:

$$\textbf{\textit{Index number}} = \frac{\textbf{\textit{Value on selected date}}}{\textbf{\textit{Value on base date}}} \times \mathbf{100}$$

Example 6.5-a Calculating the Index Number for Gasoline in 2011 Using 2002 as the Base Year

If the price of gasoline (gas) in 2002 was $0.75 per litre, and in 2011, the price had risen to $1.25 per litre, calculate the index number for gas using 2002 as the base year.

Solution

$$\textit{Index number} = \frac{\textit{Value on selected date}}{\textit{Value on base date}} \times 100$$

$$= \frac{1.25}{0.75} \times 100 = 166.666666...$$

Therefore, the index number for gas in 2011 is 166.67.

ie., percentage change = 166.67 – 100 = 66.67%.

2002 is referred to as the base date, (ie. the value 100 is the index for the base date). Since the index number for 2012 is greater than 100, the value of the item has increased.

Solution
continued

Therefore, the price of gas in 2011 has increased by 66.67% from its price in 2002.

Example 6.5-b

Calculating the Index Number for Basic Cable TV in 2012 Using 2002 as the Base Year

If the price of basic cable TV in 2002 was $39 per month, and it decreased to $25 per month in 2012, calculate the index for the price of basic cable TV in 2012 using 2002 as the base date.

Solution

$$Index\ number = \frac{Value\ on\ selected\ date}{Value\ on\ base\ date} \times 100$$

$$= \frac{25.00}{39.00} \times 100 = 64.102564...$$

Therefore, the index number for basic cable TV in 2012 is 64.10.

ie., percentage change = 64.10 – 100 = – 35.90%

Since the index number, 64.10, is less than the base index of 100, the price of basic cable TV in 2012 decreased by 35.90% from its price in 2002.

Consumer Price Index (CPI)

The Consumer Price Index (CPI) is an indicator of changes in consumer prices experienced by Canadians.

The Consumer Price Index (CPI) is a good example of how useful index numbers can be in day-to-day life. CPI is an indicator of changes in consumer prices. In Canada, Statistics Canada obtains this number by calculating the cost of a fixed basket of goods and services purchased by consumers and comparing this cost over time.

CPI is calculated by comparing the cost of a fixed basket of items at a particular period to the cost at base period. The CPI value is usually rounded to one decimal place.

Example 6.5-c

Calculating CPI in 2010 Using 2005 as the Base Year

The basket of goods and services included in the CPI cost $16,500.00 in 2005. The same basket cost $19,200.00 in 2010. Calculate the CPI in 2010 using 2005 as the base year.

Solution

$$Index\ number = \frac{Value\ on\ selected\ date}{Value\ on\ base\ date} \times 100$$

$$CPI_{2010} = \frac{19{,}200.00}{16{,}500.00} \times 100 = 116.363636...$$

Therefore, the CPI in 2010 is 116.4.

CPI for Canada is calculated and issued by Statistics Canada on a monthly basis and is released during the 3rd week of the following month (around the 20th).

For example, CPI for Sept. 2012 was released on Oct. 19 2012. (CPI for Sept. 2012 = 122.0).

When there are considerable changes in consumer spending patterns, the base period for CPI is adjusted periodically by Statistics Canada. In 2004, the base period was changed from 1992 to 2002, which is the current base period used in CPI calculations (CPI for 2002 = 100). The annual CPI from 2002 to 2011 is provided in Table 6.5.

Table 6.5

CPI from the Years 2002 to 2011

Year	2002	2003	2004	2005	2006	2007	2008	2009	2010	2011
CPI	100.0	102.8	104.7	107.0	109.1	111.5	114.4	114.4	116.5	119.9

The Purchasing Power of Money is the number of goods/services that can be purchased with a unit of currency.

Inflation is a rise on the general level of prices of goods and services in an economy over time.

Purchasing Power of a Dollar and Inflation

CPI is used to measure the purchasing power of a dollar and inflation. Wages of workers, private and public pension programs, personal income tax deductions, social and welfare payments, spousal and child support payments, etc. are adjusted periodically based on the changes in CPI.

$$\textit{Purchasing power of a dollar} = \frac{\$1}{CPI} \times 100$$

When prices increase, CPI increases and the purchasing power of money decreases. The general increase is called inflation. Inflation rate is the rate of change in CPI over a period of time.

$$\textit{Inflation rate (from Year A to Year B)} = \frac{CPI_{Year\ B} - CPI_{Year\ A}}{CPI_{Year\ A}} \times 100\%$$

Inflation is crucial in financial planning because $100 to be received in the future is worth less than $100 received today. Unless our income rises to match the price increase (inflation), we will not be able to maintain the same standard of living as before. Real income is the income after adjusting for inflation and is calculated as follows:

$$\textit{Real income} = \frac{\textit{Money income}}{CPI} \times 100\%$$

Example 6.5-d

Calculating Purchasing Power of a Dollar Given CPI

If the CPI was 116.5 for 2010 and 119.9 for 2011, determine the purchasing power of the dollar for the two years. Compare with the base year 2002.

Solution

$$\textit{Purchasing power in 2010} = \frac{\$1}{116.5} \times 100 = 0.858369...$$

$$= 85.84\%$$

Solution continued

$$Purchasing\ power\ in\ 2011 = \frac{\$1}{119.9} \times 100 = 0.834028...$$

$$= 83.40\%$$

Therefore, the dollar in 2010 could purchase 85.84% of what could be purchased in 2002, and the dollar in 2011 could purchase 83.40% of what could be purchased in 2002.

Example 6.5-e

Calculating Inflation Rate Given CPI

If the CPI was 119.9 in 2011 and 122.4 at the end of 2012, what would be the inflation rate from 2011 to 2012?

Solution

$$Inflation\ rate\ (from\ 2011\ to\ 2012) = \frac{CPI_{2012} - CPI_{2011}}{CPI} \times 100\%$$

$$Inflation\ rate\ (from\ 2011\ to\ 2012) = \frac{122.4 - 119.9}{119.9} \times 100\%$$

$$= 2.085071...$$

$$= 2.1\%$$

Therefore, the inflation rate for 2011 to 2012 would be 2.1%.

Example 6.5-f

Purchasing Power of a Dollar and Inflation

Peter's income was \$30,000 in 2002 (base year), \$40,000 in 2008, and \$42,000 in 2011. The CPI was 114.1 in 2008 and 119.9 in 2011. Determine Peter's real income in 2008 and 2011.

Solution

$$Real\ income = \frac{Money\ income}{CPI} \times 100\%$$

$$Real\ Income\ \text{in 2008} = \frac{40{,}000.00}{114.1} \times 100 = \$35{,}056.967572...$$

$$= \$35{,}056.97$$

$$Real\ Income\ \text{in 2011} = \frac{42{,}000.00}{119.9} \times 100 = \$35{,}029{,}190992...$$

$$= \$35{,}029.19$$

Therefore, the real income decreased in 2011 compared to that in 2008.

S&P/TSX is an index of stock prices of the largest companies on the Toronto Stock Exchange.

Stock Index

Stock index is an application of index numbers and is used to measure the performance of stock markets. For example, the Standard and Poor's Toronto Stock Exchange Composite index reflects the share prices of all the companies trading on the Toronto Stock Exchange. Here, the "basket" composed of ordinary goods and services that all consumers use on an average is replaced by a portfolio composed of the shares of the big companies that are listed on the Toronto Stock Exchange. This index is an indicator of the health of the Toronto Stock Exchange. If S&P/TSX goes up, it means that the overall value of the shares in the Exchange is going up; it is important to note that individually, some companies will be performing better than others, but collectively, the companies are performing well. The base value used for the S&P/TSX is 1,000, set in 1975. S&P/TSX is calculated as follows:

$$S\&P\ /\ TSX\ Composite\ Index = \frac{Value\ of\ portfolio\ on\ selected\ date}{Value\ of\ portfolio\ on\ base\ date} \times 100\%$$

In January 2012, the S&P/TSX index reached 12,000, which means that the value of the portfolio in 2012 was 12 times its value in 1975.

Example 6.5-g **Calculating S&P/TSX**

If the S&P/TSX portfolio cost $200,000.00 in 1975, and the same portfolio cost $3,125,000.00 in 2009, calculate the S&P/TSX Composite Index.

Solution

$$S\&P\ /\ TSX\ Composite\ Index = \frac{Value\ of\ portfolio\ on\ selected\ date}{Value\ of\ portfolio\ on\ base\ date} \times 100\%$$

$$= \frac{3{,}125{,}000.00}{200{,}000.00} \times 100$$

$$= 1{,}562.5$$

Therefore, in 2008, the S&P/TSX Composite Index was 1,562.5.

6.5 | Exercises

Answers to odd-numbered problems are available online.

1. Determine the index for 2009 and 2011 for the value of a car using 2005 as the base year.

Year	2005	2009	2011
Value of Car	$32,000	$35,000	$37,000

2. Determine the index for 2007 and 2010 for the price of a tire using 2002 as the base year.

Year	2002	2007	2010
Price of a Tire	$35	$43	$60

3. Determine the index for 2012 for the price of a monthly metro pass for adults and students using 2002 as the base year.

Year	Metro Pass Adult	Metro Pass Student
2002	$98.75	$83.25
2012	$126.00	$104.00

4. Determine the index for 2012 for the cost of an adult and child movie ticket using 2006 as the base year.

Year	Movie Ticket Adult	Movie Ticket Child
2006	$9.00	$6.00
2012	$12.00	$8.00

Use the index given below to answer Problems 5 to 7.

Year	1	2	3	4	5	6	7
Index	100.0	105.0	107.5	111.0	110.0	118.5	120.0

5. If an item was worth $2,500 in year 3, how much was it worth in year 5 and year 7?
6. If an item was worth $4,000 in year 2, how much was it worth in year 4 and year 6?
7. If an item was worth $2,000 in year 5, how much was it worth in year 2 and year 3?
8. If an item was worth $5,000 in year 6, how much was it worth in year 3 and year 4?

Use the CPI from year 2002 to 2011 provided in Table 6.5 to answer Problems 9 to 16.

9. What real income in 2011 would be equivalent to an income of $60,000 in 2005?
10. What real income in 2010 would be equivalent to an income of $50,000 in 2003?
11. Calculate the inflation rate for the period 2009 to 2010.
12. Calculate the inflation rate for the period 2010 to 2011.
13. The college tuition fee for the year 2008 was $3,200. What would the tuition fee be for the year 2011 if the tuition fee increased with the inflation rate during this period?
14. Tony earned $58,000 in 2004. How much would he have earned in 2011 if his earnings grew with the inflation rate during this period?
15. Calculate the purchasing power of a dollar for 2008 and 2009 relative to the base year 2002.
16. Calculate the purchasing power of a dollar for 2010 and 2011 relative to the base year 2002.

Use the following data for Problems 17 to 20:

End of the Year	2007	2008	2009	2010	2011
S&P/TSX Index	12,412	7,647	7,480	13,443	11,955

17. If you had invested $25,000 at the end of 2008, what would have been the value at the end of 2011?
18. f you had invested $75,000 at the end of 2007, what would have been the value at the end of 2011?

19. What amount invested at the end of 2009 would have resulted in a value of $50,000 at the end of 2011?

20. What amount invested at the end of 2008 would have resulted in a value of $150,000 at the end of 2011?

6 | Review Exercises

Answers to odd-numbered problems are available online.

1. A store purchases laptops for $425 each and sells each of them for $650. Calculate the amount of markup and the rate of markup.

2. A distributor buys computers for $775 each and sells each of them for $950. Calculate the amount of markup and the rate of markup.

3. Calculate the amount of markup and the selling price of an item that has a cost of $1250 and a rate of markup of 60%.

4. A furniture store buys dining tables for $375 each and sells them after a markup of 40%. Calculate the amount of markup on the selling price of each dining table.

5. A sports jacket that cost a store $150 was sold after a markup of $75. Calculate the rate of markup and the selling price.

6. Calculate the rate of markup and the selling price of a bottle of wine if the cost is $12.50 and the markup is $2.50.

7. During a sale, a humidifier that sells for $125 is marked down by $25. Calculate the sale price and the rate of markdown.

8. All winter tires in a store are marked down by $35 during a clearance sale. Calculate the sale price and the rate of markdown on a winter tire that was originally priced for $140.

9. The regular selling price of an item is $399. During a sale, it was marked down by 15%. Calculate the amount of markdown and the sale price.

10. A toaster that sells for $39.50 is marked down by 25%. Calculate the amount of markdown and the sale price.

11. After a discount of $12.50, an item was sold for $37.50. Calculate the regular selling price of the item and the rate of markdown.

12. After a markdown of $73.50, an item was sold for $416.50. Calculate the regular selling price of the item and the rate of markdown.

13. Calculate the interest earned from an investment of $7,500 for 8 months at 4.5% p.a.

14. Steve borrowed $4,250 for 15 months at 7.2% p.a. How much interest would he have to pay on the loan?

15. What amount must be invested now to earn $375 in interest in 3 years at 4% p.a.?

16. An investment at 3% p.a. earned interest of $225 over a period of 2 years. Find the amount invested.

17. At what rate (% p.a.) will an investment of $2,400 earn interest of $660 in 5 years?

18. The interest on a loan of $3,600 for 3 years is $486. Calculate the rate of interest (% p.a.) on the loan.

19. Ram's bi-weekly pay is $1,750. Calculate his annual salary and the equivalent monthly pay.

20. Sam's monthly pay is $4,680. Calculate his annual salary and the equivalent bi-weekly pay.

21. In Problem 19, if Rodney's workweek is 35 hours and the overtime factor is 2, calculate his hourly rate of pay and the overtime rate of pay.

22. In Problem 20, if Sam's workweek is 40 hours and the overtime factor is 1.5, calculate his hourly rate of pay and the overtime rate of pay.

23. Amy receives a commission rate of 6% on all sales in a month. Last month she earned $2,160. Calculate her sales during last month.

24. Roger, a real estate agent, receives a 2% commission on the sales of houses. He earned a commission of $8,500 from the sale of a house. Find the selling price of the house.

Use the following exchange rates to answer Problems 25 to 28:

£1 = A$1.5625, C$1 = £0.6280, €1 = C$1.2875, A$1 = US$1.0360

25. Convert A$1,500 to British pounds (£)

26. Convert £2,500 to Canadian dollars (C$)

27. Convert C$1,250 to Euros (€)

28. Convert US$2,000 to Australian dollars (A$)

29. Charles converted US$3,000 into Canadian dollars at a bank that charged him a commission rate of 0.75%. How much did he receive from the bank? Use C$1 = US$1.0125

30. Dylan converted £2,000 into US dollars. If the bank was charging a commission rate of 0.50%, calculate the amount he received from the bank. Use US$1 = £0.6250.

Use the CPI given in Table 6.5 to answer Problems 31 to 36.

31. If an item was worth $25,000 in 2008, how much was it worth in 2010?

32. If an item was worth $7,500 in 2009, how much was it worth in 2011?

33. What real income in 2011 would be equivalent to an income of $5,000 in 2005?

34. What real income in 2010 would be equivalent to an income of $4,000 in 2006?

35. Calculate the purchasing power of a dollar in 2007 relative to the base year 2002.

36. Calculate the purchasing power of a dollar in 2009 relative to the base year 2002.

6 | Self-Test Exercises

Answers to all problems are available online.

1. A store that sells fruits, purchase oranges for $19.75 a box and sells them after a markup of 44%. Calculate the amount of markup and the selling price of each box of oranges.

2. A hardware store purchases electric-drills at $49.50 each and sells each of them for $94.05. Calculate the amount of markup and the rate of markup.

3. After a markup of $22, an item was sold for $77. Calculate the rate of markup and the cost of the item.

4. During a sale, a snow blower that regularly sells for $749 is sold for $561.75. Calculate the amount of markdown and the rate of markdown.

5. After a markdown of $45, an item was sold for $315. Calculate the regular selling price of the item and the rate of markdown.

6. During a clearance sale, all monitors are marked down by 20%. Calculate the sale price and the amount of markdown of a monitor that was originally priced for $96.

7. At what rate of interest (% p.a.) will $650 earn interest of $62.40 in 2 years?

8. Find the principal which will earn interest of $202.50 at 3.6% p.a. in 15 months.

9. How much interest would you have to pay on a loan of $2,190 for 180 days at 4.2% p.a.?

10. Ruben's weekly pay is $810. Calculate his annual salary and the equivalent monthly pay.

11. Kathy's annual salary is \$34,944 based on a 35-hour workweek.
    a. What would be her bi-weekly pay?
    b. Calculate her hourly rate of pay.

12. Warren is paid a commission on all his sales. He is paid monthly. Last month his pay was \$2,400 and his sales were \$32,000. Calculate the commission rate.

13. A bank charges 1.25% commission for each transaction. How many Canadian dollars would you have to pay to purchase 1,500 Australian dollars? Assume the exchange rate is C\$1 = A\$1.0455

14. Anil wants to convert US\$2,250 to Canadian dollars. If the exchange rate is C\$1= US\$1.0025 and the bank's commission rate is 0.75%, how many Canadian dollars will he receive?

Use the CPI given in Table 6.5 to answer Problems 15 and 16.

15. If an item was worth \$32,500 in 2009, how much was it worth in 2011? What real income in 2011 would be equivalent to an income of \$45,000 in 2004?

16. What real income in 2011 would be equivalent to an income of \$45,000 in 2004?

Chapter 7
Basic Algebra

Learning Outcomes

- Identify exponents and evaluate exponents using rules of exponents.
- Perform basic arithmetic operations on algebraic expressions.
- Setup basic linear equations with one variable.
- Solve linear equations with one variable using various arithmetic operations.
- Create, rearrange, and use equations to solve for unknown variables.

Chapter Outline

7.1 Algebraic Expressions
7.2 Simple Algebraic Equations and Word Problems
7.3 Exponents
7.4 Logarithms
7.5 Formulas and their Applications

Algebra is a branch of mathematics that introduces the concept of using variables to represent numbers. These variables, together with numbers, use rules of operations to express statements and equations. Algebra provides a framework to derive formulas to solve general problems and will help you develop logical-thinking and problem-solving skills in a systematic and analytical way. The study of algebra is required in any occupational field, including business

7.1 | Algebraic Expressions

Introduction

Algebraic expressions consist of one or more terms, with a combination of variables, numbers, and operation signs. In order to solve most problems in business and finance mathematics, the use of equations and formulas is necessary. These equations and formulas are formed using algebraic expressions.

Algebra is a branch of mathematics that is used to analyze and solve day-to-day business and finance problems. It deals with different relations and operations by using letters and symbols to represent numbers, values, etc.

In arithmetic, we use only numbers in expressions.

For example,

$25 + 15,\qquad 75 - 22,\qquad 8 \times 9,\qquad \frac{9}{5}$

In algebra, we use both numbers and variables (letters and symbols that represent various numbers) in expressions.

For example,

$2x + 5,\qquad 30 - 5y,\qquad 6(2a + 5),\qquad \frac{b+3}{2}$

When a certain letter of the alphabet is used to represent a varying quantity, it is called a **variable**; i.e., a variable is used to represent something that can change in an algebraic expression. When a letter represents a specific quantity that does not change in value, it is called a **constant**.

For example,

(i) If 'x' represents a person's age, then 'x' is a variable as the value of 'x' changes from year to year.

(ii) If 'a' represents a person's date of birth, then 'a' is a constant as the value of 'a' is always the same.

(iii) The constant *pi* can be expressed as, $\pi = 3.14159265...$

In algebra, we use variables, numbers, and operation signs to translate word problems into equations.

For example, If the sum of two numbers is 100, it can be represented by the equation:

$x + y = 100.$

If $x = 40$, then $y = 60$.

If $x = 10$, then $y = 90$.

Note: In algebraic expressions involving multiplication, the number and the variable(s) are written together without the operation sign for multiplication.

For example,

$5a$ means $5 \times a$, or $5(a)$, or $5 \cdot a$

xy means $x \times y$, or $x\ (y)$, or $x \cdot y$

The following key words will help in translating word problems into algebraic expressions and equations:

Arithmetic Operations and their Meanings

Keyword	Meaning
Addition (+)	add, sum, plus, more than, increased by, appreciate, rise
Subtraction (−)	subtract, difference, minus, less than, decreased by, depreciate, fall
Multiplication (×), (•)	multiply, product, times, of
Division (÷)	divide, ratio, divided by, quotient
Equal (=)	is, was, gives, given by

For example,

In words	In algebraic expression
1. Ten more than a number	$x + 10$
2. A number more than ten	$10 + x$
3. A number less than twenty	$20 - x$
4. Twenty less than a number	$x - 20$
5. Product of five and a number	$5x$
6. Divide 20 by a number	$\frac{20}{x}$
7. Divide a number by 20	$\frac{x}{20}$
8. Half of a number	$\frac{1}{2}x = \frac{x}{2}$
9. Twice a number	$2x$
10. Ten more than the product of two numbers	$xy + 10$
11. 'x' less than 'y'	$y - x$
12. 'y' less than 'x'	$x - y$
13. Seventy decreased by 3 times a number	$70 - 3x$
14. 'm' subtracted from 'n'	$n - m$

Terminology used in Algebraic Expressions

Variables are letters that represent one or more numbers. For example, 'x', 'y', and 'a'.

A **term** is a number, variable, or a combination of numbers and variables which are multiplied and/or divided together. Terms are separated by addition and subtraction operators.

For example, 5, x, $5x$, $2xy$, $4ab$, $\dfrac{xy}{3}$, $\dfrac{4x}{y}$

For example, $5x + 1$ has 2 terms.

$\quad 7x^2y^2 - 4x + 3$ has 3 terms

$\quad \dfrac{x}{4} - y^2 + \dfrac{x}{y}$ has 3 terms

An **expression** is a combination of terms. It usually refers to a statement of relations among variables.

Examples of expressions with one variable:

(i) $(2x + 5)$ (ii) $(9x - 3)$

Examples of expressions with two variables:

(i) $(5x - 7y + 5)$ (ii) $(xy + 3x - 7)$

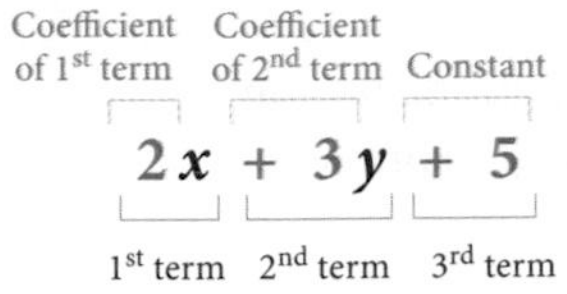

A **coefficient** is the numerical factor in front of the variable in a term.

Coefficient of 1st term Coefficient of 2nd term Constant

$2\,x + 3\,y + 5$

1st term 2nd term 3rd term

For example,

In the expression $2x + 3y + 5$, the coefficient of the first term, $2x$, is $+2$ and the coefficient of the second term, $3y$, is $+3$.

In the expression $5xy - 2x$, the coefficient of the first term, $5xy$, is $+5$ and the coefficient of the second term, $-2x$, is -2.

A **constant** is a term that has only a number without any variables.

For example,

In the expression $2x + 3y + 5$, the third term, $+ 5$, is a constant.

Like terms are terms that have the same variables and exponents.

For example,

$\quad 5x$ and $9x$ are like terms.

$\quad 30a^2$, $-4a^2$, and $9a^2$ are like terms.

Unlike terms are terms that have different variables or the same variables with different exponents.

For example,

$\quad 12y$ and $3y^2$ are unlike terms.

$\quad x^2$, x, and 1 are unlike terms.

Factors refer to each of the combinations of variables and/or numbers multiplied together in a term.

For example,

$\quad 5$ and x are factors of the term $5x$.

$\quad 3$, x, and y are factors of the term $3xy$.

A **monomial** is an algebraic expression that has only one term.

For example, 8, $7x$, $4y$, and $2xy$ are monomials.

A **binomial** is a polynomial with 2 terms.

For example, the following are binomials:

(i) $4x - 3y$ (ii) $x - 5$ (iii) $4xy + 7x$

A **trinomial** is a polynomial with 3 terms.

For example, the following are trinomials:

(i) $2x + 3y + 5$ (ii) $xy + x - 2$ (iii) $2x + xy + 3z$

A **polynomial** is an algebraic expression that has two or more terms.

For example, $8x^2 - 5x + 3$ is a polynomial with 3 terms where,

First term: $8x^2$,	Second term: $-5x$,	Third term: 3
Coefficient of first term: 8	Coefficient of second term: -5	This is a constant

Evaluating Algebraic Expressions

In an algebraic expression, when we replace all the variables with numbers and simplify the expression, it is referred to as evaluating the algebraic expression. The simplified answer is the value of the expression.

Example 7.1-a **Evaluating Algebraic Expressions**

Evaluate the following:

(i) $2x + y$, where $x = 10$ and $y = 5$

(ii) $\dfrac{3xy + 3x}{2y + 5}$, where $x = 3$ and $y = 2$

Solution

(i) $2x + y$, where $x = 10$ and $y = 5$

Substituting 10 for 'x' and 5 for 'y' in the expression,

$$2x + y = 2\,(10) + 5 = 20 + 5 = 25$$

Note that 2x means $2 \times x$.

(ii) $\dfrac{3xy + 3x}{2y + 5}$, where $x = 3$ and $y = 2$

Substituting 3 for 'x' and 2 for 'y' in the expression,

$$\frac{3(3)(2) + 3(3)}{2(2) + 5} = \frac{18 + 9}{4 + 5} = \frac{27}{9} = 3$$

Example 7.1-b **Evaluating Algebraic Expressions with Exponents**

(i) Evaluate $\dfrac{(5x)^2 \times 4y}{50}$, where $x = 2$ and $y = 3$

(ii) Evaluate $2(x^2 + 3x) - 5y$, where $x = 4$ and $y = -3$

Solution

(i) Evaluate $\dfrac{(5x)^2 \times 4y}{50}$, where $x = 2$ and $y = 3$

Solution *continued*

Substituting 2 for 'x' and 3 for 'y' in the expression,

$$\frac{[5(2)]^2 \times 4(3)}{50} = \frac{10^2 \times 12}{50} = \frac{100 \times 12}{50} = 24$$

Remember to follow BEDMAS.

(ii) Evaluate $2(x^2 + 3x) - 5y$, where $x = 4$ and $y = -3$

Substituting 4 for 'x' and -3 for 'y' in the expression,

$$2[(4)^2 + 3(4)] - 5(-3) = 2(16+12) + 15 = 56 + 15 = 71$$

Basic Arithmetic Operations with Algebraic Expressions

All arithmetic operations can be applied to algebraic expressions.

Addition and Subtraction

When adding or subtracting algebraic expressions, first collect the like terms and group them, then add or subtract the coefficients of the like terms.

Example 7.1-c

Adding and Subtracting Algebraic Expressions

(i) Add $(3x + 7)$ and $(5x + 3)$

(ii) Add $(4y^2 - 8y - 9)$ and $(2y^2 + 6y - 2)$

(iii) Subtract $(x^2 + 5x - 7)$ from $(2x^2 - 2x + 3)$

(iv) Subtract $(5y^2 + 8y - 6)$ from $(-2y^2 - 7y + 5)$

Solution

(i) $(3x + 7) + (5x + 3)$

$= 3x + 7 + 5x + 3$ Grouping like terms,

$= 3x + 5x + 7 + 3$ Adding like terms,

$= 8x + 10$

(ii) $(4y^2 - 8y - 9) + (2y^2 + 6y - 2)$

$= 4y^2 - 8y - 9 + 2y^2 + 6y - 2$ Grouping like terms,

$= 4y^2 + 2y^2 - 8y + 6y - 9 - 2$ Adding and subtracting like terms,

$= 6y^2 - 2y - 11$

(iii) $(2x^2 - 2x + 3) - (x^2 + 5x - 7)$ Expanding by distributing the negative sign to terms within the bracket,

$= 2x^2 - 2x + 3 - x^2 - 5x + 7$ Grouping like terms,

$= 2x^2 - x^2 - 2x - 5x + 3 + 7$ Adding and subtracting like terms,

$= x^2 - 7x + 10$

Solution
continued

(iv) $(-2y^2 - 7y + 5) - (5y^2 + 8y - 6)$ — Expanding by distributing the negative sign

$= -2y^2 - 7y + 5 - 5y^2 - 8y + 6$ — Grouping like terms,

$= -2y^2 - 5y^2 - 7y - 8y + 5 + 6$ — Adding and subtracting like terms,

$= -7y^2 - 15y + 11$

Multiplication

Multiplying a Monomial by a Monomial

When multiplying a monomial by a monomial, multiply the coefficients and multiply all variables. If there are any similar variables, use the exponent notation.

Example 7.1-d **Multiplying Monomials by Monomials**

(i) Multiply $6x^2y$ and $5xy$

(ii) Multiply $(3a^3)$, $(-4ab)$, and $(2b^2)$

Solution

(i) $(6x^2y)\,(5xy)$ — Grouping coefficients and variables,

$= (6)(5)(x^2)(x)(y)(y)$ — Multiplying,

$= 30x^3y^2$

(ii) $(3a^3)\,(-4ab)\,(2b^2)$ — Grouping coefficients and variables,

$= (3)(-4)(2)(a^3)(a)(b)(b^2)$ — Multiplying,

$= -24a^4b^3$

Multiplying a Polynomial by a Monomial

When multiplying a polynomial by a monomial, multiply **each term** of the polynomial by the monomial.

Example 7.1-e **Multiplying Polynomials by Monomials**

(i) Multiply $2x^3$ and $(3x^2 + 2x - 5)$

(ii) Expand and simplify $8x\,(x+3) + 4x\,(x - 4)$

Solution

(i) $2x^3\,(3x^2 + 2x - 5)$ — Expanding,

$= 6x^5 + 4x^4 - 10x^3$

(ii) $8x\,(x+3) + 4x\,(x - 4)$ — Expanding,

Solution *continued*

$= 8x^2 + 24x + 4x^2 - 16x$ Grouping like terms,

$= 8x^2 + 4x^2 + 24x - 16x$ Adding and subtracting like terms,

$= 12x^2 + 8x$

Multiplying a Polynomial by a Polynomial

When multiplying a polynomial by a polynomial, multiply each term of one polynomial by each term of the other polynomial. Then, group the like terms and simplify using addition and subtraction.

Example 7.1-f **Multiplying Polynomials by Polynomials**

(i) Multiply (x^2+5) and $(x-4)$

(ii) Multiply $(x^2 + 7)$ and $(2x^2 + 5x + 2)$

(iii) Expand and simplify $(x + 5)(2x - 6) + (3x - 4)(x - 5)$

Solution

(i) $(x^2+5)(x - 4)$

$= x^3 - 4x^2 + 5x - 20$

(ii) $(x^2 + 7)(2x^2 + 5x + 2)$ Expanding,

$= 2x^4 + 5x^3 + 2x^2 + 14x^2 + 35x + 14$ Adding like terms,

$= 2x^4 + 5x^3 + 16x^2 + 35x + 14$

(iii) $(x + 5)(2x - 6) + (3x - 4)(x - 5)$ Expanding

$= (2x2 - 6x + 10x - 30) + (3x^2 - 15x - 4x + 20)$ Grouping like terms

$= 2x^2 + 3x^2 - 6x + 10x - 15x - 4x + 20 - 30$ Adding and subtracting like terms

$= 5x^2 - 15x - 10$

Division

Dividing a Monomial by a Monomial

When dividing a monomial by a monomial, group the constants and each of the variables separately and simplify them.

Example 7.1-g **Dividing Monomials by Monomials**

(i) Divide $8x^2y$ by $6x$

(ii) Divide $9x^2$ by $2x^2$

Solution

(i) $\frac{8x^2y}{6x} = \frac{8}{6} \times \frac{x^2}{x} \times y = \frac{4}{3}xy$

(ii) $\frac{9x^2}{3x^2} = \frac{9}{3} \times \frac{x^2}{x^2} = \frac{9}{3} = 3$

Dividing a Polynomial by a Monomial

When dividing a polynomial by a monomial, divide **each term** of the polynomial by the monomial.

Example 7.1-h **Dividing Polynomials by Monomials**

(i) Divide $(9x^3 + 3x^2)$ by $6x$

(ii) Divide $(2x^3 + 4x^4 + 7x)$ and $4x^4$

Solution

(i) $\frac{9x^3 + 3x^2}{6x} = \frac{9x^3}{6x} + \frac{3x^2}{6x} = \frac{3x^2}{2} + \frac{x}{2} = \frac{3x^2 + x}{2}$

(ii) $\frac{2x^3 + 4x^4 + 7x}{4x^4} = \frac{2x^3}{4x^4} + \frac{4x^4}{4x^4} + \frac{7x}{4x^4} = \frac{1}{2x} + 1 + \frac{7}{4x^3}$

Factoring Algebraic Expressions with Common Factors

Factoring algebraic expressions means finding the common factors for both the coefficients and variables in all the terms. Once the factors are found, the expression will become a product of a monomial and a polynomial or a combination of both.

Example 7.1-i **Factoring Algebraic Expressions**

Factor the following:

(i) $12x + 18y$

(ii) $8y^2 + 18y$

(iii) $12xy^3 + 6xy^4 - 9x^3y^5 - 3xy^3$

(iv) $14(2x + y) - 7x(2x + y)$

Solution

(i) $12x + 18y$

$12x = 2 \times 2 \times 3 \times x$

$18y = 2 \times 3 \times 3 \times y$

Solution
continued

HCF is $2 \times 3 = 6$

By dividing the original expression by the HCF 6, we obtain the other factor $(2x + 3y)$.

Therefore, $12x + 18y = 6(2x + 3y)$

(ii) $8y^2 + 18y$

$8y^2 = 2 \times 2 \times 2 \times y \times y$

$18y = 2 \times 3 \times 3 \times y$

HCF is $2y$

By dividing the original expression by the HCF $2y$, we obtain the other factor $(4y + 9)$.

Therefore, $8y^2 + 18y = 2y(4y + 9)$.

(iii) $12xy^3 + 6xy^4 - 9x^3y^5 - 3xy^3$

HCF is $3xy^3$.

By dividing the original expression by the HCF $3xy^3$, we obtain the other factor $(4 + 2y - 3x^2y^2 - 1)$.

Therefore, $12xy^3 + 6xy^4 - 9x^3y^5 - 3xy^3 = 3xy^3(4 + 2y - 3x^2y^2 - 1)$.

(iv) $14(2x + y) - 7x(2x + y)$

HCF is $7(2x + y)$.

By dividing the original expression by the HCF $7(2x + y)$, we obtain the other factor $(2 - x)$.

Therefore, $14(2x + y) - 7x(2x + y) = 7(2x + y)(2 - x)$.

7.1 | Exercises

Answers to odd-numbered problems are available online.

1. Identify the following terms in the equations:
   a. 2nd term and 3rd term in $3x^2 + 7xy - 4y + 7$
   b. 3rd term and 4th term in $x^2 - 5x - y + 3$
   c. 1st term and 3rd term in $9xy + 7x - 6y + 2$
2. Identify the following terms in the equations:
   a. 1st term and 4th term in $-x^2 + 9xy + y + 7$
   b. 2nd term and 3rd term in $7xy$ # $4y + 7$
   c. 1st term and 3rd term in $10x^2 + 5xy - 6x + 7y$
3. Identify the constant and the coefficients of the terms in each of the following expressions:
   a. $5x^2 - 3xy + 5$ b. $-2y^2 + 3x + 1$ c. $-2xy^2 - 2x^2y + 7$

4. Identify the constant term and the coefficients of all the other terms in each of the following expressions:
   a. $-2y^2 + 3y - 4$ b. $y^5 - 2y^7 - 2$ c. $2x^3 - 3x^2 + 1$

Simplify the following expressions:

5. a. $13x^2 + 8x - 2x^2 + 9x$ b. $-18y - 5y^2 + 19y - 2y^2$ c. $6x - 3x + 2y^2 + y^2$
6. a. $7x + 12x^2 - 4x + 5x^2$ b. $-14y - 2y^2 + 7y + 7y^2$ c. $9x^2 - 6x^2 + 7y - 6y$
7. a. $\frac{3x + 5x}{5x}$ b. $\frac{12y - 3y}{4y + 2y}$ c. $\frac{(16y)(8x)}{(4x)(8y)}$
8. a. $\frac{8x}{x + 5x}$ b. $\frac{20y - 5y}{-4y + 7y}$ c. $\frac{(20y)(4x)}{(2x)(5y)}$
9. $3[5 - 3(4 - x)] - 2 - 5[3(5x - 4)+8] - 9x$
10. $5 - \frac{1}{4}\{x - 8[3 - 5(2x - 3) + 3x] - 3\}$
11. $6[4(8 - y) - 5(3+3y)] - 21 - 7[3(7+4y) - 4] + 198y$
12. $\frac{1}{5}\{y - 15[2 - 3(3y - 2) - 7y] - 4\} + 7$
13. $y - \{4x - [y - (2y - 9) - x] + 2\}$
14. $2y + \{-6y - z[3x + (-4x + 3)] + 5\}$
15. $(x - 1) - \{[x - (x - 3)] - x\}$
16. $9x - \{3y + [4x - (y - 6x)] - (x + 7y)\}$
17. $5\{-2y + 3[4x - 2(3 + x)]\}$
18. $4\{-7y + 8[5x - 3(4x + 6)]\}$
19. $2y + \{8[3(2y - 5) - (8y + 9) + 6]\}$
20. $7x - \{5[4(3x - 8) - (9x + 10)] + 14\}$

Simplify the following expressions:

21. $(2y - 1)(y - 4) - (3y + 2)(3y - 1)$
22. $(y + 4)(y - 3) + (y - 2)(y - 3)$
23. $(2x + 3)(2x - 1) - 4(x^2 - 7)$
24. $4(2x - 1)(x + 3) - 3(x - 2)(3x - 4)$
25. $(5x - 6)^2 - (x + 5)^2$
26. $(2y - 3)^2 - (y + 3)^2$
27. $\frac{-x^2y - xy^2}{xy}$
28. $\frac{x^2y - 3xy^2}{xy}$
29. $\frac{x^2y - 3xy^2 + 4x^2y + xy}{xy}$
30. $\frac{3x^3y^3 + 6x^2y - 3xy^2 + 3xy}{3xy}$
31. $\frac{6xy^2}{7} \times \frac{21x^2}{y} \times \frac{1}{36xy^2}$
32. $\frac{12x^2y^3}{5} \times \frac{15x^2}{4xy} \times \frac{1}{30x^3y}$
33. $\frac{3x + 9}{14} \times \frac{7x + 21}{x + 3}$
34. $\frac{16}{3x^2y + 4x} \times \frac{6x^2y + 8x}{12}$
35. $\frac{x^2 - 5x}{2x + 10} \times \frac{3x + 15}{4x}$
36. $\frac{3xy + 4y}{8y} \times \frac{12y^2}{3x + 4}$

37. $\dfrac{15xy - 15y}{4x - 12} \times \dfrac{3x - 9}{4x - 12}$

38. $\dfrac{x^2 + xy}{7x - 14} \times \dfrac{14x - 28}{x + y}$

Evalute the following expressions, given x = 2 and y = 3:

39. a. $\dfrac{19x - 5y}{9}$ b. $x^2 + 6x + 8$

40. a. $\dfrac{7x - 5y}{3}$ b. $-x^2 + 10x + 7$

41. a. $\dfrac{(3x)^2(5y)}{6y}$ b. $-2x^2 + 3x + 8y$

42. a. $\dfrac{(2x)^2(2y)}{5y}$ b. $4x^2 + 10x - 4y$

Simplify and evaluate the following expressions:

43. a. $6y + 4y - 7y$, where $y = 10$ b. $2z - z + 7z$, where $z = 7$

44. a. $3x + 5x - 8x$, where $x = 4$ b. $3A - A + 6A$, where $A = 10$

45. a. $(6x)(3x) - (5x)(4x)$, where $x = 3$ b. $(2x)(0.5x + 4x)(5x + x)$, where $x = 5$

46. a. $(10x \times 4.5x) - (11x \times 4x)$, where $x = 50$ b. $(4x)(12x + 0.25x)(0.5x + x)$, where $x = 3$

Identify like terms:

47. a. $12A + 4B - 7A - B$ b. $6x + 8y - 5x - 3y + 7$

48. a. $6B + 8A - A - 2B$ b. $14 - 3x + 10y + 4y$

49. a. $-2x + 8x - 12x + 5y + 7y$ b. $6xy^2 - 2x^2y - 4x^2 + 2xy^2 + 3x^2y + 2x^2 + 4$

50. a. $3x + 6x - 20x + 8y + 8y + 5x$ b. $3x^2y - 12xy^2 - 6x^2y - 5xy - 2xy - 4xy^2$

Identify like terms, group them, simplify, and evaluate:

51. $3a + 6b - 16c - a + 8b + 4c + 2$, where $a = 3$, $b = 2$, $c = 1$

52. $3x - 60y - 17z - 2x + 62y + 4z + 1$, where $x = 5$, $y = 8$, $z = 2$

53. $x^2 - x + 2x^2 - x$, where $x = 5$

54. $-a^2 - 3a + 3a^2 + 4a$, where $a = 15$

Factor the following expressions:

55. $6x^2y - 3xy - 9y$

56. $10ab - 8bc$

57. $15y^2 - 12y - 3$

58. $8a^3 - 4a^2$

59. $6ab - 8bc + 7ac + 3cb$

60. $10x^2 - 6x - 4x^2$

61. $6xy - 9yz$

62. $12a^2b - 16ab - 24b$

63. $10x^3 - 4x^2$

64. $33x^2 - 3x - 11x^2$

65. $60y^2 - 40y - 180y^2$

66. $4xy - 12yz + 3xz + 15zy$

67. $5x(y + 2) + 3(y + 2)$

68. $7x(m - 4) + 3(m - 4)$

69. $4y(x - 5) - x^2 + 5x$

70. $3y(x - 1) + 2x^2 - 2x$

71. $xy - 2y + 5x - 10$

72. $4x - xy - 20y + 5y^2$

73. $x^2 + x - xy - y$

74. $2x^2 + 3y + 2x + 3xy$

75. $x^2 - 4y + 4x - xy$

76. $5x^2y - 10x^2 + y^2 - 2y$

7.2 | Simple Algebraic Equations and Word Problems

Introduction

An algebraic equation is a mathematical statement that shows the equality between two algebraic expressions or between an algebraic expression and a number.

For example,

Equality between two algebraic expressions: $5x + 7 = x + 19$

Equality between an algebraic expression and a number: $2x + 5 = 13$

The value of 'x' that satisfies an equation is known as being the solution to that equation.

Examples of Writing Simple Algebraic Equations with One Variable

Six more than a number, 'n', is 15.

$n + 6 = 15$

In 20 years, A will be 60 years old.

$A + 20 = 60$

Fourteen decreased by twice a number is six.

$14 - 2x = 6$

The product of five and the sum of a number and four is sixty.

$5(x + 4) = 60$

Six divided by a number is three.

$\frac{6}{n} = 3$

Equivalent Equations

Equations with the same solutions are called equivalent equations.

For example,

$2x + 5 = 13$ (Equation 1)

$2x = 8$ (Equation 2)

$x = 4$ (Equation 3)

Equations 1, 2, and 3 are equivalent equations because $x = 4$ satisfies each equation.

Performing the same operation on both sides of an equation will result in an equivalent equation.

Principle of Equations

If $a = b$, then $b = a$

For example,

If $14 + 9 = x$

Then, $x = 14 + 9$

If $'c'$ is any number and $a = b$, then,

$a + \mathbf{c} = b + \mathbf{c}$ Addition Principle

$a - \mathbf{c} = b - \mathbf{c}$ Subtraction Principle

$a \times \mathbf{c} = b \times \mathbf{c}$ Multiplication Principle

$\frac{a}{\mathbf{c}} = \frac{b}{\mathbf{c}}$ Division Principle

Steps to Solve Algebraic Equations with One Variable

Step 1: Clear the equation of fractions and/or decimals whenever possible, to make calculations and rearrangements easier.

Step 2: Expand and clear brackets in the equation, if present, by following the order of arithmetic operations (BEDMAS).

Step 3: Use the addition and subtraction principles to collect and group all **variable** terms on the **left side** of the equation and all **constants** on the right side of the equation.

Step 4: Use the division and multiplication principles to ensure that the coefficient of the variable is +1.

Step 5: You should now have a single variable on the left side and one or more numbers on the right side. Compute the right side of the equation to find the solution.

Step 6: Verify the answer by substituting into the original problem.

Step 7: State your answer.

Example 7.2-a **Solving Equations Using the Addition Principle**

Solve the following and verify the solution:

(i) $x - 11 = 4$

(ii) $x - \frac{2}{3} = \frac{1}{5}$

Solution

(i) $x - 11 = 4$ Adding **11** to both sides,

$x - 11 + \mathbf{11} = 4 + \mathbf{11}$

$x = \mathbf{15}$

Solution *continued*

Check: Substituting 15 for x,

$$x - 11 = 4$$
$$\mathbf{15} - 11 = 4$$
$$4 = 4$$

(ii) $x - \frac{2}{3} = \frac{1}{5}$ Adding $\frac{2}{3}$ to both sides,

$$x - \frac{2}{3} + \mathbf{\frac{2}{3}} = \frac{1}{5} + \mathbf{\frac{2}{3}}$$

Using LCD of 15,

$$x = \frac{1}{5} + \frac{2}{3}$$
$$x = \frac{13}{15} + \frac{10}{15}$$
$$x = \frac{13}{15}$$

Check: Substituting $\frac{13}{15}$ for x,

$$x - \frac{2}{3} = \frac{1}{5}$$

Using LCD of 15,

$$\frac{13}{15} - \frac{2}{3} = \frac{1}{5}$$
$$\frac{13}{15} - \frac{10}{15} = \frac{13}{15}$$
$$\frac{3}{15} = \frac{3}{15}$$

Example 7.2-b

Solving Equations Using the Subtraction Principle

(i) $8 + x = 20$

(ii) $x + \frac{2}{5} = \frac{3}{4}$

Solution

(i) $8 + x = 20$ Subtracting 8 from both sides,

$$8 - \mathbf{8} + x = 20 - \mathbf{8}$$
$$x = 12$$

(ii) $x + \frac{2}{5} = \frac{3}{4}$ Subtracting $\frac{2}{5}$ from both sides,

$$x + \frac{2}{5} - \frac{2}{5} = \frac{3}{4} - \frac{2}{5}$$

Using LCD of 20,

$$x = \frac{3}{4} - \frac{2}{5}$$
$$x = \frac{15}{20} - \frac{8}{20}$$
$$x = \frac{7}{20}$$

Example 7.2-c **Solving Equations Using the Multiplication and Division Principles**

(i) $5x = 20$

(ii) $\frac{3}{8}x = 12$

Solution

(i) $5x = 20$ Dividing both sides by 5,

$$\frac{5x}{\mathbf{5}} = \frac{20}{\mathbf{5}}$$

$$x = 4$$

(ii) $\frac{3}{8}x = 12$ Multiplying both sides by $\frac{8}{3}$,

$$\frac{3}{8}x\left(\frac{\mathbf{8}}{\mathbf{3}}\right) = 12\left(\frac{\mathbf{8}}{\mathbf{3}}\right)$$

$$x = 4 \times 8$$

$$x = 32$$

Or,

$\frac{3}{8}x = 12$ Multiplying both sides by 8,

$$\frac{3}{8}x(\mathbf{8}) = 12(\mathbf{8})$$

$3x = 96$ Dividing both sides by 3,

$$\frac{3x}{\mathbf{3}} = \frac{96}{\mathbf{3}}$$

$$x = 32$$

Example 7.2-d **Solving Equations Using All the Principles**

(i) $\frac{x}{3} + 5 = 7$

(ii) $8x + 7 - 3x = -6x - 15 + x$

(iii) $2(3x - 7) = 28 - 3(x + 1)$

Solution

(i) $\frac{x}{3} + 5 = 7$

$\frac{x}{3} + 5 - \mathbf{5} = 7 - \mathbf{5}$ Subtracting 5 from both sides,

$\frac{x}{3} = 2$ Multiplying both sides by 3,

$$\frac{x}{3} \times \mathbf{3} = 2 \times \mathbf{3}$$

$$x = 6$$

Solution
continued

(ii) $8x + 7 - 3x = -6x - 15 + x$ Grouping like terms on both sides,

$8x - 3x + 7 = -6x + x - 15$

$5x + 7 = -5x - 15$ Adding $5x$ to both sides,

$5x + \mathbf{5x} + 7 = -5x + 5x - 15$

$10x + 7 = -15$ Subtracting 7 from both sides,

$10x + 7 - \mathbf{7} = -15 - 7$

$10x = -22$ Dividing both sides by 10,

$\frac{10x}{\mathbf{10}} = -\frac{22}{\mathbf{10}}$

$x = -2.2$

(iii) $2(3x - 7) = 28 - 3(x + 1)$ Expanding both sides,

$6x - 14 = 28 - 3x - 3$ Adding $3x$ to both sides and simplifying,

$9x - 14 = 25$ Adding 14 to both sides and simplifying,

$9x = 25 + 14$

$9x = 39$ Dividing both sides by 9 and simplifying,

$x = \frac{39}{9}$

$x = 4\frac{1}{3} = 4.333333...$

Steps to Solve Word Problems

Step 1: Read the entire problem and understand the situation.

Step 2: Identify the given information and the question to be answered.

Step 3: Look for key words. Some words indicate certain mathematical operations.

Step 4: Choose a variable to represent the unknown(s).

Step 5: State what that variable represents, including the unit of measure.

Step 6: Where necessary, draw a simple sketch to identify the information. This helps with envisioning the question more clearly.

Step 7: Create an equation (or set of equations) to describe the relationship between the variables and the constants in the question.

Step 8: Rearrange the equation(s) and solve for the unknowns.

Example 7.2-e

Solving a Word Problem Using Algebraic Equations

If Harry will be 65 years old in 5 years, how old is he today?

Solution

Let Harry's age today be x years.

Therefore, in 5 years,

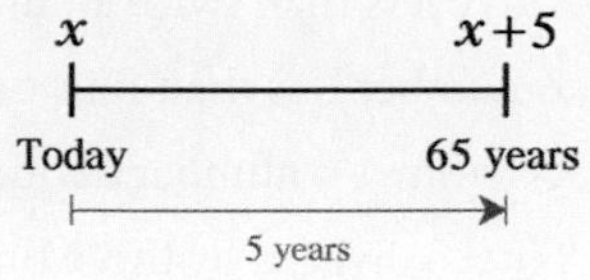

Harry's age will be, $x + 5 = 65$

Solving for x, $x = 65 - 5$

$= 60$

Therefore, Harry is 60 years old today.

Example 7.2-f

Solving a Word Problem Using Algebraic Equations

The perimeter of a rectangular garden is 50 metres. The length is 5 metres more than the width. Find the dimensions of the garden. (Hint: perimeter = 2 times the length + 2 times the width).

Solution

Let the width be w metres.

Therefore, the length is: $length = (w+5)$ metres

$Perimeter = 2(length) + 2(width)$

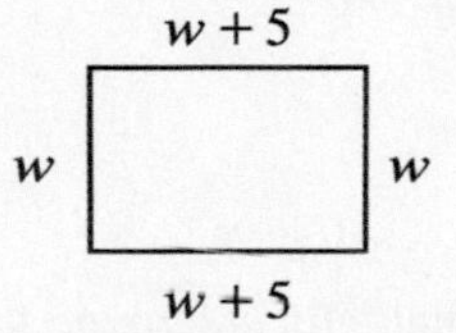

Perimeter = 50m

$50 = 2(w+5) + 2w$

$50 = 2w + 10 + 2w$

$2w + 10 + 2w = 50$

$4w + 10 = 50$

$4w = 50 - 10$

$4w = 40$

$w = 10$

Therefore, the width of the garden is 10 metres, and the length = 10 + 5 = 15 metres.

7.2 | Exercises

Answers to odd-numbered problems are available online.

Write the algebraic expression for the following:

1. Three less than twice a number.
2. A number less than four times a number.
3. Two times a number divided by five.
4. Fifteen divided by three times a number.
5. Six times the total of three and a number.
6. Seven times the sum of a number and five
7. Twenty-five increased by three times a number.
8. Twenty increased by twice a number.

Write the algebraic equation for the following and solve the equation:

9. The sum of a number and six is ten.
10. A number decreased by fifteen is five.
11. Six times a number is seventy-two.
12. The product of a number and four is twenty-eight.
13. A number divided by five is four.
14. A number divided by three is three.
15. Two-thirds a number is twelve.
16. Two-fifths a number is six.

Solve the following algebraic equations using principles of equations, and round the answer to 2 decimal places, wherever applicable:

17. $x - 20 = 10$
18. $x - 25 = 17$
19. $22 = 40 - x$
20. $54 = 23 - x$
21. $21 + x = 4$
22. $50 + x = 45$
23. $16 + x = 22$
24. $12 + x = 38$
25. $x - \frac{4}{5} = \frac{3}{5}$
26. $x - \frac{1}{6} = \frac{5}{6}$
27. $\frac{10}{15} = x - \frac{4}{3}$
28. $7x - 16 = 22$
29. $x + \frac{2}{5} = \frac{1}{4}$
30. $x + 0.13 = 70$
31. $5x = 20$
32. $4x = 24$
33. $11x + 4 = 17$
34. $\frac{8}{2}x = 20$
35. $10y - 0.09y = 17$
36. $\frac{x}{7} + 15 = 24$
37. $8x + 7 - 3x = -6x - 15 + x$
38. $x - 2 - 4x = -3x - 8 + 5x$

39. $2(3x - 7) = 28 - 3(x + 1)$

40. $4(2x - 5) = 32 - 4(x - 2)$

41. $(4 + 6)(2 + 4x) = 45 - 2.5(x + 3)$

42. $(5 + 0.5x)(1 + 3) = -1.2(2x + 4) + 25$

43. $\frac{x - 7}{2} + \frac{x + 2}{3} = 41$

44. $\frac{7}{12}(2x + 1) + \frac{3}{4}(x + 1) = 3$

45. $\frac{5}{y + 4} = \frac{3}{y - 2}$

46. $\frac{3}{x + 1} = \frac{2}{x - 3}$

47. $\frac{7}{5x - 3} = \frac{5}{4x}$

48. $\frac{5}{y + 2} = \frac{3}{y}$

49. $15 + 5(x - 10) = 3(x - 1)$

50. $2(x - 3) + 3(x - 5) = 4$

51 $4(y + 7) - 2(y - 4) = 3(y - 2)$

52. $8(2y + 4) - 6(3y + 7) = 3y$

53. If three times a number plus twenty is seven times that number, what is the number?

54. Fifteen less than three times a number is twice that number. What is the number?

55. A 25-metre long wire is cut into 2 pieces. One piece is 7 metres longer than the other. Find the length of each piece.

56. A 9-metre long pipe is cut into 2 pieces. One piece is twice the length of the other piece. Find the length of each piece.

57. \$500 is shared between Andy and Becky. Andy's share is \$150 less than Becky's share. Calculate the size of each of their shares.

58. \$200 is shared between Bill and Ann. Ann's share is \$50 more than Bill's share. Calculate the size of each of their shares.

59. Movie tickets that were sold to children were \$3 cheaper than those sold to adults. If a family of 2 adults and 2 children paid \$34 to watch a movie at the cinema, what was the price of the adults' ticket, and what was the price of the children's ticket?

60. Giri had twice the number of quarters (25 cents) in his bag than dimes (10 cents). If he had a total of 54 coins, how many of them were quarters? What was the total dollar value of these coins?

61. A square garden, with sides of length x, is widened by 4 metres and lengthened by 3 metres. Write the equation for the area (A) of the expanded garden. If each side was originally 10 metres in length, find the new area. (Hint: Area of a Rectangle = Length × Width)

62. A square garden, with sides of length x, has had its width reduced by 4 metres and its length reduced by 2 metres. Write the equation for the Area (A) of the shrunken garden. If each side was originally 20 metres in length, find the new area.

7.3 | Exponents

Introduction

The concept of exponents was covered in Chapter 3, Section 3.1, where exponents were used to express repeated multiplication or division of the same numbers.

$$\underbrace{a \times a \times a \times a \ldots \times a}_{\text{'n' factors of 'a'}} = a^n \qquad \frac{1}{\underbrace{a \times a \times a \times a \times a \times \ldots \times a}_{\text{'n' factors of 'a'}}} = \frac{1}{a^n} = a^{-n}$$

For example,

$\underbrace{2 \times 2 \times 2 \times 2 \times 2}_{\text{5 factors of 2}}$ is represented by: 2^5 (5 = exponent, 2 = base)

$\frac{1}{\underbrace{8 \times 8 \times 8}_{\text{3 factors of 8}}}$ is represented by: $\frac{1}{8^3} = 8^{-3}$ (−3 = exponent, 8 = base)

The above exponential principle is applied to express repeated multiplication of a variable or an algebraic term.

In algebra, when 'n' is a positive integer, the general form for writing exponential expressions using variables is represented by:

$$\underbrace{x \times x \times x \times \ldots \times x}_{\text{'n' factors of 'x'}} = x^n \qquad \frac{1}{\underbrace{x \times x \times x \times \ldots \times x}_{\text{'n' factors of 'x'}}} = \frac{1}{x^n} = x^{-n}$$

Some useful applications of the above with examples are provided below:

	Exponential Form	Expanded Form	Example
(i)	$-x^n = -(x)^n$	$= -(x \times x \times x \times x \ldots \times x)$	$-2^5 = -(2 \times 2 \times 2 \times 2 \times 2) = -32$ $-2^4 = -(2 \times 2 \times 2 \times 2) = -16$
(ii)	$(-x)^n$	$= (-x)(-x)(-x) \ldots (-x)$	$(-2)^5 = (-2)(-2)(-2)(-2)(-2) = -32$ $(-2)^4 = (-2)(-2)(-2)(-2) = 16$
(iii)	$-x^{-n} = -(x)^{-n}$	$= -\frac{1}{x^n}$ $= -\frac{1}{x \times x \times x \times x \ldots \times x}$	$-2^{-5} = -(2)^{-5} = -\frac{1}{2^5}$ $= -\frac{1}{2 \times 2 \times 2 \times 2 \ldots \times 2} = -\frac{1}{32}$
(iv)	$(-x)^{-n}$	$= \frac{1}{(-x)^n}$ $= \frac{1}{(-x) \times (-x) \times (-x) \times (-x) \ldots \times (-x)}$	$(-2)^{-5} = \frac{1}{(-2)^5}$ $= \frac{1}{(-2) \times (-2) \times (-2) \times (-2) \times (-2)}$ $= \frac{1}{-32} = \frac{-1}{32}$ $(-2)^{-4} = \frac{1}{(-2)^4} = \frac{1}{(-2)(-2)(-2)(-2)} = \frac{1}{16}$
(v)	ax^n	$= a(x \times x \times x \times x \ldots \times x)$	$3x^4$, where $x = 2$, $= 3(2)^4 = 3(2 \times 2 \times 2 \times 2) = 48$
(vi)	$(ax)^n$	$= (ax) \times (ax) \times (ax) \times (ax) \ldots \times (ax)$	$(3x)^4$, where $x = 2$, $(3 \times 2)^4 = 6^4 = 6 \times 6 \times 6 \times 6 = 1{,}296$

Note: The examples above assume that x is a positive number.

Rules of Exponents and Evaluation of Exponents

Rules of exponents' are also referred to as 'laws of exponents' or 'properties of exponents'. When the bases of exponents are the same, there are eight basic rules, as follows:

Note: There are no rules for addition or subtraction of exponents. These operations would have to be done separately.

For example, $2^3 + 2^5 = (2 \times 2 \times 2) + (2 \times 2 \times 2 \times 2 \times 2)$

$= 8 + 32 = 40$

The exponent button on the Texas Instruments BA II Plus calculator is the y^x button, as shown in this picture.

Table 7.3 **Rules of Exponents**

Rule #	Rule	Rule in Exponential form	Example
1	Product Rule	$(x^m)(x^n) = x^{m+n}$	$2^4 \times 2^3 = 2^{(4+3)} = 2^7 = 128$
2	Quotient Rule	$\frac{x^m}{x^n} = x^{m-n}$	$\frac{3^5}{3^3} = 3^{5-3} = 3^2 = 9$
3	Power of a power	$(x^m)^n = x^{mn}$	$(2^4)^2 = 2^{4\times2} = 2^8 = 256$
4	Power of a product	$(xy)^m = x^m y^m$	$(3 \times 5)^4 = 3^4 \times 5^4$ $= 81 \times 625 = 50{,}625$
5	Power of a quotient	$\left(\frac{x}{y}\right)^m = \frac{x^m}{y^m}$	$\left(\frac{3}{5}\right)^4 = \frac{3^4}{5^4} = \frac{81}{625}$
6	1 or −1 as an exponent	$x^1 = x$ and $x^{-1} = \frac{1}{x}$	If $x = 7$ and $n = 1$, then $7^1 = 7$ and $7^{-1} = \frac{1}{7}$
7	Negative exponent	$\left(\frac{x}{y}\right)^{-m} = \frac{y^m}{x^m}$	$\left(\frac{2}{3}\right)^{-4} = \left(\frac{3}{2}\right)^4 = \frac{3^4}{2^4} = \frac{81}{16}$
8	Zero (0) as an exponent	* $x^0 = 1$	If $x = 9$ and $n = 0$, then $9^0 = 1$

* $\frac{x^n}{x^n} = x^{(n-n)} = x^0$ Also, $\frac{x^n}{x^n} = 1$, therefore, $x^0 = 1$

Example 7.3-a **Solving Expressions Using the Product Rule and the Quotient Rule**

Solve: $(2^2)^3 \times 2^7 \div 2^9$

Solution

$2^6 \times 2^7 \div 2^9$

$2^{(6+7-9)} = 2^4 = 16$

Example 7.3-b

Solving Expressions that have Exponents with Different Bases

Solve: $2^4 \times 3^4$

Solution

$2^4 \times 3^4 = (2 \times 2 \times 2 \times 2) \times (3 \times 3 \times 3 \times 3) = 16 \times 81 = 1,296$

Example 7.3-c

Solving Expressions that have Negative Exponents

Solve: $\left(\frac{5}{4}\right)^{-2} \times \left(\frac{2}{3}\right)^{-3}$

Solution

$\left(\frac{5}{4}\right)^{-2} \times \left(\frac{2}{3}\right)^{-3}$

$= \left(\frac{4}{5}\right)^{2} \times \left(\frac{3}{2}\right)^{3}$

$= \frac{4^2}{5^2} \times \frac{3^3}{2^3}$

$= \frac{16}{25} \times \frac{27}{8}$

$= \frac{2}{25} \times \frac{27}{1}$

$= \frac{54}{25}$

$= 2\frac{4}{25} = 2.16$

Fractional Exponent

When the exponent, *'n'*, of a variable is a fraction, we call it a fractional exponent. The fractional exponent, $\frac{1}{n}$, replaces the radical sign, $\sqrt{\ }$.

For example,

The square root of $x = \sqrt{x} = x^{\frac{1}{2}}$

The cube root of $x = \sqrt[3]{x} = x^{\frac{1}{3}}$

Similarly, the nth root of $x = \sqrt[n]{x} = x^{\frac{1}{n}}$

$x^{\frac{1}{n}} = \sqrt[n]{x}$

$x^{\frac{m}{n}} = \sqrt[n]{x^m}$

$x^{-\frac{1}{n}} = \frac{1}{x^{\frac{1}{n}}} = \frac{1}{\sqrt[n]{x}}$

$x^{-\frac{m}{n}} = \frac{1}{x^{\frac{m}{n}}} = \frac{1}{\sqrt[n]{x^m}}$

Fractional exponents obey all the rules of exponents.

(i) $x^{\frac{1}{n}} = \sqrt[n]{x}$

For example, if $x = 16$ and $n = 4$,

then, $16^{\frac{1}{4}} = \sqrt[4]{16}$ Read as the 4th root of 16

$= 2$

(ii) $x^{\frac{m}{n}} = \left(x^{\frac{1}{n}}\right)^m = [\sqrt[n]{x}]^m$

This refers to finding the nth root of x, then raising the result to the power of m.

For example, if $x = 16$, $m = 3$, and $n = 4$,

then, $16^{\frac{3}{4}} = \left(16^{\frac{1}{4}}\right)^3 = [\sqrt[4]{16}]^3 = [2]^3 = 8$

Or

$$x^{\frac{m}{n}} = (x^m)^{\frac{1}{n}} = \sqrt[n]{x^m}$$

This refers to raising 'x' to the power of 'm', then finding the nth root of the result.

For example, if $x = 16$, $m = 3$, and $n = 4$,

then, $16^{\frac{3}{4}} = (16^3)^{\frac{1}{4}} = \sqrt[4]{16^3} = \sqrt[4]{4{,}096} = 8$

Note: The first method is easier because finding the nth root first results in a smaller number, which is easier to raise to the power of 'm'.

(i) $x^{-\frac{m}{n}} = \dfrac{1}{x^{\frac{m}{n}}} = \dfrac{1}{(\sqrt[n]{x})^m}$

For example, if $x = 27$, $m = 4$, and $n = 3$,

then, $24^{-\frac{4}{3}} = \dfrac{1}{24^{\frac{4}{3}}} = \dfrac{1}{(\sqrt[3]{27})^4} = \dfrac{1}{(3)^4} = \dfrac{1}{81}$

7.3 | Exercises

Answers to odd-numbered problems are available online.

For Problems 1 to 24, simplify and then evaluate.

1. a. $5^4 - 4^2$ b. $\dfrac{3^9 \times 3^2}{3^5}$
2. a. $10^3 - 7^2$ b. $\dfrac{2^9 \times 2^1}{2^5}$
3. a. $\dfrac{(2^5)^4}{4^6}$ b. $4^0 - 4^4$
4. a. $\dfrac{(2^5)^4}{16^3}$ b. $3^0 + 3^4$
5. a. $\dfrac{10^6}{10^0}$ b. $\dfrac{3^7}{27}$
6. a. $\dfrac{8^5}{8^3}$ b. $\dfrac{5^6}{125}$
7. a. $\left(\dfrac{5}{2}\right)^2\left(\dfrac{5}{2}\right)^3$ b. $-10^4 \times 10^3$
8. a. $\left(\dfrac{5}{3}\right)^3\left(\dfrac{3}{5}\right)^2$ b. $-2^4 \times 2^2$

9. a. $(-5)^2 \times (4)^2$ b. $3^4 \times 3^{(4+2)}$

10. a. $(-2)^2 \times (3)^2$ b. $10^4 \times 10^{(3+2)}$

11. a. $(2 \times 3^2)^4$ b. $3^{-2} \times 3^3$

12. a. $(5 \times 2^2)^3$ b. $12^{-8} \times 12^9$

13. $\sqrt[4]{25^2 \times 25^2}$ 14. $\sqrt[4]{5^2 \times 25^3}$ 15. $\sqrt[2]{3^4 \times 2^4}$ 16. $\sqrt[6]{9^3 \times 27^4}$

17. $(2^6)^{\frac{1}{3}}$ 18. $(5^{15})^{\frac{1}{5}}$ 19. $\left(\frac{3^9}{3^3}\right)^{\frac{1}{3}}$ 20. $\left(\frac{2^{12}}{2^4}\right)^{\frac{1}{4}}$

21. $(9)^{\frac{3}{2}}$ 22. $(16)^{\frac{3}{4}}$ 23. $-5^3(-25)^3$ 24. $-100^2 \times (-10)^4$

For Problems 25 to 56, simplify the expressions and write your answers with positive exponents.

25. $(5x)(4x^2)$ 26. $(3x)(6x^2)$ 27. $(x^9) \times (x^2) \div x^5$ 28. $x^{10} \times x^{20} \div x^{30}$

29. $(x^5)^4 \div x^3$ 30. $(x^5)^4 \div x^{20}$ 31. $\frac{x^6}{x^0}$ 32. $\frac{x^0}{x}$

33. $\left(\frac{x}{y}\right)^2\left(\frac{x}{y}\right)^3\left(\frac{x}{y}\right)^2$ 34. $\left(\frac{x}{y}\right)^4\left(\frac{x}{y}\right)^2\left(\frac{x}{y}\right)^{-8}$ 35. $\left(\frac{x}{y}\right)^2\left(\frac{x}{y}\right)^3$ 36. $\left(\frac{x}{y}\right)^5\left(\frac{x}{y}\right)^{-3}$

37. $-x^4 \times x^3$ 38. $x^6 \times (-x)^5$ 39. $(-y)^4(y)^2$ 40. $(-y)^5 \times (y)^1$

41. $(xy^2)^4$ 42. $(x^3y^2)^5$ 43. $x^{-5} \times x^7$ 44. $x^0 \times x^{(2 \times 3)}$

45. $(x^3)^2(x^2)^3(x^{3-1})$ 46. $(x^{5-1})(x^3)^2(x^2)^{-3}$ 47. $\sqrt[4]{x^6x^{10}}$ 48. $\sqrt[4]{x^8x^4}$

49. $\sqrt[3]{x^9x^6}$ 50. $\sqrt[2]{x^{10}y^{-6}}$ 51. $(27x^6)^{\frac{1}{3}}$ 52. $(81x^8)^{\frac{1}{4}}$

53. $\left(\frac{x^9}{x^3}\right)^{\frac{1}{3}}$ 54. $\left(\frac{x^{19}}{x^4}\right)^{\frac{1}{4}}$ 55. $\frac{(-x)^3(-x)^4}{x^5}$ 56. $\frac{(-x)^6(-x)^4}{x^9}$

7.4 | Logarithms

Concept of Logarithm and its Relation to Exponents

We know that multiplication is a faster method for finding the answer to repeated addition.

For example, 5 + 5 + 5 + 5 + 5 + 5 + 5 is the same as 7×5.

Similarly, the use of logarithm is a faster method of solving for an unknown exponent.

Exponential Form

$10^3 = 1{,}000$

$5^2 = 25$

Exponent → x; Base → a; Number → y

$$a^x = y$$

Read as: base 'a' raised to the 'x' is 'y' or 'a' to the power of 'x' is 'y'.

Logarithmic Form

$\log_{10} 1{,}000 = 3$

$\log_5 25 = 2$

Number → y; Base → a; Logarithm (exponent) → x

$$\text{Log}_a y = x$$

Read as: logarithm of 'y' to the base 'a' is 'x' or log 'y' to the base 'a' is 'x'.

As seen above, a logarithm is the exponent to which the base is raised to get the number.

Any positive number can be used as the base for logarithms.

For example, 100 is the same as 10^2. Here, the base is 10 and the exponent is 2. Therefore, the logarithm of 100 to the base 10 is 2.

$$\underbrace{10^2 = 100}_{\textbf{Exponential form}} \quad \text{is the same as} \quad \underbrace{\log_{10} 100 = 2}_{\textbf{Logarithmic form}}$$

Similarly, 125 is the same as 5^3. Here, the base is 5 and the exponent is 3; therefore, the logarithm of 125 to the base 5 is 3.

$$\underbrace{5^3 = 125}_{\textbf{Exponential form}} \quad \text{is the same as} \quad \underbrace{\log_5 125 = 3}_{\textbf{Logarithmic form}}$$

Common Logarithms (log)

Common logarithms are always to the base 10. If no base is shown in the common logarithmic expression, it is assumed to have base 10 and is referred to by the symbol 'log'.

Common Logarithmic Form	Exponential Form
$\log_{10} 1{,}000 = 3 = \log 1{,}000 = 3$	$10^3 = 1{,}000$
$\log_{10} 100 = 2 = \log 100 = 2$	$10^2 = 100$
$\log_{10} 10 = 1 = \log 10 = 1$	$10^1 = 10$
$\log_{10} 1 = 0 = \log 1 = 0$	$10^0 = 1$
$\log_{10} y = x = \log y = x$	$10^x = y$

The natural logarithm key on the Texas Instruments BA II Plus calculator is the 'LN' button, as shown in this picture.

We know $x^0 = 1$

Thus, $10^0 = 1$

and $e^0 = 1$

Therefore,

$\log_{10} 1 = 0 \longrightarrow \log 1 = 0$

$\ln_e 1 = 0 \longrightarrow \ln 1 = 0$

Natural Logarithms (ln)

Natural logarithms are always to the base 'e' where the constant $e = 2.718282...$ 'e' is a special number in mathematics (similar to π, which is equal to 3.141592...) and is found by $\left(1 + \frac{1}{n}\right)^n$, where '$n$' is a large number.

Assume $n = 100{,}000$ then $e = \left(1 + \frac{1}{100{,}000}\right)^{100{,}000} = 2.718282...$

In business and financial calculators, the natural logarithm key, ln, is the only logarithmic key available. The common logarithm key, **log**, is not available. Natural logarithm is referred to by the symbol '**ln**' (pronounced "lawn"), which has the base 'e'.

If the base of a logarithmic expression is 'e', then it is simply expressed by '**ln**'.

Natural Logarithmic Form	Exponential Form
$\log_e 1 = \ln 1 = 0$	$e^0 = 1$
$\log_e e = \ln e = 1$	$e^1 = 2.718282...$
$\log_e 10 = \ln 10 = 2.302585...$	$e^{2.302585} = 10$
$\log_e 1.005 = \ln 1.005 = 0.00498754...$	$e^{0.00498754} = 1.005$

The rules of logarithms are used to evaluate the exponent 'n' in business and finance mathematics formulas, which you will study in subsequent chapters.

Rules of Logarithms

Common logarithms (log) and natural logarithms (ln) follow the same rules.

Table 7.4 Rules of Logarithms

Rule		Common Logarithms (log)		Natural Logarithms (ln)	
		Rule in Common Logarithmic Form	Example	Rule in Natural Logarithmic Form	Example
1	Product Rule	$\log(AB) = \log A + \log B$	$\log(50 \times 10) = \log 50 + \log 10$	$\ln(AB) = \ln A + \ln B$	$\ln(50 \times 10) = \ln 50 + \ln 10$
2	Quotient Rule	$\log\left(\frac{A}{B}\right) = \log A - \log B$	$\log\left(\frac{50}{10}\right) = \log 50 - \log 10$	$\ln\left(\frac{A}{B}\right) = \ln A - \ln B$	$\ln\left(\frac{50}{10}\right) = \ln 50 - \ln 10$
3	Power Rule	$\log(A)^n = n \log A$	$\log(50)^2 = 2 \log 50$	$\ln(A)^n = n \ln A$	$\ln(50)^2 = 2 \ln 50$
4	Zero as a power or One as logarithm	$\log(A)^0 = \log 1 = 0$	$\log(50)^0 = \log 1 = 0$	$\ln(A)^0 = \ln 1 = 0$	$\ln(50)^0 = \ln 1 = 0$

Example 7.4-a

Solving Equations using Natural Logarithms (ln)

Solve for 'n' in the following equations:

(i) $1{,}024 = 2^n$

(ii) $3{,}749 = 1{,}217(1.005)^n$

Solution

(i) $1{,}024 = 2^n$ Taking ln on both sides,

$\ln 1{,}024 = \ln 2^n$ Using Power Rule,

$\ln 1{,}024 = n \ln 2$

$$n = \frac{\ln 1{,}024}{\ln 2} = 10$$

(ii) $3{,}749 = 1{,}217(1.005)^n$ Taking ln on both sides,

$$\frac{3{,}749}{1{,}217} = (1.005)^n$$

Using Power Rule,

$$\ln\left(\frac{3{,}749}{1{,}217}\right) = \ln(1.005)^n$$

$$\ln\left(\frac{3{,}749}{1{,}217}\right) = n \ln 1.005$$

$$n = \frac{\ln\left(\frac{3{,}749}{1{,}217}\right)}{\ln 1.005} = \frac{1.125100\ldots}{0.004987\ldots} = 225.582147\ldots$$

7.4 | Exercises

Answers to odd-numbered problems are available online.

Express in logarithmic form:

1. a. $10^5 = 100{,}000$ b. $4^5 = 1{,}024$
2. a. $10^4 = 10{,}000$ b. $4^4 = 256$
3. a. $2^6 = 64$ b. $6^5 = 7{,}776$
4. a. $2^3 = 8$ b. $6^4 = 1{,}296$
5. a. $3^2 = 9$ b. $9^4 = 6{,}561$
6. a. $3^3 = 27$ b. $8^2 = 64$

Express in exponential form:

7. a. $\log_{10}100 = 2$ b. $\log_4 64 = 3$
8. a. $\log_{10}1{,}000 = 3$ b. $\log_4 4{,}096 = 6$
9. a. $\log_2 32 = 5$ b. $\log_5 625 = 4$
10. a. $\log_2 4 = 2$ b. $\log_5 125 = 3$

11. a. $\log_3 729 = 6$ b. $\log_6 216 = 3$

12. a. $\log_3 243 = 5$ b. $\log_6 1{,}296 = 4$

Calculate the following (rounding to 4 decimal places):

13. a. ln 2,250 b. ln 154 c. ln 27

14. a. ln 39 b. ln 276 c. ln 1,550

15. a. ln 10.05 b. ln 1.005 c. ln 0.675

16. a. ln 0.165 b. ln 1.02 c. ln 12.51

Solve for 'n' (rounding to 2 decimal places):

17. $250 = (30)^n$

18. $320 = (15)^n$

19. $7{,}500 = (45)^n + 500$

20. $8{,}000 = (35)^n + 1{,}500$

21. $10{,}000 = 2{,}000(1.2)^n$

22. $15{,}000 = 5{,}000\,(1.04)^n$

23. $(1.05)^n = 1.31$

24. $2.5 = (1.05)^n$

Express the following as a sum or difference of two or more natural logarithms:

25. $\ln\left(\frac{3}{7}\right)$

26. $\ln\left(\frac{40}{13}\right)$

27. $\ln(4 \times 9)$

28. $\ln(7 \times 8)$

29. $\ln\left(\frac{AB}{C}\right)$

30. $\ln\left(\frac{x}{ab}\right)$

31. $\ln\left(\frac{X}{YZ}\right)$

32. $\ln\left(\frac{xy}{c}\right)$

33. $\ln\left(\frac{3x}{2yz}\right)$

34. $\ln\left(\frac{5x}{2ab}\right)$

Express as a single natural logarithm:

35. $\ln 8 + \ln 5$

36. $\ln 25 + \ln 4$

37. $\ln 15 - \ln 3$

38. $\ln 60 - \ln 15$

39. $2\ln 5 + 3\ln 3$

40. $2\ln 8 + 3\ln 3$

41. $5\ln 2 - 2\ln 3$

42. $4\ln 5 - 3\ln 2$

43. $3\ln a + 2\ln b - 5\ln c$

44. $4\ln x - 2\ln y + 3\ln z$

45. $2\ln 5$

46. $5\ln 2$

47. $3\ln 6$

48. $6\ln 3$

49. $2\ln\frac{x}{y}$

50. $5\ln\frac{a}{b}$

51. $4\ln(a \times b)$

52. $3\ln(xy)$

53. $3\ln 2 + 4\ln 3 - 2\ln 4$

54. $2\ln 3 + 3\ln 2 - 4\ln 2$

Solve for 'n' (rounding to 2 decimal places):

55. $n = \ln\left(\frac{4,285}{4,000}\right)$

56. $n = \ln\left(\frac{6,750}{3,200}\right)$

57. $n = \ln\left(\frac{3,645}{2,175}\right)$

58. $n = \ln\left(\frac{75,000}{2,200}\right)$

59. $n = \frac{\ln\left(\frac{7,200}{4,725}\right)}{\ln(1.01)}$

60. $n = \frac{\ln\left(\frac{5,120}{2,250}\right)}{\ln(1.005)}$

61. $n = \frac{\ln(2.5)}{\ln(1.03)}$

62. $n = \frac{\ln(3)}{\ln(1.02)}$

7.5 | Formulas and their Applications

Formulas are similar to equations. In formulas, the relationship among many variables is written as a rule for performing calculations. To solve for one of the variables in a formula, rearrange the formula to isolate the required variable, simplify, and then solve for the required variable. Rearrangement can be performed using the rules that you have learned in the previous sections of this chapter.

To solve for a required variable using a formula, it is important to know what each symbol in the formula represents. For example, consider the formula for simple interest: $I = Prt$. In this simple interest formula, 'I' represents the amount of simple interest, 'P' represents the amount of investment or loan, also known as principal, 'r' represents the interest rate per annum, and 't' represents the time period in years.

To solve for any of the variables, 'I', 'P', 'r', or 't' in this simple interest formula, we can rearrange the variables as shown below:

$I = Prt$ is the same as $Prt = I$

Solving for 'P':

$$\frac{Prt}{rt} = \frac{I}{rt}$$ Dividing both sides by 'rt',

$$P = \frac{I}{rt}$$

Solving for 'r':

$$\frac{Prt}{Pt} = \frac{I}{Pt}$$ Dividing both sides by 'Pt',

$$r = \frac{I}{Pt}$$

Solving for 't':

$$\frac{Prt}{Pr} = \frac{I}{Pr}$$ Dividing both sides by 'Pr',

$$t = \frac{I}{Pr}$$

Example 7.5-a

Rearranging to Isolate Variables

Rearrange and isolate the variable:

(i) 'M' in $S = C + M$

(ii) 'P' in $C + E + P = S$

(iii) 'R' and 'B' in $P = RB$

(iv) 'b' and 'm' in $y = mx + b$

(v) 'P' in $S = P(1 + rt)$

Solution

(i) $S = C + M$

$M + C = S$ Subtracting 'C' on both sides,

$M + C - \mathbf{C} = S - \mathbf{C}$

$M = S - C$

(ii) $C + E + P = S$ Subtracting 'C' and 'E' on both sides,

$C + E + P - \mathbf{C} - \mathbf{E} = S - \mathbf{C} - \mathbf{E}$

$P = S - C - E$

(iii) $P = RB$

Isolating 'R'

$RB = P$

Dividing both sides by 'B',

$$\frac{RB}{B} = \frac{P}{B}$$

$$R = \frac{P}{B}$$

Isolating 'B'

$RB = P$

Dividing both sides by 'R',

$$\frac{RB}{R} = \frac{P}{R}$$

$$B = \frac{P}{R}$$

(iv) $y = mx + b$

Isolating 'b'

$mx + b = y$

Subtracting 'mx' from both sides,

$mx - \mathbf{m}x + b = y - \mathbf{m}x$

$b = y - mx$

Isolating 'm'

$mx + b = y$

Subtracting 'b' from both sides

$mx + b - \mathbf{b} = y - \mathbf{b}$

$mx = y - b$

Dividing both sides by 'x',

$$\frac{mx}{x} = \frac{y - b}{x}$$

$$m = \frac{y - b}{x}$$

(v) $P(1 + rt) = S$

Isolating 'P' by dividing both sides by '$(1 + rt)$',

Solution
continued

$$\frac{P(1+rt)}{(1+rt)} = \frac{S}{(1+rt)}$$

$$P = \frac{S}{(1+rt)}$$

Example 7.5-b

Solving for Variables Using the Rearranged Simple Interest Formula

In the simple interest formula $I = Prt$, find:

(i) 'I', when $P = \$1{,}000$, $r = 5\% = 0.05$, $t = 3$ years

(ii) 'P', when $I = \$150$, $r = 3\% = 0.03$, $t = 1$ year

(iii) 'r', when $I = \$500$, $P = \$8{,}000$, $t = 2$ years

(iv) 't', when $I = \$40$, $P = \$800$, $r = 5\% = 0.05$

Round your answers to 2 decimal places, wherever applicable.

Solution

(i) Substitute the values for 'P', 'r', and 't' in the formula: $I = Prt$

$$I = 1{,}000 \times 0.05 \times 3 = \$150.00$$

(ii) Substitute the values for 'I', 'r', and, 't' in the rearranged formula:

$$P = \frac{I}{rt}$$

$$P = \frac{150}{(0.03 \times 1)} = \$5{,}000.00$$

(iii) Substitute the values for 'I', 'P', and 't' in the rearranged formula:

$$r = \frac{I}{Pt}$$

$$r = \frac{500}{8{,}000 \times 2} = 0.03125 = 3.125\% = 3.13\%$$

(Rounded to 2 decimal places)

(iv) Substitute the values for 'I', 'P', and 'r' in the rearranged formula:

$$t = \frac{I}{Pr}$$

$$t = \frac{40}{800 \times 0.05} = 1 \text{ year}$$

Formulas to Find the Perimeter (P) and Area (A) of Common Plane Figures

1. Square:

$$P = 4S$$
$$A = S^2$$

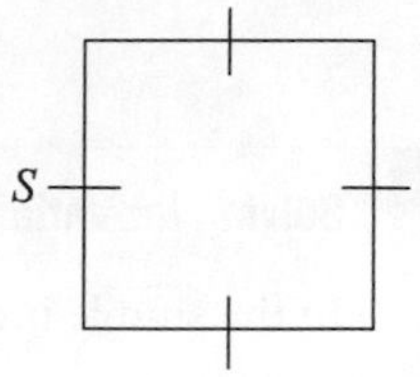

2. Rectangle:

$$P = 2(l + w)$$
$$A = l \times w$$

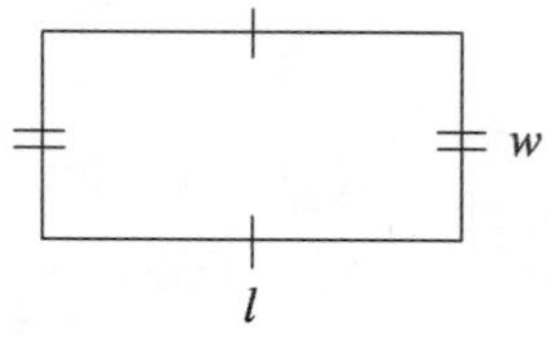

3. Triangle:

$$P = a + b + c$$
$$A = \frac{1}{2} b \times h$$

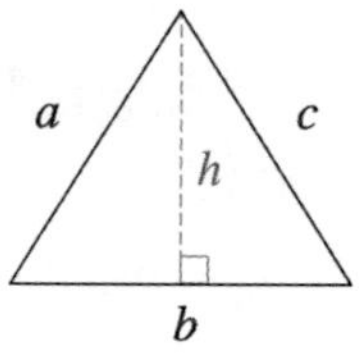

4. Parallelogram:

$$P = 2\,(a + b)$$
$$A = b \times h$$

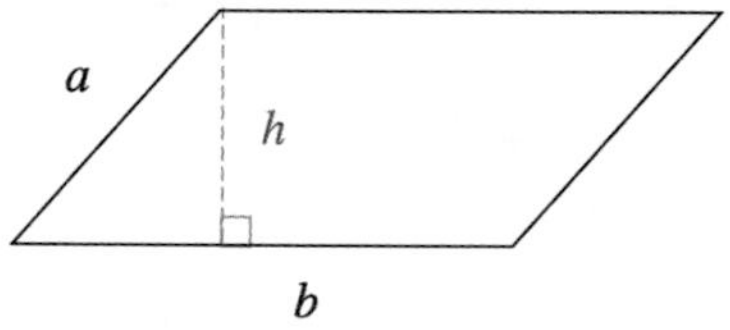

5. Trapezium:

$$P = a + b + c + d$$
$$A = \frac{(a + b)}{2} \times h$$

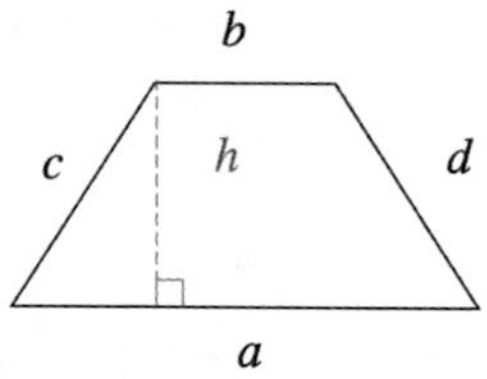

6. Circle:

$$P = \text{Circumference } (C)$$
$$C = 2\pi r$$
$$A = \pi r^2$$

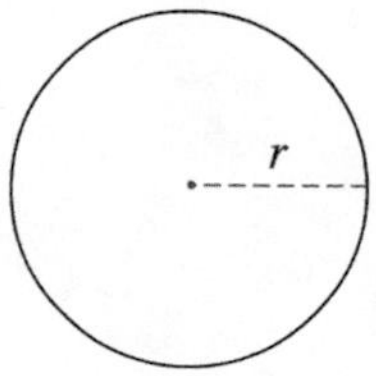

Formulas to Find the Surface Area (SA) and Volume (V) of Common Solid Objects

1. Square Prism (Cube):

$$SA = 6s^2$$
$$V = s^3$$

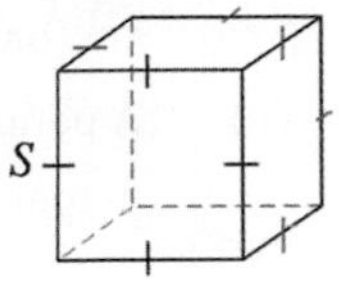

2. Rectangular Prism:

$$SA = 2(l \times w + l \times h + w \times h)$$
$$V = l \times w \times h$$

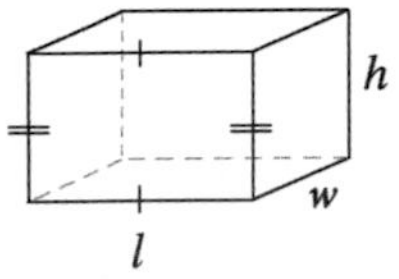

3. Triangular Prism:

$$SA = \text{Area of all 5 faces}$$
$$V = B \times h$$

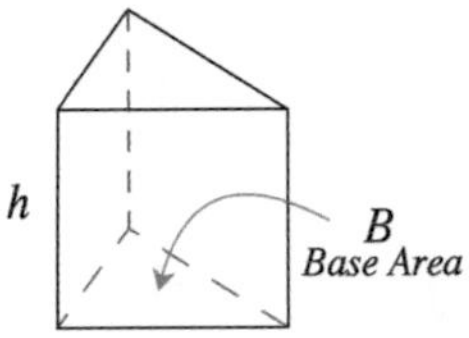

4. Cylinder:

$$SA = 2\pi rh + 2\pi r^2$$
$$V = \pi r^2 h$$

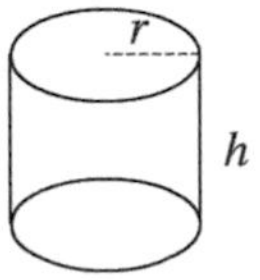

5. Cone:

$$SA = \pi r^2 + \pi rs$$
$$V = \frac{1}{3}\pi r^2 h$$

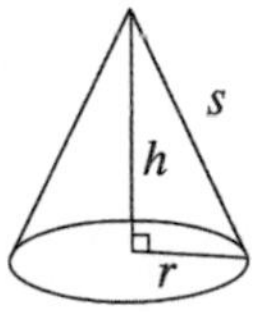

6. Triangular pyramid:

$$SA = \text{Area of all 4 faces}$$
$$V = \frac{1}{3}B \times h$$

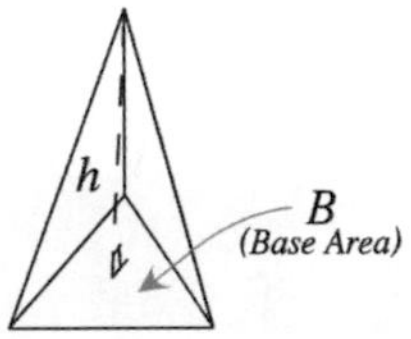

7. Sphere:

$$SA = 4\pi r^2$$
$$V = \frac{4}{3}\pi r^3$$

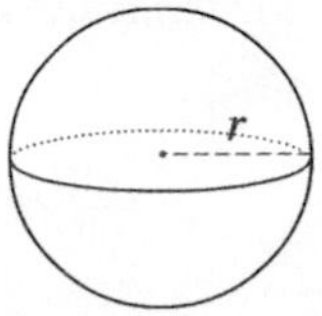

Example 7.5-c

Calculating the Perimeter and Area of Plane Figures Using Formulas

Find the perimeter and area of the following plane figures:

(i) A triangle with sides of 5 cm, 8 cm, and 10 cm (base) and a height of 4 cm.

(ii) A parallelogram with sides of 9 cm and 6 cm and a perpendicular distance of 5 cm between the 9 cm sides.

Solutions

(i) Triangle:

$P = a + b + c = 5 + 8 + 10 = 23$ cm

Area $= \frac{1}{2} b \times h = \frac{1}{2} \times 10 \times 4 = 20$ cm^2

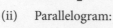

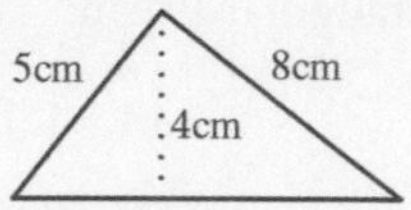

(ii) Parallelogram:

$P = 2(a + b) = 2(9 + 6) = 30$ cm

Area $= b \times h = 9 \times 5 = 45$ cm^2

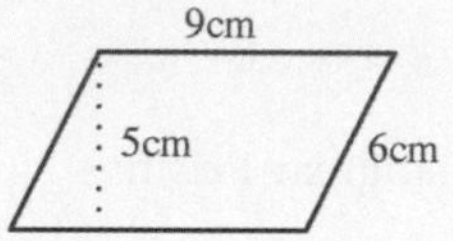

Example 7.5-d

Calculating Surface Area and Volume of Solid Objects Using Formulas

Find the surface area and volume of the following solid objects:

(i) A sphere with a radius of 12 cm.

(ii) A cylinder with a height of 15 cm and a base with a radius of 6 cm.

Solution

(i) Sphere:

$SA = 4\pi r^2 = 4\pi(12^2) = 1{,}809.557368... = 1{,}809.56$ cm^2

$V = \frac{4}{3}\pi r^3 = \frac{4}{3}\pi(12^3) = 7{,}238.229474... = 7{,}238.23$ cm^3

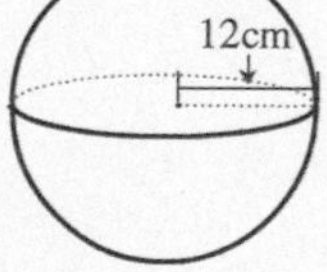

(ii) Cylinder:

$SA = 2\pi rh + 2\pi r^2 = 2\pi(6)(15) + 2\pi(6^2)$

$= 791.681348... = 791.68$ cm^2

$V = \pi r^2 h = \pi(6^2)(15) = 1{,}696.460033... = 1{,}696.46$ cm^3

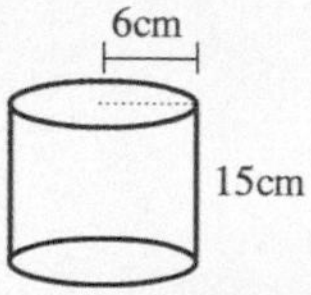

7.5 | Exercises

Answers to odd-numbered problems are available online.

Rearrange and isolate the indicated variables:

1. 'L' in $N = L(1 - d)$
2. 'b' in $A = \frac{b - h}{2}$
3. 'C' in $S = C + M$
4. 'R' in $P = R \times B$
5. 'E' in $C + E + P = S$
6. 'C' in $C + E + P = S$

7. 'r' in $C = 2\pi r$

8. 'd' in $N = L - dL$

9. 'r' in $S = P(1 + rt)$

10. 't' in $S = P(1 + rt)$

11. 'a' and 'c' in $b = \dfrac{ac}{1 - a}$

12. 'a' and 'c' in $b = \dfrac{c + ac}{a - 2}$

13. 'a' and 'b' in $c = \dfrac{a - c}{b}$

14. 'a' and 'b' in $c = \dfrac{ab - b}{4 + a}$

In the simple interest formula $I = Prt$, find:

15. 't', when $I = \$21$, $P = \$700$, $r = 0.01$

16. 'r', when $I = \$500$, $P = \$5{,}000$, $t = 0.75$

In the trade discount formula $N = L(1 - d)$, find:

17. 'L', when $N = \$300$, $d = 0.40$

18. 'd', when $L = \$900$, $N = \$630$

Find the perimeter and area of the following plane figures:

19. A rectangle with sides of 15 m and 20 m.
20. A square with sides 8 mm long.
21. A circle with a radius of 8 cm.
22. A circle with a radius of 25 cm.
23. A triangle with sides of 9 cm, 4 cm, and 6 cm (base) and a height of 5 cm.
24. A triangle with sides of 16 cm, 14 cm, and 5 cm(base) and a height of 13 cm.
25. A parallelogram with sides of 12 cm and 4 cm and a perpendicular distance of 3.5 cm between the 12 cm parallel sides.
26. A parallelogram with sides of 14 cm and 7 cm and a perpendicular distance of 5.5 cm between the 14 cm parallel sides.
27. Find the surface area and volume of the following solid objects:
    a. A rectangular prism with sides of 40 cm, 80 cm, and 150 cm.
    b. A sphere with a radius of 20 cm.
    c. A cylinder with a height of 15 cm and a base with a diameter of 12 cm.
28. Find the surface area and volume of the following solid objects:
    a. A rectangular prism with sides of 60 cm, 200 cm, and 30 cm.
    b. A sphere with a diameter of 50 cm.
    c. A cylinder with a height of 51 cm and a base with a radius of 5 cm.
29. Find the volume of a cone with a base area of 140 cm^2 and a height of 40 cm.
30. Find the volume of a triangular pyramid with a base area of 270 m^2 and a height of 15 m.

7 | Review Exercises

Answers to odd-numbered problems are available online.

Simplify the following expressions then evaluate:

1. a. $-4x^2 + 3x - 5 + 7x^2 - 2x + 3$, where $x = 2$

   b. $4x^2 - 5 + 7x - 2x^2 - x - 3$, where $x = -1$

2. a. $3x^2 - x + 2 + x^2 - 5x - 2$, where $x = 3$

   b. $-5y^2 - 7y + 3 + y^2 - 5y + 2$, where $y = -2$

3. a. $-y^2 + 4xy + x^2 - 6y^2 - xy - 11x^2$, where $x = 1$ and $y = 2$

   b. $(x - 4)(x + 2) + 3(x + 2)$, where $x = 3$

4. a. $-4x^2 + 6xy - 6y^2 + 6x^2 - 2xy + 3y^2$, where $x = 2$ and $y = 1$

   b. $(y - 2)(y - 3) + 2(y - 2)$, where $y = 4$

Factor the following expressions then evaluate:

5. a. $6x^2 - 4x$, $x = 1$

   b. $3y^3 - 12y^2$, $y = -2$

6. a. $8y^2 - 64y$, $y = 2$

   b. $16x^2 - 4x^3$, $x = -1$

7. a. $7xy + 14x^2$, $x = 3$ and $y = 2$

   b. $9x^3 - 6x^2 + 3x$, $x = 1$

8. a. $15y^2 + 10xy$, $x = -1$ and $y = 2$

   b. $16x^3 + 8x^2 - 4x$, $x = 2$

Write in algebraic expressions:

9. a. Twelve increased by three times a number.

   b. The difference between a number and five.

10. a. Eight decreased by twice a number.

    b. Six less than the total of a number and ten.

11. a. The product of three more than a number and the number.

    b. Sum of ten times a number and fifteen.

12. a. Sum of 15 and half of a number.

    b. Product of two times a number and seven.

Write the following in algebraic equation and solve:

13. a. Seventeen more than five times a number is forty-two

    b. A number divided by fifteen is forty-five.

14. a. The product of five and a number is seventy-five.

    b. Three more than two times a number is nine.

15. a. The difference between a number and ten is ten.

    b. The product of four times a number and three is thirty-six.

16. a. The sum of two times a number and eight is one hundred.

    b. A number divided by three is seven.

Solve for the unknown variable, x, using principle of equations:

17. a. $5x - 5 = 10$

    b. $\frac{x}{3} + 4 = 10$

18. a. $3x - 5 = -17$

    b. $\frac{x}{4} - 2 = 1$

19. a. $12 - 3x = 3 - 4x$

    b. $4(x + 4) = 24$

20. a. $4x - 2 = 13 - 6x$

    b. $3(2x - 5) = 3$

Simplify and evaluate:

21. a. $(-3)^2 + 2^3$
    b. $(-3)^2(2^3)$
    c. $\frac{2^8}{2^4}$
22. a. $(-5)^3 + 3^2$
    b. $2^3(-2)^4$
    c. $\frac{3^7}{3^5}$
23. a. $\left(\frac{4}{9}\right)^{-\frac{1}{2}}$
    b. $\sqrt[3]{125}$
    c. $\frac{4^9}{4^5 \times 4^2}$
24. a. $\left(\frac{1}{8}\right)^{-\frac{2}{3}}$
    b. $\sqrt[5]{32}$
    c. $\frac{3^4 \times 3^2}{3^3}$

Simplify the expression and express your answer with a positive exponent:

25. a. $(x^4)(3x^3)$
    b. $\frac{x^6}{x^2}$
    c. $\left(\frac{x^2}{y}\right)^3\left(\frac{x}{2y^2}\right)^2$
26. a. $(x^3)(2x^5)$
    b. $\frac{x^9}{x^6}$
    c. $\left(\frac{2x^2}{y}\right)^2\left(\frac{3x}{y^2}\right)^3$
27. a. $\left(\frac{4x^3}{2y^2}\right)^3$
    b. $(8x^6)^{\frac{1}{3}}$
    c. $\left(\frac{x^7}{x^0}\right)^2$
28. a. $\left(\frac{3x^2}{4y^3}\right)^2$
    b. $\left(\frac{x^0}{y^3}\right)^3$
    c. $(4x^2)^{\frac{1}{2}}$

Solve for 'n' and express the answer to 2 decimal places:

29. a. $2{,}060 = 1{,}225(1.02)^n$
    b. $5{,}215 = (1.005)^n + 600$
    c. $2{,}187 = 3^n$
30. a. $6{,}075 = 4{,}150(1.03)^n$
    b. $4{,}815 = (1.04)^n + 900$
    c. $15{,}625 = 5^n$
31. a. $n = \frac{\ln\left(\frac{2{,}775}{1{,}200}\right)}{\ln(1.03)}$
    b. $n = \frac{\ln(3)}{\ln(1.02)}$
    c. $n = \frac{\ln(500)}{\ln(2)}$
32. a. $n = \frac{\ln\left(\frac{4{,}950}{1{,}250}\right)}{\ln(1.005)}$
    b. $n = \frac{\ln(1{,}200)}{\ln(5)}$
    c. $n = \frac{\ln\left(\frac{4{,}235}{1{,}615}\right)}{\ln(1.048)}$

33. A sphere has a surface area of 450 cm^2.
    a. Find its radius to 2 decimal places.
    b. Find its volume to the nearest cm^3.
34. A cylinder with a height of 15 cm has a volume of 3,000 cm^3.
    a. Find its base radius to 2 decimal places.
    b. Find its surface area to the nearest cm^2.
35. Rearrange the formula $V = \frac{1}{3}\pi r^2 h$ to isolate the variable 'h'. Find 'h', when $r = 11$ cm and $V = 4{,}560$ cm^3. Round your answer to 2 decimal places.
36. Rearrange the formula $V = \frac{1}{3}\pi r^2 h$ to isolate the variable 'r'. Find 'r', when $V = 2{,}280$ cm^3 and $h = 15$ cm. Round your answer to 2 decimal places.

7 | Self-Test Exercises

Answers to all problems are available online.

Simplify the following expressions then evaluate:

1. a. $2x^2 + 5x + 1 - 4 - 3x - x^2$, where $x = 2$

   b. $-3x^2 + 2x + 2x^2 - 8x + 10$. where $x = -3$

2. a. $9x^2 - 4xy + y^2 - 6y^2 - 3xy + 10x^2$, where $x = 1$ and $y = 2$

   b. $5(2x - 3y) - 2(3x - 2y) + 7$, where $x = 2$ and $y = 1$

Factor the following expressions then evaluate:

3. a. $18y^2 - 12y$ $\quad y = -2$

   b. $15y^3 + 12y^2 + 3y$ $\quad y = 1$

4. a. $14xy - 21x^2$ $\quad x = 2$ and $y = 1$

   b. $8xy^2 - 6x^2y$ $\quad x = 1$ and $y = -1$

Write the following in algebraic expressions:

5. a. Twenty-five less than three times a number.

   b. A number increased by eighteen.

6. a. The difference between twice a number and six.

   b. A number divided by three..

Write the following as algebraic equations and solve:

7. a. Nine less than twice a number is twenty-one.

   b. Twenty-two is five times a number decreased by 3.

8. a. Four times eight is sixteen times a number.

   b. Thirty is a product of six and a number.

Solve for the unknown variable x, using principles of equations:

9. a. $24 - 5x = 4$

   b. $\frac{x}{3} - 2 = 4$

10. a. $8 + 2x = 4 - 5x$

    b. $3(3x - 3) = 33$

Simplify, evaluate, and express your answer with a positive exponent:

11. a. $(-2)^3(-2)^4$

    b. $(-5)^3 + 2^2$

    c. $\frac{(-10)^5}{(-10)^2}$

12. a. $(216)^{\frac{1}{3}}$

    b. $\frac{5^3 \times 5^4}{5^2}$

    c. $\sqrt[3]{27}$

Simplify the expression and express your answer with a positive exponent:

13. a. $(3x^3)^2$

    b. $(4x^2y^3)^2$

    c. $(16x^0y^4)^{\frac{1}{2}}$

14. a. $\left(\frac{x^6}{x^2}\right)^{-\frac{1}{2}}$

    b. $(x^{-3}y)^2$

    c. $\frac{x^{-7}x^{-3}}{x^{-10}}$

Solve for 'n' and express the answer to 2 decimal places:

15. a. $n = \frac{\ln\left(\frac{2,200}{1,200}\right)}{\ln(1.04)}$

    b. $n = \frac{\ln(1,475)}{\ln(10)}$

    c. $n = \frac{\ln(5,000)}{\ln(3)}$

16. a. $460 = 240(1.05)^n$

    b. $750 = (1.05)^n + 600$

    c. $1,296 = 6^n$

17. In the formula $f = (1 + i)^{m} - 1$, solve for 'f' when,

    a. $i = \frac{0.05}{12}$ and $m = 2$

    b. $i = 0.005$ and $m = 2$

18. In the formula $S = P(1 + rt)$,

    a. Isolate 't'

    b. Find the value of 't' when, $S = \$1{,}200$, $P = \$1{,}000$, and $r = 0.10$

Chapter 8
Graphs of Linear Equations

Learning Outcomes

- Identify the basic terminology of rectangular coordinate systems.
- Express linear equations in standard form and slope-intecept form.
- Determine the slope and y-intercept of a line from its equation.
- Construct a table of values for a linear equation.
- Graph a linear equation using the table of values, slope-intercept, and x- and y-intercepts.
- Determine the equation of a line from a graph.

Chapter Outline

8.1 Rectangular Coordinate System
8.2 Graphing Linear Equations

A linear graph is an illustrative way to express an equation with two variables. A linear equation describes a relationship in which the value of one of the variables depends on the value of the other variable. Therefore, the solutions are a set of ordered pairs replacing the respective variables in the equation. In this chapter, you will learn how to graph linear equations and how these graphs represent the solution to these equations.

8.1 | Rectangular Coordinate System

Introduction

Graphs provide information in a visual form and graphs are drawn on a rectangular coordinate system known as the Cartesian coordinate system (invented by René Descartes). Understanding the rectangular coordinate system is important in order to be able to read and draw graphs.

This system uses a horizontal and a vertical number line, each known as an axis. These two perpendicular axes cross at a perpendicular at the point (O), known as the origin.

The horizontal number line (moving to the left or the right) is called the X-axis and the vertical number line (moving up or down) is called the Y-axis, as illustrated in Exhibit 8.1-a.

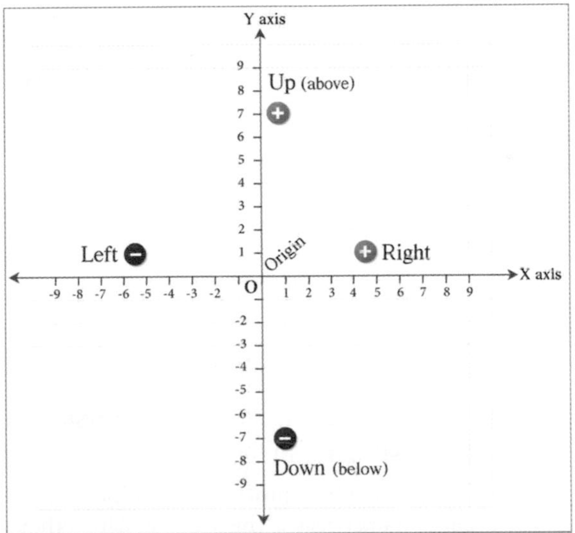

Exhibit 8.1-a Rectangular Coordinate System

Sign Convention

The numbers to the **right** of the origin along the X-axis are **positive** (+) and those to the left are **negative** (–). The numbers **above** the origin along the Y-axis are **positive** (+) and those below are **negative** (–).

The purpose of the rectangular coordinate system and the sign convention is to locate a point relative to the X- and Y-axes and in reference to the origin 'O'.

Each ordered pair, (x, y), represents only one point on the graph. The x and y values of the ordered pair determine the location of that point.

Ordered pairs are used to locate a point in the coordinate system. The ordered pair (x, y) describes a point in the plane by its x- and y-coordinates. Ordered pairs are usually written within brackets with x always first, followed by y, and separated by a comma. The origin is identified by the coordinates (0, 0) since both its x and y values are 0.

As illustrated in Exhibit 8.1-b, the coordinate of a point P written as an ordered pair (2, 3) refers to the point P which is 2 units to the right and 3 units above, in reference to the origin.

Note: The first value in the bracket gives the x-coordinate (horizontal distance from the Y-axis) and the second value in the bracket gives the y-coordinate (vertical distance from the X-axis) of the point; i.e., the x-coordinate of point P is 2 units and the y-coordinate of point P is 3 units, as illustrated in Exhibit 8.1-b.

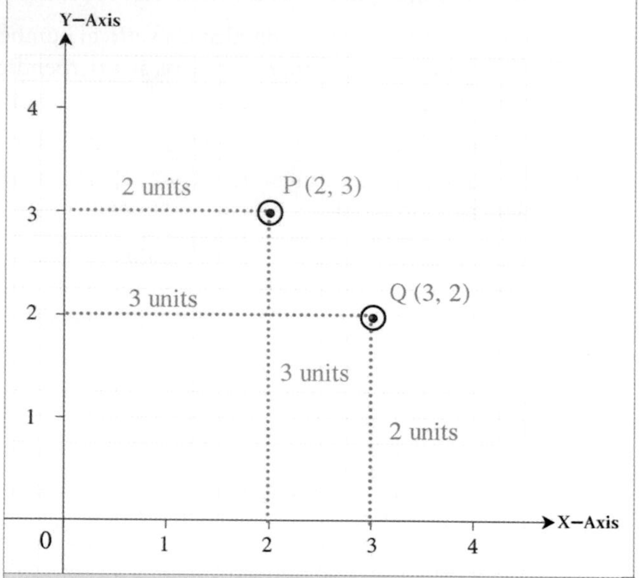

Exhibit 8.1-b Ordered Pairs

It is called a rectangular coordinate system because the x- and y-coordinates form a rectangle with the X- and Y- axes.

It is important to identify the coordinate numbers in their order. They are called ordered pairs because the order in which they appear determines their position on the graph. Changing their order will result in a different point.

Pay close attention to the order in which coordinate pairs are written.

For example,

(2, 3) and (3, 2) are different points.

(2, 3) refers to a point 'P', which is 2 units to the right of the origin and 3 units above the origin.

(3, 2) refers to a point 'Q', which is 3 units to the right of the origin and 2 units above the origin.

Quadrants

The X- and Y- axes divide the coordinate plane into 4 regions, called **quadrants**. Quadrants are numbered counter-clockwise from one (I) to four (IV), as illustrated in Exhibit 8.1-c.

That is, the upper right quadrant is Quadrant I, the upper left quadrant is Quadrant II, the lower left quadrant is Quadrant III, and the lower right quadrant is Quadrant IV. Table 8.1-a shows the sign convention of coordinates in each of the quadrants with examples that are plotted on the graph in Exhibit 8.1-d.

Table 8.1 **Sign Convention of Coordinates in Different Quadrants, Axes, and Origin**

Quadrant, Axis, Origin	Sign of x-coordinate	Sign of y-coordinate	Example as plotted in Exhibit 8.1-d
Quadrant I	Positive (+)	Positive (+)	A (3, 2)
Quadrant II	Negative (−)	Positive (+)	B (−3, 4)
Quadrant III	Negative (−)	Negative (−)	C (−5, −2)
Quadrant IV	Positive (+)	Negative (−)	D (5, −3)
X−Axis	Positive (+) or Negative (−)	Zero (0)	E (4,0), F (−2,0)
Y−Axis	Zero (0)	Positive (+) or Negative (−)	G (0,3) H (0,−4)
Origin	Zero (0)	Zero (0)	0 (0,0)

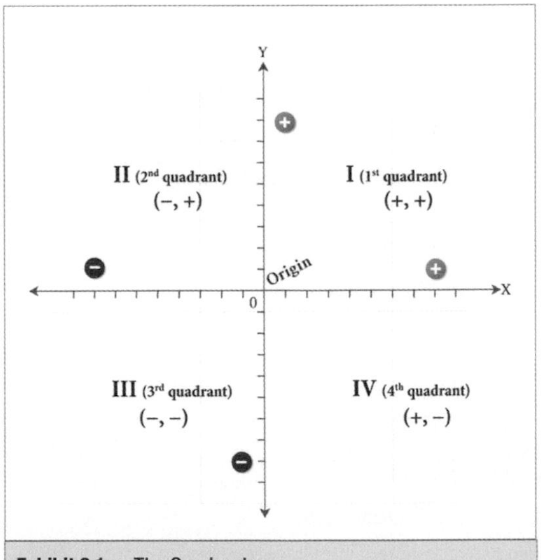

Exhibit 8.1-c The Quadrants

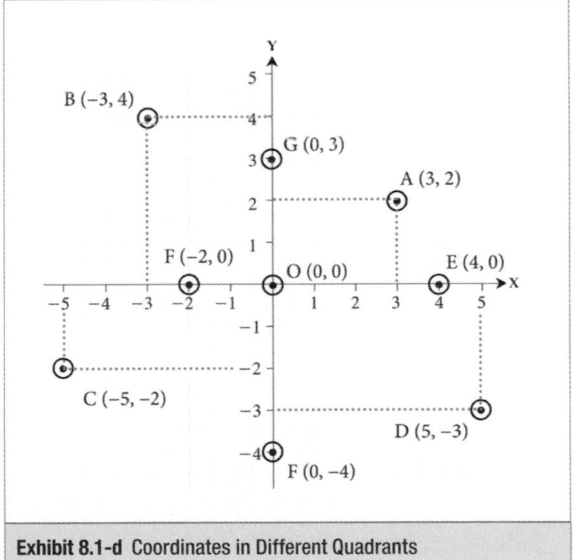

Exhibit 8.1-d Coordinates in Different Quadrants

Example 8.1-a

Identifying x- and y-Coordinates

Find the x- and y-coordinates of the points; A, B, C, D, E, F, G and H labelled in the graph.

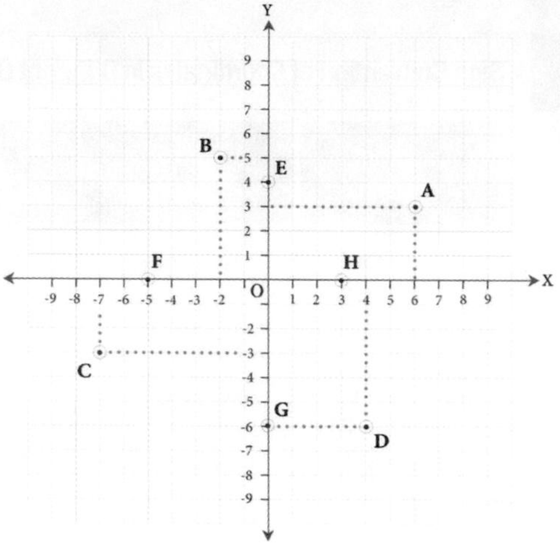

Solution

A: (6, 3)	B: (−2, 5)	C: (−7, −3)	D: (4, −6)
E: (0, 4)	F: (−5, 0)	G: (0, −6)	H: (3, 0)

Example 8.1-b

Identifying the Quadrant or the Axis

Identifying the quadrant or the axis in which the following points are located:

a. (−15, 20)	b. (20, 5)	c. (9, 0)	d. (0, 20)
e. (12, −18)	f. (0, −6)	g. (−30, −15)	h. (−1, 0)

Solution

a. (−15, 20) ⟶ (−, +) = 2nd Quadrant

b. (20, 5) ⟶ (+, +) = 1st Quadrant

c. (9, 0) ⟶ (+, 0) = X-Axis

d. (0, 20) ⟶ (0, +) = Y-Axis

e. (12, −18) ⟶ (+, −) = 4th Quadrant

f. (0, −6) ⟶ (0, −) = Y-Axis

g. (−30, −15) ⟶ (−, −) = 3rd Quadrant

h. (−1, 0) ⟶ (−, 0) = X-Axis

8.1 | Exercises

Answers to odd-numbered problems are available online.

Plot the following points on a graph:

1. a. A (−3, 5) b. B (5, −3) c. C (0, −4)
2. a. A (−6, 0) b. B (4, −2) c. C (0, −7)
3. a. D (6, 0) b. E (−2, 4) c. F (5, 2)
4. a. D (8, 0) b. E (−3, −5) c. F (5, 5)

In which quadrant or axis do the following points lie?

5. a. A (−1, 2) b. B (5, −1) c. C (3, 5)
6. a. A (1, 6) b. B (4, −3) c. C (−7, 3)
7. a. D (−4, 0) b. E (−2, −7) c. F (0, 5)
8. a. D (6, 0) b. E (−1, −13) c. F (0,−7)

Plot the following pairs of points on a graph and calculate the length of each horizontal line joining the pair of points:

9. a. (3, 4) and (5, 4) b. (−7, 1) and (2, 1)
10. a. (5, 6) and (5, 2) b. (7, 2) and (7, −4)
11. a. (−5, 3) and (0, 3) b. (−2, −2) and (6, −2)
12. a. (−3, 5) and (−3, −4) b. (−3, 5) and (−3, 0)
13. Three vertices of a square, ABCD, have points *A* (−3, 3), B (1, 3), and C (1, −1). Find the coordinates of the 4th vertex, D.
14. Three vertices of a rectangle, PQRS, have points P (−3, 4), Q (6, 4), and R (6, −1). Find the coordinates of the 4th vertex, S.
15. A vertical line has a length of 7 units and the coordinates of one end of the line is (1, 5). Find the possible coordinates of the other end of the line.
16. A horizontal line has a length of 6 units and the coordinates of one end of the line is (−1, 3). Find the possible coordinates of the other end of the line.

8.2 | Graphing Linear Equations

Introduction

A linear equation is an algebraic equation with one or two variables (each to the power of one), which produces a straight line when plotted on a graph.

Examples of linear equations with one variable are:

$3x - 5 = 0,$ $x - 3 = 0,$ $5y + 7 = 0,$ $y + 2 = 0$

Examples of linear equations with two variables are:

$2x - 3y + 3 = 0,$ $y = 2x + 3,$ $4y = 3x,$ $x + y = 0$

Linear equations with two variables are generally represented by variables x and y and expressed either in the form of $Ax + By = C$ (A, B, and C are integers) or in the form of $y = mx + b$ (m and b are integers or fractions).

The process of finding the value of the variables for which the equation(s) are true is called solving the equations.

Linear Equation in Standard Form

The 'standard' form for a linear equation in two variables, x and y, is usually written as $Ax + By = C$, where A, B *and* C are integers, A is positive, and A, B, and C, have no common factors other than 1.

For example, consider the following simple linear equation with two variables: $2x - y = -3$

This equation is in the form of $Ax + By = C$ and is called the equation in 'standard' form, where $A = 2$, $B = -1$, and $C = -3$.

- If a given equation has fractions, then multiply each term by the lowest common denominator (LCD) and rearrange to the standard form.
- If a given equation has decimals, then multiply each term by a multiple of 10 to eliminate the decimals and rearrange to the standard form.
- If a given equation has no fractions or decimals, then rearrange to the standard form.

Example 8.2-a

Writing Linear Equations in Standard Form

Write the following equations in standard form:

(i) $\frac{2}{3}x + \frac{1}{2}y - 3 = 0$ (ii) $0.3x = 1.25y + 2$

(iii) $5 - 2x - 3y = 0$

Solution

(i) $\frac{2}{3}x + \frac{1}{2}y - 3 = 0$ Multiplying by LCD, 6,

$4x + 3y - 18 = 0$ Rearranging,

$4x + 3y = 18$

Therefore, the equation $\frac{2}{3}x + \frac{1}{2}y - 3 = 0$, in standard form, is $4x + 3y = 18$.

(ii) $0.3x = 1.25y + 2$ Multiplying by 100,

Solution continued

$30x = 125y + 200$ Dividing by 5,

$6x = 25y + 40$ Rearranging,

$6x - 25y = 40$

Therefore, the equation $0.3x = 1.25y + 2$, in standard form, is $6x - 25y = 40$.

(iii) $5 - 2x - 3y = 0$ Rearranging,

$-2x - 3y = -5$ Multiplying by -1,

$2x + 3y = 5$

Therefore, the equation $5 - 2x - 3y = 0$, in standard form, is $2x + 3y = 5$.

Linear Equation in Slope-Intercept Form

The 'slope-intercept' form for a linear equation in two variables, x and y is written in the form of $\boldsymbol{y = mx + b}$, where $\boldsymbol{m}$ and $\boldsymbol{b}$ are usually either integers or a fractions. '$\boldsymbol{m}$' represents the slope and '$\boldsymbol{b}$' represents the y-intercept.

For example, consider a simple linear equation such as $y = 2x + 3$. This equation is in the form of $y = mx + b$ and is called the equation in 'slope-intercept' form, where the slope, $m = 2$, and the y-intercept, $b = 3$.

Example 8.2-b

Writing Linear Equations in Slope-Intercept Form

Write the following equations in slope-intercept form and identify the slope of the y-intercept.

(i) $4x + 3y = 18$ (ii) $6x = 25y + 40$

Solution

(i) $4x + 3y = 18$ Rearranging the term with y on the left,

$3y = -4x + 18$ Dividing by 3,

$y = -\frac{4}{3}x + 6$ This is of the form $y = mx + b$

Therefore, the slope is $-\frac{4}{3}$ and the y-intercept is 6.

(ii) $6x = 25y + 40$ Rearranging the term with y on the left,

$-25y = -6x + 40$ Multiplying by -1,

$25y = 6x - 40$ Dividing by 25 and simplifying,

$y = \frac{6}{25}x - \frac{8}{5}$ This is of the form $y = mx + b$.

Therefore, the slope is $\frac{6}{25}$ and the y-intercept is $-\frac{8}{5}$.

It is not possible to solve equations that are either in standard form or in slope-intercept form because they have two variables, x and y. However, it is possible to solve for a set of values by replacing one variable (either x or y) with any number and then solving for the value of the other variable. Therefore, if an equation has two variables, then the solution is a pair of values.

Consider the equation:

$y = 2x + 3$ Substituting for $x = 1$ in the equation,

$y = 2(1) + 3 = 5$

Therefore, $x = 1$ and $y = 5$ is one of the solutions of the equation; i.e., (1, 5) is a point on the line that represents the equation.

Similarly, we can obtain any number of points on the line by using different values for x.

$y = 2x + 3$ Substituting for $x = 2$ in the equation,

$y = 2(2) + 3 = 7$

Therefore, $x = 2$ and $y = 7$ is another solution to the equation; i.e., (2, 7) is another point on the line.

Graphing a linear equation means representing the solution of the equation on a graph. Conversely, any point on the line is a solution to the linear equation.

Drawing a linear graph requires only two points. However, at least 3 points will ensure that the formed line truly represents the given linear equation.

Graphing Linear Equations Using a Table of Values

Steps in graphing a linear equation using a table of values:

1. Create a table of values by choosing a value for the variable x.
2. Compute the corresponding value for the variable y.
3. Form the ordered pair (x, y).
4. Repeat steps one to three 2 more times to create 3 ordered pairs.
5. Plot the ordered pairs (points) on the coordinate system, choosing a scale.
6. Join the points in a straight line.
7. Label the graph with the equation of the line.

Let us consider a linear equation, $y = 2x + 3$. Find 4 ordered pairs that are on this line by choosing values for x and finding the corresponding values for y, then draw the graph.

Choose, $x = 3$,

$$\begin{aligned} y &= 2x + 3 \\ &= 2(3) + 3 \\ &= 6 + 3 = 9 \end{aligned}$$

(3, 9) is a point on the line.

Choose, $x = 2$,

$$\begin{aligned} y &= 2x + 3 \\ &= 2(2) + 3 \\ &= 4 + 3 = 7 \end{aligned}$$

(2, 7) is a point on the line.

Choose, $x = 1$,

$$\begin{aligned} y &= 2x + 3 \\ &= 2(1) + 3 \\ &= 2 + 3 = 5 \end{aligned}$$

(1, 5) is a point on the line.

Choose, $x = 0$,

$$\begin{aligned} y &= 2x + 3 \\ &= 2(0) + 3 \\ &= 0 + 3 = 3 \end{aligned}$$

(0, 3) is a point on the line.

$y = 2x + 3$		
x	y	(x, y)
3	9	(3, 9)
2	7	(2, 7)
1	5	(1, 5)
0	3	(0, 3)

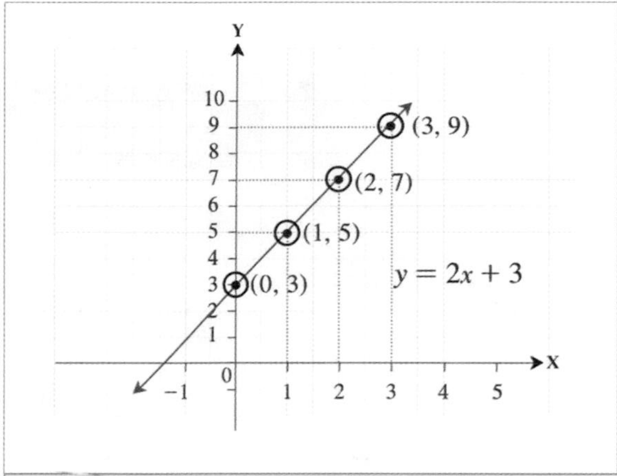

Exhibit 8.2-a Graphing a Linear Equation Using a Table of Values

Graphing Linear Equations Using the x-intercept and the y-intercept

We may use the x-intercept and y -intercept as two points to draw a linear graph and use a 3rd point to test the drawn line.

Let us consider a linear equation, $y = 3x + 9$. Find the x-intercept, y-intercept, one ordered pair, and draw the graph.

x-intercept: it is the point at which the line crosses the X-axis and where the y-coordinate is zero.

Substituting $y = 0$ in the above equation and solving for x,

$0 = 3x + 9$, thus, $x = -3$.

Therefore, $(-3, 0)$ is the x-intercept.

y-intercept: it is the point at which the line crosses the Y-axis

and where the x-coordinate is zero.

Substituting $x = 0$ in the above equation and solving for y,

$y = 3(0) + 9$, thus, $y = 9$.

Therefore, (0, 9) is the y-intercept.

Let us find one ordered pair on this line.

Let $x = -1$.

Substituting this in the equation,

$y = 3(-1) + 9 = 6$

Since the point $(-1, 6)$ falls on the line when plotted on the graph, it verifies that the plotted line represents the equation.

$y = 3x + 9$		
x	y	(x, y)
-3	0	$(-3, 0)$
0	9	$(0, 9)$
−1	6	$(-1, 6)$

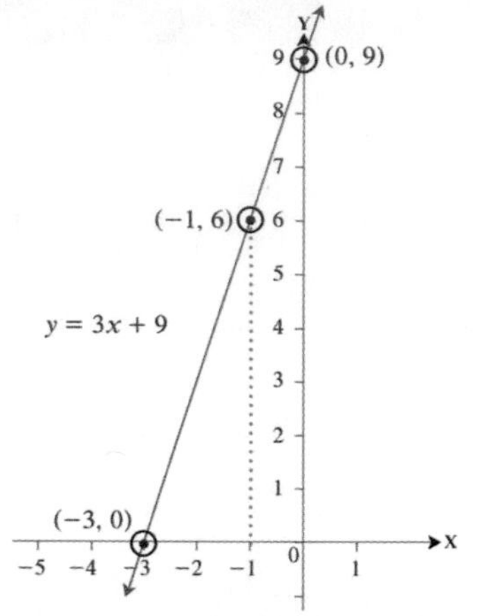

Exhibit 8.2-b Graphing a Linear Equation Using the x-intercept and the y-intercept

Graphing Linear Equations Using the Slope and the y-intercept

We know a linear equation in the form of $y = mx + b$ is known as the equation in slope-intercept form, where 'm' is the slope and 'b' is the y-intercept.

If the equation is in the standard form $Ax + By + = C$, it can be rearranged to represent the slope-intercept form, as follows:

$$Ax + By = C$$

$$By = -Ax + C$$

$$y = -\frac{A}{B}x + \frac{C}{B}$$

This is of the form $y = mx + b$.
Where slope, $m = -\frac{A}{B}$ and the y-intercept, $b = \frac{C}{B}$.

The Slope and y-intercept of a Line

The slope (m) is the steepness of the line relative to the X-axis. It is the ratio of the change in value of y (called 'rise') to the corresponding change in value of x (called 'run').

If $P(x_1, y_1)$ and $Q(x_2, y_2)$ are two different points on a line, then the slope of the line between the points PQ is given by,

$$m = \frac{\text{Change in } y \text{ value}}{\text{Change in } x \text{ value}} = \frac{\Delta y}{\Delta x} = \frac{\text{Rise}}{\text{Run}} = \frac{y_2 - y_1}{x_2 - x_1}$$

This is illustrated in Exhibit 8.2-c and Exhibit 8.2-d:

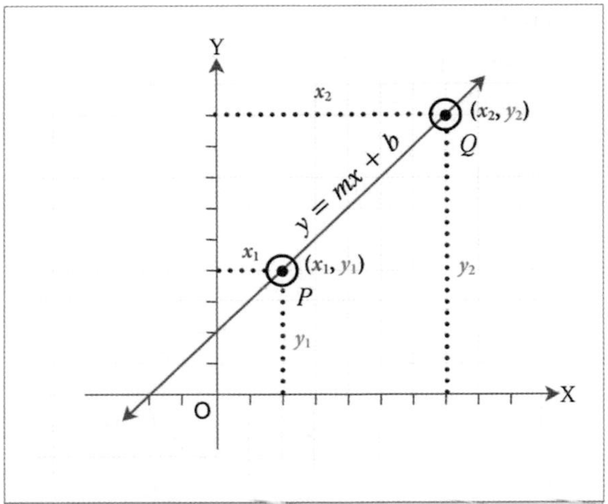

Exhibit 8.2-c Coordinates of Points P and Q

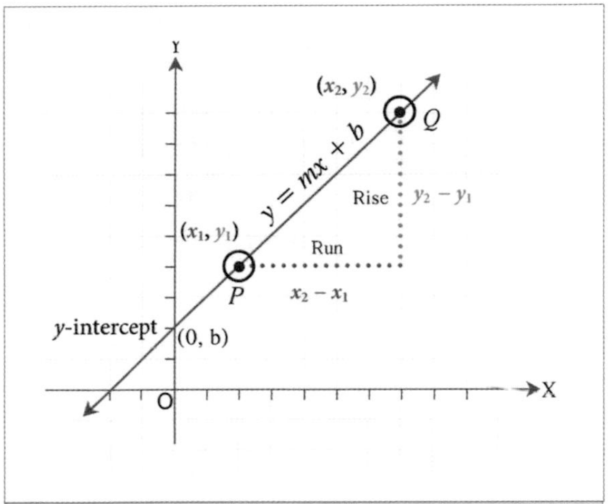

Exhibit 8.2-d Rise and Run Between Points P and Q

Example 8.2-c **Finding the Slope and y-intercept of an Equation and Graphing the Equation**

Find the slope and y-intercept of the linear equation $-2x + 3y - 12 = 0$ and graph the equation.

Solution

Rearranging, $-2x + 3y - 12 = 0$

$3y = 2x + 12$

Therefore, $y = \frac{2}{3}x + 4$

This is in the form, $y = mx + b$,

Where, the y-intercept, $b = 4$, and the slope $m = \frac{2}{3}$.

Therefore, (0, 4) is a point on the line and

Slope, $m = \frac{\text{Change in } y \text{ value}}{\text{Change in } x \text{ value}} = \frac{\text{Rise}}{\text{Run}} = \frac{2}{3}$

Solution *continued*

Representing this on a graph:

(i) First plot the y-intercept (0, 4).

(ii) From this point, move 3 units to the right and then move 2 units up to locate the new point (3, 6). This is the same as moving 2 units up, then 3 units to the right to locate the new point (3, 6).

(iii) Similarly, from the point (3, 6) move 3 units to the right and 2 units up to locate another point (6, 8).

(iv) Draw the line through these points to graph the equation.

<u>**Or,**</u>

(i) From the y-intercept (0,4), move 3 units to the left and then move 2 units down to locate a point (−3, 2).

(ii) Similarly, by using the same order for both the rise and the run find another point, (−6, 0).

(iii) Draw the line through these points to graph the equation.

Note: *All the points will lie on the same line.*

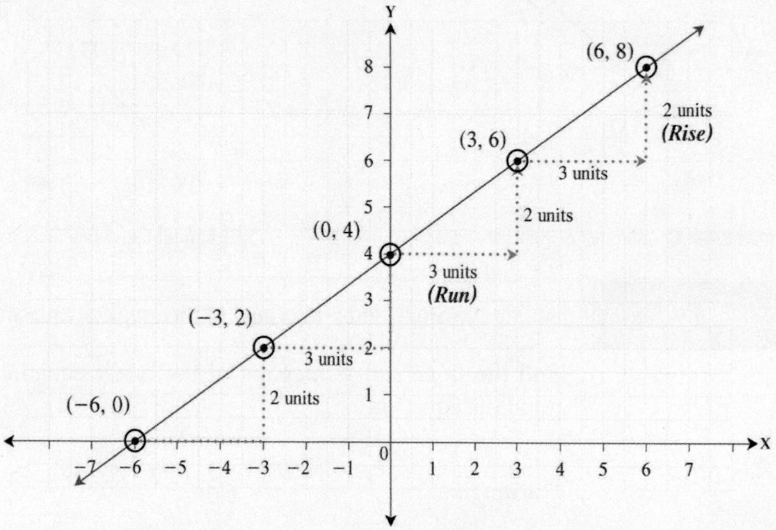

Example 8.2-d

Graphing a Linear Equation in the Slope-Intercept Form

Graph the equation $y = -\frac{3}{4}x - 2$.

Solution

The equation is in the form $y = mx + b$.

Therefore, the slope,

$$m = \frac{\text{Change in } y \text{ value}}{\text{Change in } x \text{ value}}$$

Solution
continued

$$m = \frac{\text{Rise}}{\text{Run}} = -\frac{3}{4}$$

$$m = \frac{-3}{4} \; or = \frac{3}{-4}$$

The y-intercept = – 2, which gives the point (0, – 2).

First plot the point (0, – 2). Then, using the slope, $m = \frac{-3}{4}$, from the point (0, – 2), move 4 units to the right and 3 units down to locate the new point, (4, – 5).

Alternatively, first plot the point (0, – 2). Then, using the slope, $m = \frac{3}{-4}$, from the point (0, – 2), move 4 units to the left and 3 units up to get another point on the line, (– 4, 1).

Draw a line through these points to graph the equation.

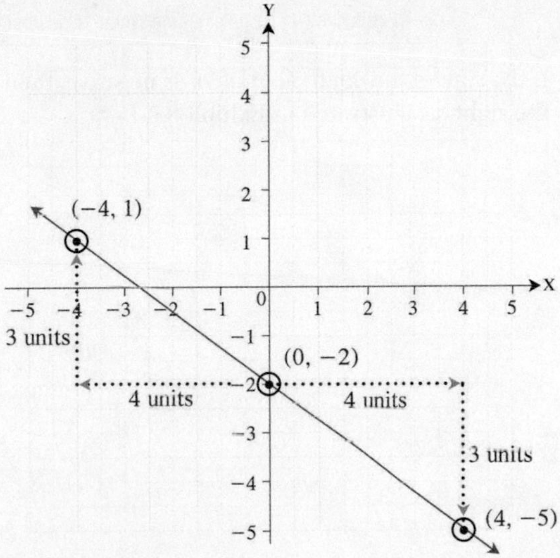

***Note**: The sign of the coefficient 'm' of the equation $y = mx + b$ indicates the direction of the line.*

If the sign of the coefficient *'m'* is positive, then the line slopes upwards to the right, as illustrated in Exhibit 8.2-e.

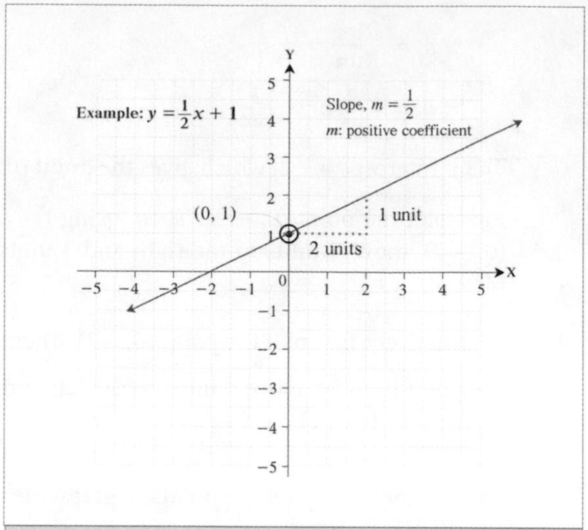

Exhibit 8.2-e Slope of a Line When 'm' is Positive

If the sign of the coefficient of *'m'* is negative, then the line slopes downwards to the right, as illustrated in Exhibit 8.2-f.

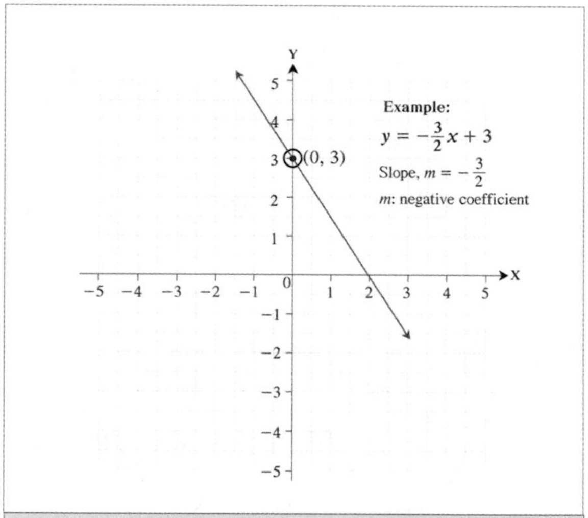

Exhibit 8.2-f Slope of a Line When 'm' is Negative

The slope of a line parallel to the X-axis is zero; i.e., if the slope of a line is zero, then the line is horizontal, as shown in Exhibit 8.2-g. For example, in the equation, $y = 3$, ($y = 0x + 3$), the slope is zero and the value of the y-coordinate is 3 for all values of x. Therefore, the line is horizontal and passes through (0, 3), as illustrated in Exhibit 8.2-g.

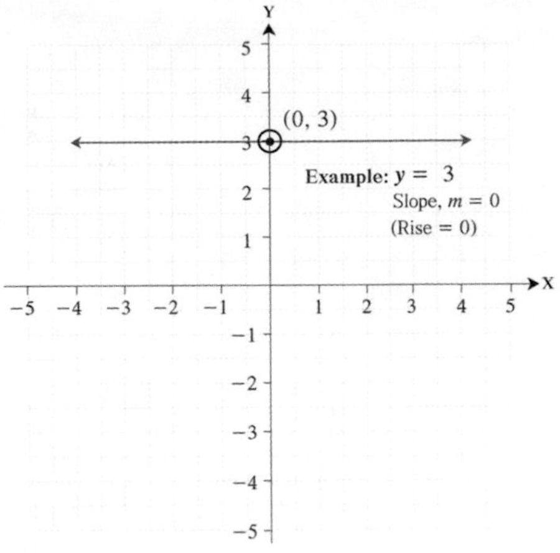

Exhibit 8.2-g Slope of a Line Parallel to the X-axis

The slope of a line parallel to the Y-axis is undefined; i.e., if the slope of a line is undefined, then the line is vertical, as shown in Exhibit 8.2-h. For example, in the equation, $x = 2$, the value of the x-coordinate is 2 for all values of y. Therefore, the line is vertical and passes through (2, 0), as illustrated in Exhibit 8.2-h.

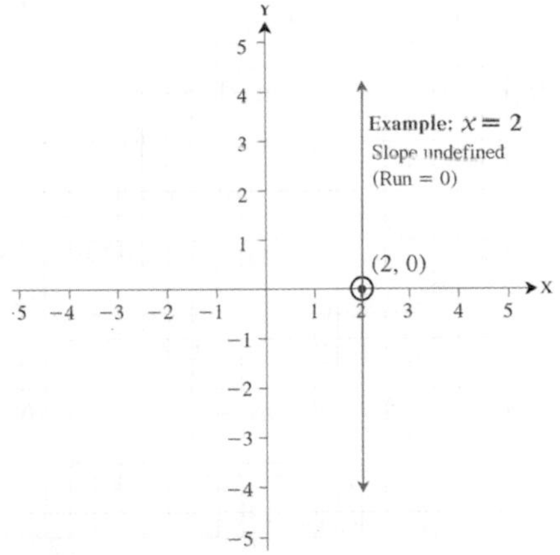

Exhibit 8.2-h Slope of a Line Parallel to the Y-axis

An equation with a y-intercept equal to 0 will have the graph passing through the origin.

For example, in the equation, $\boldsymbol{y = 2x}$,

Slope $(m) = 2 = \frac{2}{1}$, and y-intercept $= 0$.

Therefore, the line passes through (0, 0), as illustrated in Exhibit 8.2-i.

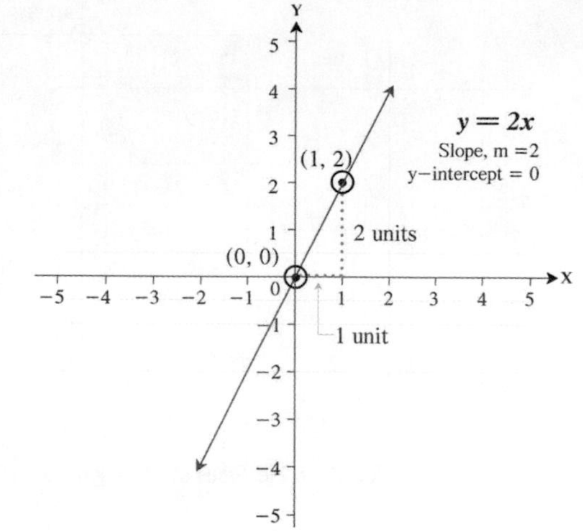

Exhibit 8.2-i Slope of a Line When the y-intercept is 0

Example 8.2-e **Finding the Slope and the Equation of a Line Given 2 Points**

Find the equation of a line that passes through points (3, 2) and (4, 5).

Solution

Step 1: Calculate the slope.

$$m = \frac{\text{Change in } y \text{ value}}{\text{Change in } x \text{ value}} = \frac{y_2 - y_1}{x_2 - x_1} = \frac{5 - 2}{4 - 3} = \frac{3}{1}$$

Step 2: Replace m with the calculated slope.

Substituting for m in the slope-intercept equation $y = mx + b$, we obtain $y = 3x + b$.

Step 3: Substitute one ordered pair into the equation to solve for b.

Substituting the coordinate (3, 2) into the above equation to solve for b,

$2 = 3(3) + b$,

$b = -7$

Step 4: Write the equation $y = mx + b$, substituting for the values of m and b, as calculated.

Therefore, the equation of the line is $y = 3x - 7$.

Example 8.2-f

Finding the Equation of a Line Given the Slope and One Point

Find the equation of a line having a slope of −2 and passing through (3, 5).

Solution

$m = -2$, point = (3, 5)

Substituting for m in the slope-intercept equation $y = mx + b$, we obtain,

$y = -2x + b.$

Substituting the coordinates of the given point (3, 5) in the above equation to solve for b,

$$5 = -2(3) + b,$$

$$b = 5 + 6 = 11$$

Therefore, the equation of the line is $y = -2x + 11$.

Example 8.2-g

Finding the Equation of a Line Given a Graph

Find the equation of the line that is plotted in the graph shown:

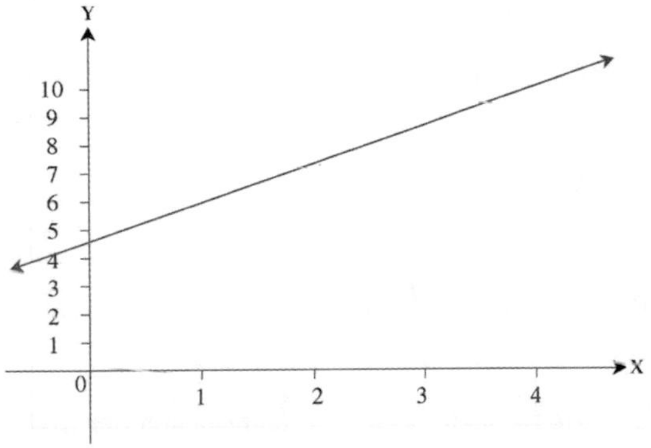

Solution

Start by choosing any 2 points (with integer coordinates) on the line: e.g., (1, 6) and (4, 10).

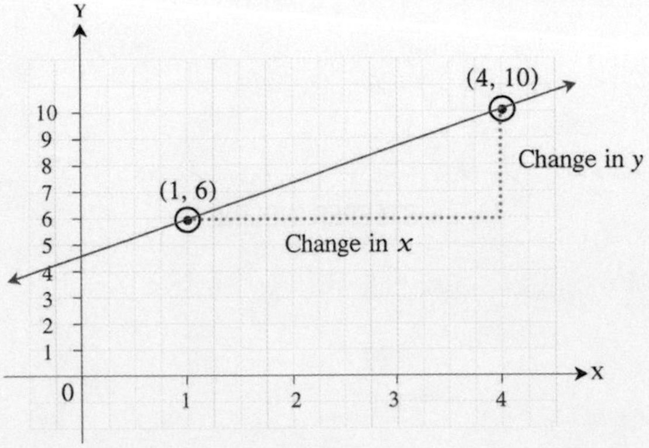

Solution
continued

The slope of the line is, $m = \dfrac{y_2 - y_1}{x_2 - x_1} = \dfrac{10 - 6}{4 - 1} = \dfrac{4}{3}$.

Let the equation of the line be $y = mx + b$ Substituting $m = \dfrac{4}{3}$

Therefore, $y = \dfrac{4}{3}x + b$

Substituting the coordinates of one of the points (1, 6) into the above equation,

$$y = \frac{4}{3}(x) + b$$

$$6 = \frac{4}{3}(1) + b$$

Solving for b,

$$b = 6 - \frac{4}{3}(1) = \frac{14}{3}$$

Therefore, the equation of the line is

$$y = \frac{4}{3}x + \frac{14}{3}$$

This is in the slope-intercept form.
Multiplying both sides by 3,

$$3y = 4x + 14.$$

Rearranging, $4x - 3y = -14$

Therefore, the equation of the line, in standard form, is $4x - 3y = -14$.

A higher value for a slope (m) indicates a steeper incline.

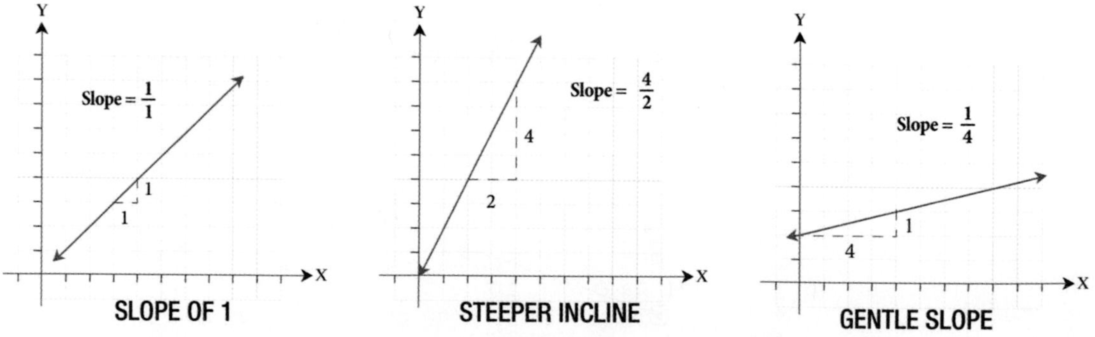

Parallel and Perpendicular Lines

Parallel Lines

Lines having the same slope are parallel to each other. All vertical lines are parallel to each other and all horizontal lines are parallel to each other.

(i) For example, lines represented by the equations $y = \frac{3}{2}x + 6$, $y = \frac{3}{2}x + 3$, and $y = \frac{3}{2}x - 6$ all have the same slope (equal to $\frac{3}{2}$). Therefore, they are parallel to each other.

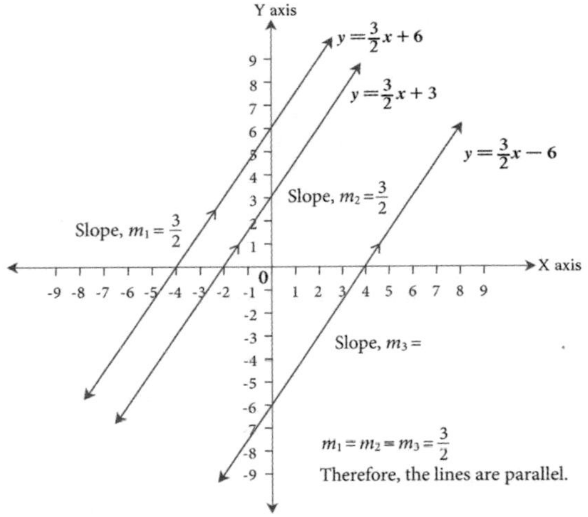

All points on a vertical line will have the same x-coordinate and the slope is undefined. The equation of a vertical line is of the form $x = k$, where k represents the x-coordinate of the line.

(ii) For example, lines represented by the equations $x = -4$, $x = 2$, and $x = 5$ are vertical lines and have undefined slopes. Therefore, they are parallel to each other. Vertical lines are parallel to the y-axis.

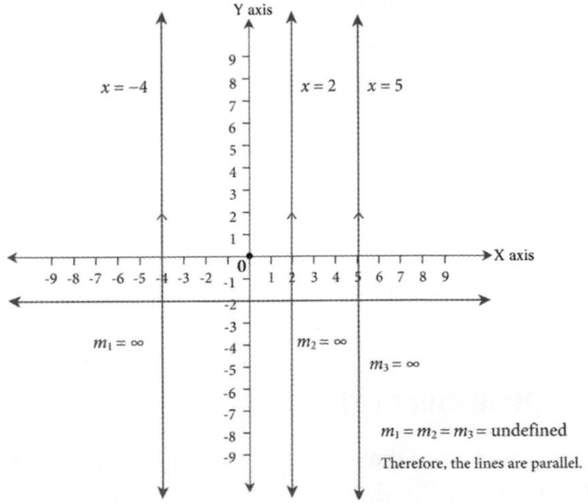

All points on a horizontal line will have the same y-coordinate - and the slope is zero. The equation of a horizontal line is of the form $y = b$, where b is the y- intercept of the line.

(iii) For example, lines represented by the equations $y = 4$, $y = 2$, and $y = -2$ are horizontal lines and have slopes equalling zero. Therefore, they are parallel to each other. Horizontal lines are parallel to the x-axis.

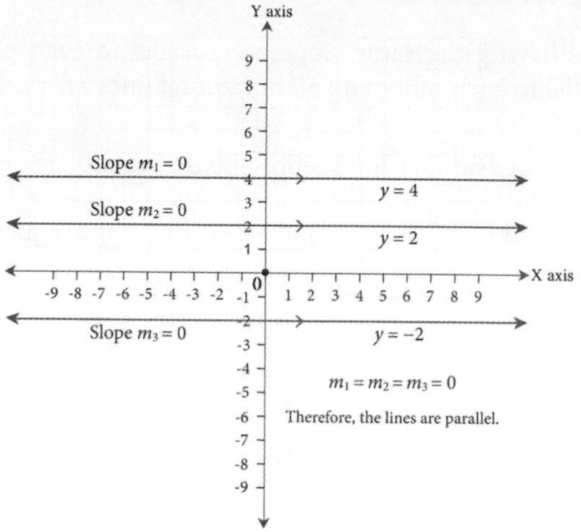

Example 8.2-h

Writing the Equation of a Line Parallel to a Given Line and Passing Through a Given Point

Write the equation of a line parallel to $3x + y = 5$ and that passes through the point P (2, 4).

Solution

$3x + y = 5$ Rearranging to slope-intercept form,

$y = -3x + 5$ Therefore, the slope, $m = -3$.

The slope of the line parallel to this will have the same slope, $m = -3$.

Let the equation of the line parallel to $3x + y = 5$ be $y = mx + b$. It passes through (2, 4) and has a slope, $m = -3$.

Substituting the values,

$$y = mx + b$$
$$4 = -3(2) + b$$
$$4 = -6 + b$$
$$b = 10$$

Therefore, the equation of the line that is parallel to $3x + y = 5$ and that passes through the point P(2, 4) is $y = -3x + 10$.

Two lines are perpendicular if the product of their slopes is -1. The lines are also perpendicular if one of them is vertical and the other is horizontal.

Perpendicular Lines

If the product of the slopes of two lines is -1, then the two lines are perpendicular to each other. This is the same as stating that if the slope of one line is the negative reciprocal of the other, then the two lines are perpendicular to each other.

For example, lines represented by $y = 2x + 4$ and $y = -\frac{1}{2}x + 1$ are perpendicular to each other because their slopes are negative reciprocals of each other. $m_1 = 2, m_2 = -\frac{1}{2}$.

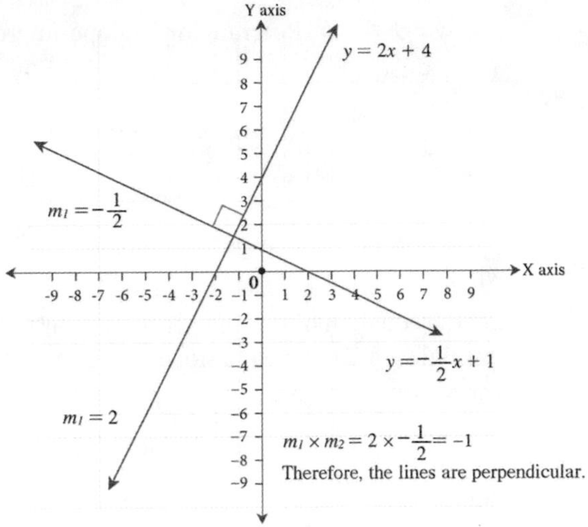

Also, all vertical lines (slope = undefined) and horizontal lines (slope = zero) are perpendicular to each other. For example, lines represented by $y = 2$ and $x = 4$ are perpendicular to each other.

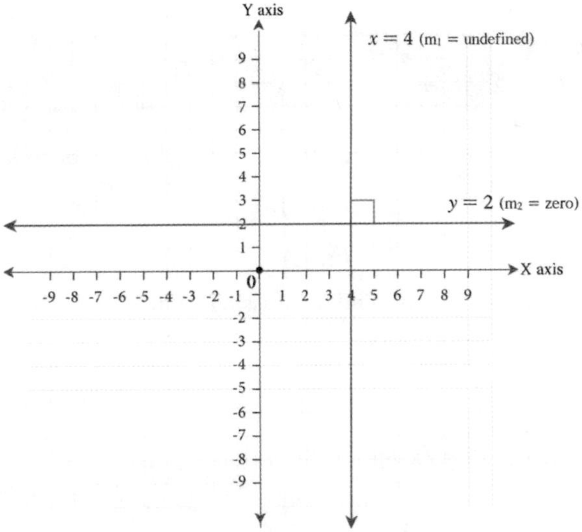

Example 8.2-i **Writing the Equation of a Line Perpendicular to a Given Line and Passing Through a Given Point**

Write the equation of the line perpendicular to $x + 3y = 9$ that passes through the point $(-4, 2)$.

Solution

$x + 3y = 9$ Rearranging to slope-intercept form,

$3y = -x + 9$

$y = \frac{-1}{3}x + 3$ Therefore, the slope, $m = -\frac{1}{3}$.

The slope of the line perpendicular to this will be the negative reciprocal, which is 3.

Let the equation of the line perpendicular to $x + 3y = 9$ be $y = mx + b$. It passes through $(-4, 2)$ and has a slope, $m = 3$.

Substituting the values,

$$y = mx + b$$

$$2 = 3(-4) + b$$

$$2 = -12 + b$$

$$b = 14$$

Therefore, the equation of the line that is perpendicular to $x + 3y = 9$ and that passes through the point $P(-4, 2)$, is $y = 3x + 14$.

8.2 | Exercises

Answers to odd-numbered problems are available online.

1. For the equation $2x + 3y = 18$, find the missing values in the following ordered pairs:

   a. (3, ?) b. (−6, ?) c. (0, ?)

   d. (?, 0) e. (?,−4) f. (?, 2)

2. For the equation $x + 5y = 20$, find the missing values in the following ordered pairs:

   a. (0, ?) b (−15, ?) c. (5, ?)

   d. (?, 6) e. (?,−3) f. (?, 0)

Graph the following equations using a table of values:

3. $y = x + 3$
4. $y = 3x + 2$
5. $y = -5x + 1$
6. $y = -2x + 3$
7. $2x + y + 1 = 0$
8. $4x + y + 2 = 0$
9. $2x - y - 3 = 0$
10. $x - y - 1 = 0$

Find the x-intercepts and y-intercepts for the following equations:

11. $3x + y = -2$
12. $5x + y = -3$
13. $x + y - 3 = 4$
14. $x + y - 4 = 7$
15. $y = 2x + 4$
16. $y = 4x + 1$
17. Point 'A' is in the 3rd quadrant and Point 'B' is in the 1st quadrant.Find the sign of the slope of the line AB.
18. Point 'C' is in the 4th quadrant and Point 'D' is in the 2nd quadrant. Find the sign of the slope of the line CD.

Find the slopes and y-intercepts of the following equations and graph the equations:

19. $2x - 3y - 18 = 0$
20. $5x - 2y + 10 = 0$
21. $-4x + 7y - 21 = 0$
22. $-7x + 8y - 32 = 0$

Find the equations of the lines that pass through the following points:

23. (1, 2) and (5, 2)
24. (5, 0) and (4, 5)
25. (−3, −5) and (3, 1)
26. (−4, −7) and (5, 2)

Find the equations of the lines that have:

27. Slope = 1 and passing through (2, 6).
28. Slope = −5 and passing through (3, −2).
29. Slope = 2 and passing through the origin.
30. Slope = 4 and passing through the origin.
31. x-intercept = 4 and y-intercept = −5.
32. x-intercept = −3 and y-intercept = 3.

Find the slopes of the lines passing through:

33. (2, 1) and (6, 1)
34. (−6, 4) and (2, 4)
35. (−5, 4) and (3, −1)
36. (5, 6) and (5, −4)
37. The slope of a line is 3. The line passes through A (4, y) and B (6, 8). Find y.
38. The slope of a line is 2. The line passes through A (x, 8) and B (2, 4). Find x.
39. Points A (2, 3), B (6, 5), and C (10, y) are on a line. Find y.
40. Points D (3, 2), E (6, 5), and F (x, 1) are on a line. Find x.

41. Find the equation of the line (in standard form) for the graph shown below:

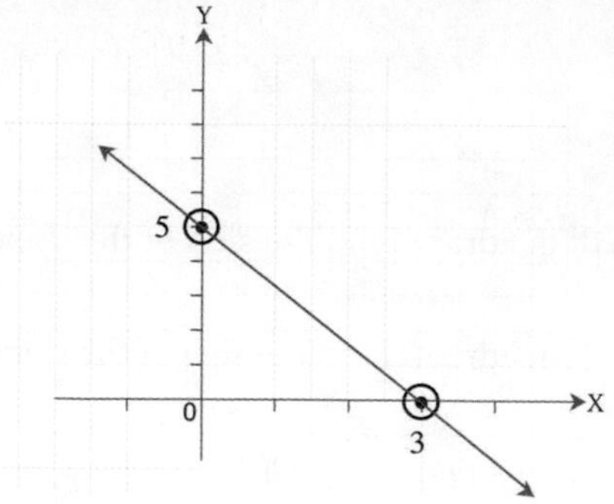

42. Find the equation of the line (in standard form) for the graph shown below:

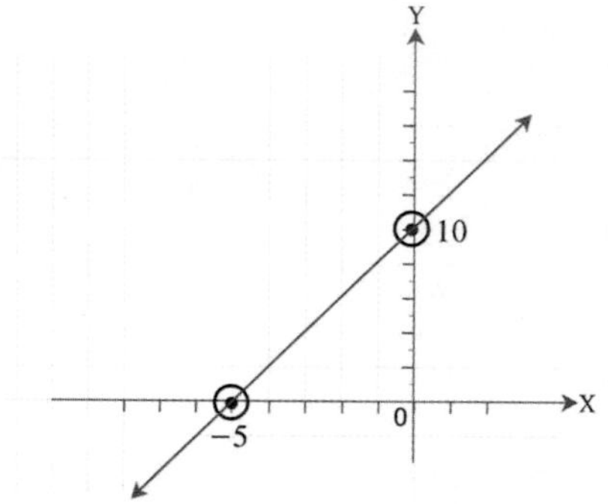

Determine the equations for the following lines:

43. A line parallel to $3y - 2x = 6$ and passing through the point P(2, −3).
44. A line parallel to $y = 3x - 1$ and passing through the point P(−2, −4).
45. A line parallel to $3x - 9y = -2$ and passing through the y-intercept of the line $5x - y = 20$.
46. A line parallel to $3x + y = -2$ and passing through the x-intercept of the line $2x + 3y - 4 = 0$.
47. A line perpendicular to $x + y = 3$ and passing through the point P(−2, 5).
48. A line perpendicular to $4x + y + 1 = 0$ and passing through the point P(3, 4).
49. A line perpendicular to $2x - y = 5$ and passing through the x-intercept of the line $3x + 2y - 6 = 0$.
50. A line perpendicular to $3x + y + 9 = 0$ and passing through the y-intercept of the line $2x + 3y - 10 = 0$.

8 | Review Exercises

Answers to odd-numbered problems are available online.

1. In which quadrant or on which axis do the following points lie?

   a. A (5, –1) b. B (–2, 3)
   c. C (3, 0) d. D (4, –2)
   e. E (2, 0) f. F (0, 4)

2. In which quadrant or axis do the following points lie?

   a. A (4, –1) b. B (–5, 0)
   c. C (–2, –7) d. D (0, –3)
   e. E (6, 6) f. F (5, 4)

3. Plot the following points and join them in the order A, B, C, D. Identify the type of quadrilateral and find its area and perimeter.

   a. A (6, –3) b. B (6, –6)
   c. C (–2, –6) d. D (–2, –3)

4. Plot the following points and join them in the order P, Q, R, S. Identify the type of quadrilateral and find its area and perimeter.

   a. P (−2, 4) b. Q (−8, 4)
   c. R (−8, −2) d. S (−2, −2)

Graph the following equations using a table of values with four points:

5. $4x - y = 2$
6. $2x + 3y = 12$
7. $x + y - 4 = 0$
8. $x + 2y - 4 = 0$
9. $y = \frac{1}{2}x + 2$
10. $y = -\frac{1}{3}x - 2$

Graph the following equations using the x-intercept, y-intercept, and another point:

11. $3x - 4y = 12$
12. $x - 2y = -1$
13. $x - 2y - 6 = 0$
14. $3x + y - 4 = 0$
15. $y = 4x$
16. $x = 2y$

Graph the following equations using the slope and y-intercept method:

17. $y = 4x + 6$
18. $y = 5x + 4$
19. $3x + 2y - 12 = 0$
20. $2x + 3y + 6 = 0$
21. $y = -\frac{3}{4}x - 1$
22. $y = -\frac{1}{3}x - 1$

Find the equation of the line that passes through the following points:

23. (3, 2) and (7, 5)
24. (4, 6) and (2, 4)
25. (5, −4) and (−1, 4)
26. (0, −7) and (−6, −1)
27. (1, −2) and (4, 7)
28. (3, −4) and (−1, 4)
29. Write the equation of a line parallel to $3x - 4y = 12$ and that passes through the point P(−2, 3).
30. Write the equation of a line parallel to $2x - 3y = 9$ and that passes though the point P(2, −3).
31. Write the equation of a line perpendicular to $2y = x + 4$ and that passes through the point P(−2, 5).
32. Write the equation of a line perpendicular to $3x + 4y + 6 = 0$ and that passes through the point P(4, −1).

8 | Self-Test Exercises

Answers to all problems are available online.

1. Write the following equations in the form $Ax + By = C$:

   a. $y = \frac{2}{3}x - \frac{4}{2}$

   b. $6y - 2x + \frac{1}{4} = 0$

2. Three vertices of a rectangle ABCD have the points A $(-3, 4)$, B $(5, 4)$, and C $(5, -1)$. Find the coordinate of the 4th vertex and the area of the rectangle.

3. Find the slopes and y-intercepts of the following lines:

   a. $2x - 3y + 6 = 0$

   b. $3x + 4y - 5 = 0$

4. Find the equation of the line, in standard form, that passes through the points P $(-4, 5)$ and Q $(1, 1)$.

5. Graph the equation $2x - 3y = 9$ using a table of values with 4 points.

6. Use the slope of the lines to determine whether the pairs of lines are parallel:

   a. $3y = 6x - 9$ and $4x - 2y = -6$

   b. $3y + 4x = 0$ and $3x + 4y = 2$

7. Write the equation of a line, in standard form, that is parallel to $3x - 2y + 9 = 0$ and that passes through the point $(-6, -3)$.

   (Hint: Parallel lines will have the same slope.)

8. Graph the equation $3y + 4x = 0$ using the x-intercept, y-intercept, and another point on the line.

9. Given the following slopes (m) and y-intercepts (b), write the following equations in standard form:

   a. $m = -\frac{1}{2}, b = -4$

   b. $m = \frac{2}{3}, b = -2$

10. Graph the line that contains the points $(-3, 5)$ and that has a slope of $\frac{-3}{4}$.

11. Write the equation of a line parallel to $2x + 3y = 6$ and that passes through the point P$(-6, -1)$.

12. Write the equation of the line perpendicular to $5x - y = 4$ and that passes through the point P$(1, 2)$.

13. Write the equation of the line passing through the points P$(-3, 5)$ and Q$(5, -1)$.

14. Write the equation of the line that passes through the origin and that is perpendicular to the line passing through the points P$(-3, 5)$ and Q$(5, -1)$.

15. Write the equation of the line having an x-intercept equal to 5 and y-intercept equal to -3.

16. Write the equation of the line passing through the origin and parallel to $y = 5x - 1$.

Chapter 9
Systems of Linear Equations with Two Variables

Learning Outcomes

- Classify systems of linear equations.
- Solve linear systems graphically.
- Solve linear systems using the substitution method.
- Solve linear systems using the elimination method.
- Write and solve systems of equations to word problems.

Chapter Outline

Many word problems can be solved easily by translating them to systems of equations with two or more variables. A 'system' of equations is a set of equations considered together. 'Linear' equations produce straight lines when we graph them. The simplest linear system is one with two equations and two variables. A system of linear equations can be solved by several methods. In this chapter, you will learn to solve them by plotting the equations on the same graph or by using algebraic approaches, such as the substitution and elimination methods.

9.1 | Solving Systems of Linear Equations With Two Variables Graphically

Introduction

In Chapter 8, you learned that a linear equation with two variables produces a straight line when plotted on a graph. If the graph of an equation is linear, then all the points (**ordered pairs**) on the line are the solution to that linear equation. For example, $2x + y = 4$ is a linear equation with two variables, x and y. The graph of this equation is a line and all the points (ordered pairs) on this line are solutions to this equation as shown in the diagram below.

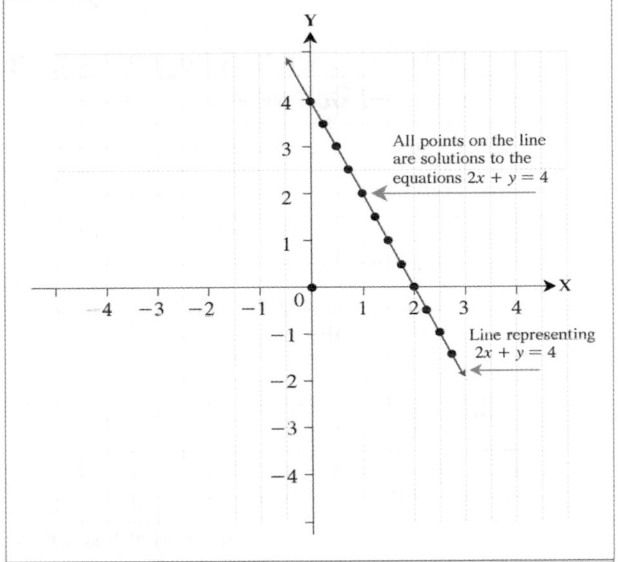

Exhibit 9.1-a Graph of $2x + y = 4$

System of Equations

Two or more equations analyzed together are called a system of equations. In this section, we will be analyzing two linear equations with two variables.

The solution to a system of two equations with two variables is an ordered pair of numbers (coordinates) that satisfy both equations.

If we graph a system of two linear equations, and if they intersect, then the point at which the two lines intersect will be the solution to both lines.

For example, $2x + y = 4$ and $x - 2y = -3$ form a system of two linear equations. The graphs of these equations intersect at (1, 2) as shown in the following diagram. This point (1, 2) is the solution to the system of two linear equations.

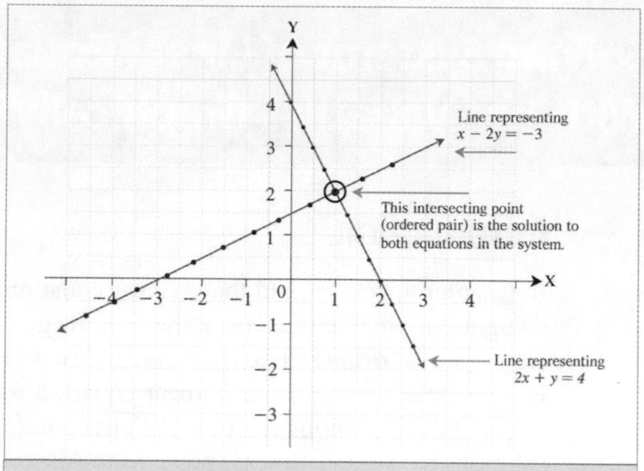

Exhibit 9.1-b Graph of 2x + y = 4 and x – 2y = -3

Graphs of Two Linear Equations May Intersect at One Point, Not Intersect, or Coincide

- **If they intersect (*lines are not parallel*)**, it indicates that there is only one solution.
- **If they do not intersect (*lines are parallel and distinct*)**, it indicates that there is no solution.
- **If they coincide (*lines are the same*)**, it indicates that there are an infinite number of solutions.

If the graphs of 2 linear equations intersect at one point or if the lines coincide (representing the same line) then they are "consistent" as a system. Otherwise, they are "inconsistent" as a system.

Consistent and Inconsistent Systems

A linear system of two equations that has **one or many solutions** is called a **consistent linear system.**

A linear system of two equations that has **no solution** is called an **inconsistent linear system.**

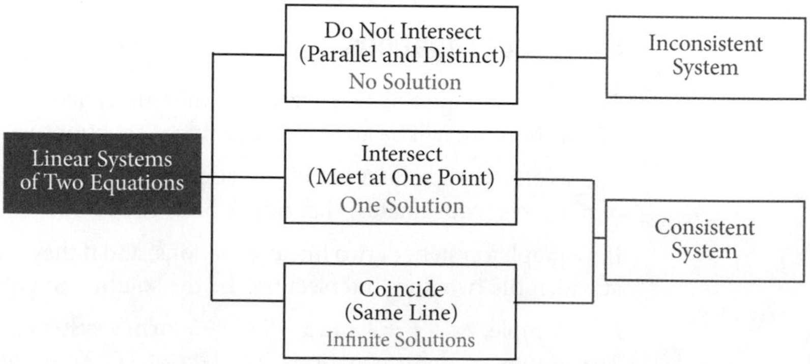

Dependent and Independent Equations

If a system of equations has an **infinite number of solutions** then the **equations are dependent**.

If a system of equations has **one or no solution,** then the **equations are independent**.

If the graphs of 2 linear equations coincide (represents the same line), then they are called a "dependent system of equations" otherwise they are called an "independent system of equations".

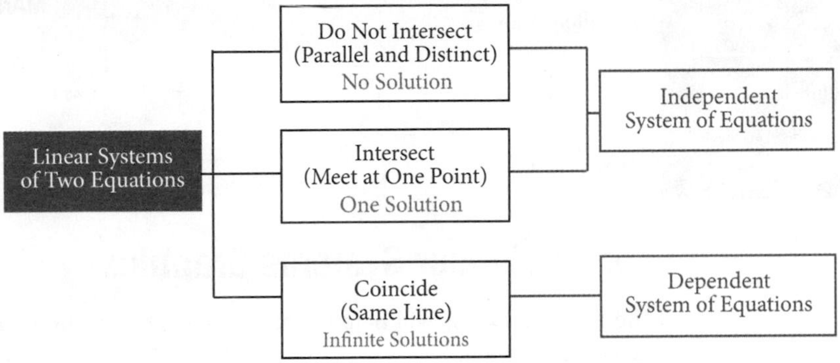

Intersecting Lines

Slopes of lines:	Different
y-intercepts:	May or may not be the same. *Will be different, unless the lines intersect on the Y-axis or at the origin.*
Number of solutions:	One
System:	Consistent
Equations:	Independent

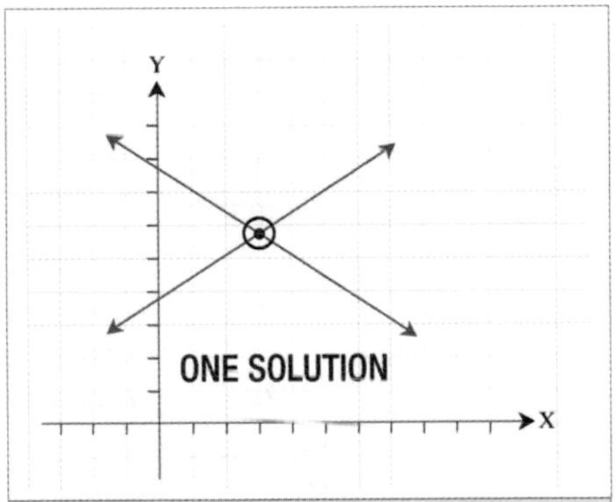

Exhibit 9.1-c Intersecting Lines

Parallel and Distinct Lines

Slopes of lines:	Same
y-intercepts:	Different
Number of solutions:	None
System:	Inconsistent
Equations:	Independent

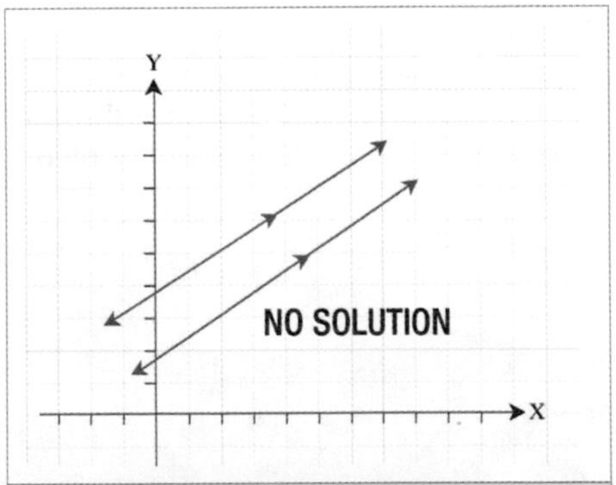

Exhibit 9.1-d Parallel and Distinct Lines

Coincident Lines

Slopes of lines:	Same
y-intercepts:	Same
Number of solutions:	Infinitely many
System:	Consistent
Equations:	Dependent

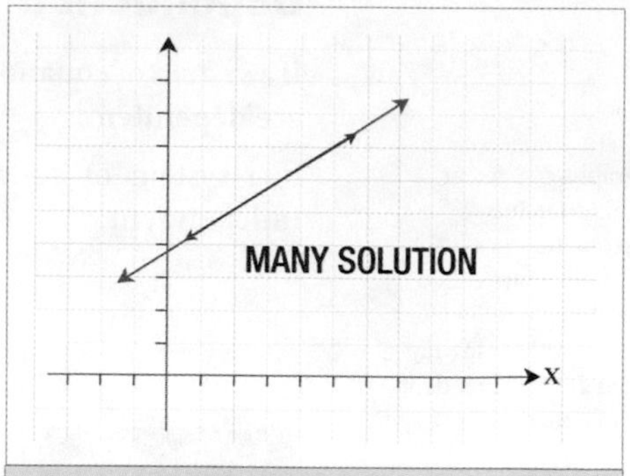

Exhibit 9.1-e Coincident Lines

Solving Linear Systems Graphically

The following steps will help to solve systems of two linear equations with two variables graphically:

Step 1: Rewrite both equations in the form of $y = mx + b$ (or $Ax + By = C$) and clear off any fractions or decimal numbers.

Step 2: Graph the first equation by either using the slope and y-intercept method (or using the x-intercept and y-intercept) or using a table of values. The graph will be a straight line.

Step 3: Graph the second equation on the same axes as in **Step 2**. It will be another straight line.

Step 4: If the two lines intersect at a point, then the point of intersection is the solution to the given system of equations, also known as an ordered pair (x, y).

Step 5: Check the solution obtained for the variables by substituting the values in each of the original equations. If the answer satisfies the equations, then it is the solution to the given systems of equations.

Note: In Step 2, the order in which the equations are graphed or the method used to graph the equations does not matter.

Example 9.1-a **Solving and Classifying Systems of Linear Equations**

Solve the following system of equations by graphing, and classify the system as consistent or inconsistent and the equations as dependent or independent.

$x - y + 1 = 0$

$x + y - 3 = 0$

Solution

Step 1:	$x - y + 1 = 0$	Writing the equation in $y = mx + b$ form,
	$y = x + 1$	Equation (i)
	$x + y - 3 = 0$	Writing the equation in $y = mx + b$ form,
	$y = -x + 3$	Equation (ii)

Solution
continued

Step 2: Equation (i): $y = x + 1$

$m = 1$ and $b = 1$

Therefore, the slope is $\frac{1}{1}$ and the y-intercept is (0, 1).

Step 3: Equation (ii): $y = -x + 3$

$m = -1$ and $b = 3$

Therefore, the slope is $\frac{-1}{1}$ and the y-intercept is (0, 3).

Graphing equations (i) and (ii) using the slope and y-intercept form:

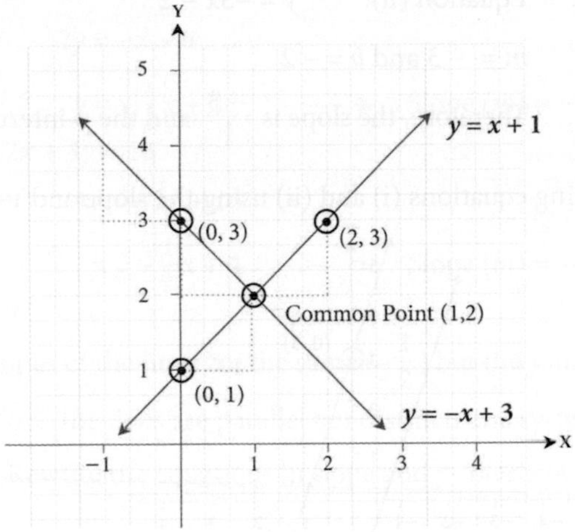

Step 4: The two lines intersect at the common point (1, 2).

Step 5: Check the solution (1, 2) in Equations (i) and (ii).

Equation (i), $y = x + 1$

$LS = y = 2$

$RS = x + 1 = 1 + 1 = 2$

Therefore, LS = RS

Equation (ii), $y = -x + 3$

$LS = y = 2$

$RS = -x + 3 = -1 + 3 = 2$

Therefore, LS = RS

Therefore, the solution is (1, 2). The system is consistent and the equations are independent.

Example 9.1-b

Classifying Systems of Linear Equations

Solve this system of equations by graphing, and classify the system as consistent or inconsistent and the equations as dependent or independent.

$3x + y - 3 = 0$

$3x + y + 2 = 0$

3. $y = -x + 2$

   $2y = -2x + 6$

4. $y = 2x + 6$

   $2y = -3x + 6$

5. $y = -4x + 7$

   $2y + 8x = 14$

6. $y = -2x + 3$

   $2y + 4x = 6$

7. $3x - y - 8 = 0$

   $6x - 2y - 1 = 0$

8. $y = 2x - 4$

   $3y = -2x + 4$

9. $y - x + 1 = 0$

   $y + 2x - 5 = 0$

10. $y = x - 2$

    $3y = -2x + 9$

11. $5x + y + 9 = 0$

    $x - 3y + 5 = 0$

12. $3x - 2y + 1 = 0$

    $y + 4x - 6 = 0$

13. $3x + 2y = -4$

    $y + \frac{3}{2}x + 2 = 0$

14. $2x - y = 6$

    $6x - 3y = 15$

15. $4x - 2y = 6$

    $-2y + 4x - 8 = 0$

16. $2y - x - 6 = 0$

    $y = \frac{1}{2}x + 3$

17. $x - y = 6$

    $2x + y = 3$

18. $4x - 8y = 0$

    $2x - 4y = -8$

19. $y + \frac{1}{2}x + 1 = 0$

    $4y - x - 4 = 0$

20. $y = x + 5$

    $x + 2y = 10$

For Problems 21 to 28, without graphing, determine whether each system has one solution, no solution, or many solutions.

21. $3x + 4y = 4$

    $2x + y = 6$

22. $3x - 2y = 6$

    $x + 2y = 6$

23. $x - y = 1$

    $2x + y = 5$

24. $x + y = 7$

    $2x - y = 8$

25. $3y - 2x = 1$

    $12y - 8x = -4$

26. $2x - y - 4 = 0$

    $6x - 3y + 12 = 0$

27. $2x = 3y - 1$

    $8x = 12y + 4$

28. $x + 2y = 5$

    $x + 4y = 9$

29. Find the value of 'A' for which the lines $Ax - 2y - 5 = 0$ and $8x - 4y + 3 = 0$ are parallel.
30. Find the value of 'B' for which the lines $3x + 2y + 8 = 0$ and $6x - By - 3 = 0$ are parallel.
31. Find the value of 'A' for which the lines $x + 3y + 1 = 0$ and $Ay + 2x + 2 = 0$ are coincident.
32. Find the value of 'B' for which the lines $y = Bx + 3$ and $x - 2y + 6 = 0$ are coincident.

9.2 | Solving Systems of Linear Equations With Two Variables Algebraically

Introduction

Solving systems of linear equations using algebraic methods is the most accurate for the following reasons:

1. It eliminates graphing errors.
2. It provides the exact answer for systems of equations that have fractions or that have fractional answers.

There are basically two methods involved in solving systems of linear equations. They are the **Substitution method** and the **Elimination method**.

Substitution Method

The substitution method is preferable if either one of the equations in the system has a variable with a coefficient of 1 or −1.

In this method, the following steps are used to solve systems of two linear equations with two variables:

Step 1: Rewrite both the equations in the form of $Ax + By = C$, where A, B, and C are integers.

Step 2: Choose the simplest equation from 'Step 1' and solve to find an expression for one variable in terms of the other variable.

Step 3: Substitute the expression for the variable from 'Step 2' into the other equation, the one not used in Step 2. This will result in an equation in one of the variables.

Step 4: Solve the equation in 'Step 3' for the one variable.

Step 5: Solve for the other variable using any one of the equations in 'Step 1' and by substituting the value of the known variable.

The answer for the two variables found in 'Step 4' and 'Step 5' will be the solution to the given system of equations.

Step 6: Check if the solution obtained for the variables is true by substituting these values in each of the original equations. If the solution satisfies the equations, then it is the solution to the given systems of equations.

Note: In 'Step 2', if possible, it is best to select the equation in which the coefficient on any one of the variables is equal to one, since this will make the calculations in 'Steps 3 and 4' easier.

Example 9.2-a **Solving a System of Equations by Substituting for the Variable 'y'**

Solve the system of equations given below:

$y - 3x + 2 = 0$

$3y + x - 14 = 0$

Solution

Step 1: Rewriting the equations in the form of $Ax + By = C$,

$$y - 3x + 2 = 0$$

$$y - 3x = -2 \quad \text{Equation (i)}$$

$$3y + x - 14 = 0$$

$$3y + x = 14 \quad \text{Equation (ii)}$$

Step 2: The coefficient of y in Equation (i) is one.

Equation (i), $y - 3x = -2$

$$y = 3x - 2$$

Step 3: Substituting $3x - 2$ for y in Equation (ii),

$$3y + x = 14$$

$$3(3x - 2) + x = 14$$

Step 4: Solving for 'x',

$$9x - 6 + x = 14$$

$$9x + x = 14 + 6$$

$$10x = 20$$

$$x = 2$$

Step 5: Substituting for $x = 2$ in Equation (i),

$$y - 3x = -2$$

$$y - 3(2) = -2$$

$$y - 6 = -2$$

$$y = 6 - 2$$

$$y = 4$$

Therefore, the solution is (2, 4).

Step 6: Checking the solution in Equations (i) and (ii),

Equation (i), $y - 3x = -2$

$$LS = y - 3x$$

$$LS = 4 - 3(2)$$

$$= -2$$

$$= RS \text{ (True)}$$

Therefore, LS = RS.

Equation (ii), $3y + x = 14$

$$LS = 3y + x$$

$$LS = 3(4) + 2$$

$$= 14$$

$$= RS \text{ (True)}$$

Therefore, LS = RS.

Example 9.2-b

Solving a System of Equations by Substituting for the Variable 'x'

Solve the system of equations given below:

$x + 2y = 6$

$4x + 3y = 4$

Solution

Step 1: The equations are in the form of $Ax + By = C$,

$x + 2y = 6$ Equation (i)

$4x + 3y = 4$ Equation (ii)

Step 2: The coefficient of x in Equation (i) is one.

$x + 2y = 6$

$x = 6 - 2y$

Step 3: Substituting $6 - 2y$ for x in Equation (ii),

$4x + 3y = 4$

Step 4: Solving for 'y',

$4(6 - 2y) + 3y = 4$

$24 - 8y + 3y = 4$

$5y = 20$

$y = 4$

Step 5: Substituting $y = 4$ in Equation (i),

$x + 2y = 6$

$x + 2(4) = 6$

$x = -2$

Therefore, the solution is $(-2, 4)$.

Step 6: Checking the solution in Equations (i) and (ii),

Equation (i),	Equation (ii),
$x + 2y = 6$	$4x + 3y = 4$
$LS = x + 2y$	$LS = 4x + 3y$
$LS = -2 + 2(4)$	$LS = 4(-2) + 3(4)$
$= -2 + 8$	$= -8 + 12$
$= 6$	$= 4$
$= RS$ (True)	$RS =$ (True)
Therefore, LS = RS.	Therefore, LS = RS.

Elimination Method

The elimination method is preferable if none of the equations in the system has a variable with a coefficient of 1 or −1.

In this method, the following steps are used to solve systems of two linear equations with two variables:

Step 1: Rewrite both equations in the form of $Ax + By = C$, where, A, B, and C are integers.

Step 2: Multiply one or both equations by a suitable integer so that it will create the same (or opposite) coefficient for any one of the variables in both equations.

The purpose is to eliminate one of the variables by subtracting (or adding) these two equations.

Step 3: Subtract (or add) the two equations from 'Step 2' to obtain one equation with only one variable.

Step 4: Solve the equation in 'Step 3' to find the one variable.

Step 5: Solve for the other variable using either one of the equations in 'Step 1' and by substituting the value of the known variable.

The answer for the two variables found in 'Step 4' and 'Step 5' will be the solution to the given system of equations.

Step 6: Check if the solution obtained for the variables is true by substituting these values in each of the original equations.

Note:

In 'Step 2' it does not matter which of the variables you choose to create the same (or opposite) coefficient in both equations.

In 'Step 3' you will **subtract** if both equations have the same coefficient for the variable to be eliminated. If the coefficients are opposite, then you will **add** to eliminate that variable.

Example 9.2-c

Solving a System of Equations by Eliminating the Variable 'x'

Solve the system of equations given below:

$2x + 3y = 13$

$-3x + 6y = 12$

Solution

Step 1: The equations are in the form of $Ax + By = C$,

$2x + 3y = 13$ Equation (i)

$-3x + 6y = 12$ Equation (ii)

Step 2: Choosing the variable to be eliminated; in this case, 'x'.

The variable 'x' in Equations (i) and (ii) has coefficients of 2 and −3, respectively.

Solution *continued*

Multiplying Equation (i) by 3, and multiplying Equation (ii) by 2,

$$3(2x + 3y) = 3(13) \qquad 2(-3x + 6y) = 2(12)$$

$$6x + 9y = 39 \qquad -6x + 12y = 24$$

$$6x + 9y = 39 \quad \text{Equation (iii)}$$

$$-6x + 12y = 24 \quad \text{Equation (iv)}$$

Step 3: Adding Equations (iii) and (iv),

$$(6x + 9y) + (-6x + 12y) = 39 + 24$$

Step 4: Solving for 'y',

$$6x - 6x + 9y + 12y = 63$$

$$21y = 63,$$

$$y = \frac{63}{21} = 3$$

Step 5: Substituting $y = 3$ in Equation (i) and solving for 'x',

$$2x + 3y = 13$$

$$2x + 3\,(3) = 13$$

$$2x = 13 - 9 = 4$$

$$x = 2$$

Therefore, the solution is (2, 3).

Step 6: Checking the solution in Equations (i) and (ii),

Equation (i),

$$2x + 3y = 13$$

$$\text{LS} = 2x + 3y$$

$$\text{LS} = 2(2) + 3(3)$$

$$= 4 + 9$$

$$= 13$$

$$= \text{RS (True)}$$

Therefore, LS = RS.

Equation (ii),

$$-3x + 6y = 12$$

$$\text{LS} = -3x + 6y$$

$$\text{LS} = -3(2) + 6(3)$$

$$= -6 + 18$$

$$= 12$$

$$= \text{RS (True)}$$

Therefore, LS = RS.

Example 9.2-d Solving a System of Equations by Eliminating the Variable 'y'

Solve the system of equations given below:

$3x + 2y = 8$

$8x + 5y = 18$

Solution

Step 1: The equations are in the form of $Ax + By = C$,

$3x + 2y = 8$ Equation (i)

$8x + 5y = 18$ Equation (ii)

Step 2: Choosing the variable to be eliminated; in this case, 'y',

The variable 'y' in Equations (i) and (ii) has coefficients of 2 and 5, respectively.

Multiplying Equation (i) by 5, and multiplying Equation (ii) by 2,

$$5(3x+ 2y) = 5(8) \qquad 2(8x + 5y) = 2(18)$$

$$15x + 10y = 40 \qquad 16x + 10y = 36$$

$15x + 10y = 40$ Equation (iii)

$16x + 10y = 36$ Equation (iv)

Step 3: Subtracting Equation (iii) from (iv),

$(16x + 10y) - (15x + 10y) = 36 - 40$

Step 4: Solving for 'x',

$$16x + 10y - 15x - 10y = -4$$

$$x = -4$$

Step 5: Substituting $x = -4$ in Equation (i) and solving for 'y',

$$3x + 2y = 8$$

$$3(-4) + 2y = 8$$

$$-12 + 2y = 8$$

$$2y = 12 + 8$$

$$2y = 20$$

$$y = 10$$

Therefore, the solution is $(-4, 10)$.

Step 6: Checking the solution in Equations (i) and (ii),

Equation (i),

$3x + 2y = 8$

$$LS = 3x + 2y$$

$$LS = 3(-4) + 2(10)$$

$$= -12 + 20$$

$$= 8$$

$= RS$ (True)

Therefore, LS = RS.

Equation (ii),

$8x + 5y = 18$

$$LS = 8x + 5y$$

$$LS = 8(-4) + 5(10)$$

$$= -32 + 50$$

$$= -18$$

$= RS$ (True)

Therefore, LS = RS.

Solving Systems of Equations With Fractions

When one or more of the variables in a system of equations has fractional coefficients, clear the fraction by multiplying each equation by its lowest common denominator **(LCD)**.

For example, consider the follwing system of equations:

$$\frac{2}{3}x + \frac{1}{2}y = 1$$

$$\frac{1}{3}x - \frac{3}{4}y = -2$$

To clear the fractions, multiply each equation by its **LCD** (lowest common denominator).

$\frac{2}{3}x + \frac{1}{2}y = 1$	The LCD is 6; therefore, multiplying each term by 6,
$4x + 3y = 6$	Equation (i)
$\frac{1}{3}x - \frac{3}{4}y = -2$	The LCD is 12; therefore, multiplying each term by 12,
$4x - 9y = -24$	Equation (ii)

Therefore, the equations of the given system are equivalent to:

$$4x + 3y = 6$$

$$4x - 9y = -24$$

This system can then be solved by the Elimination method.

Solving Systems of Equations With Decimal Numbers

When one or more of the variables in a system of equations has decimal numbers in its coefficients, clear the decimal numbers by multiplying each equation by 10 or by 100, etc., depending on the number of decimal places.

For example, consider the following system of equations:

$$0.05x + 0.15y = 2.4$$

$$2.5x + 0.5y = 2.2$$

To clear the decimal numbers, multiply the first equation by 100 (to eliminate 2 decimal places) and the second equation by 10 (to eliminate 1 decimal place).

$0.05x + 0.15y = 2.4$	Multiplying by 100,
$5x + 15y = 240$	Dividing by 5,
$x + 3y = 48$	Equation (i)
$2.5x + 0.5y = 2.2$	Multiplying by 10,
$25x + 5y = 22$	Equation (ii)

Therefore, the equations of the given system are equivalent to:

$$x + 3y = 48$$

$$25x + 5y = 22$$

This system can then be solved by the Substitution or Elimination method.

System With No Solutions

If a false equation is obtained (such as 0 = 4) when solving a system of two linear equations with two variables, then the system has no solutions. That is, the graph of the equation will be parallel and distinct.

Example 9.2-e **Solving a System With No Solutions**

Solve the following system of equations by Elimination:

$2x + 3y = 5$

$6x + 9y = 12$

Solution

Step 1: $2x + 3y = 5$ Equation (i)

$6x + 9y = 2$ Equation (ii)

Step 2: Choosing the variable to be eliminated; in this case, 'x'.

The variable 'x' in Equations (i) and (ii) has coefficients of 2 and 6, respectively.

Multiplying Equation (i) by 3,

$$3(2x+ 3y) = 5$$

$$6x + 9y = 5 \quad \text{Equation (iii)}$$

Step 3: Subtracting Equation (ii) from (iii),

$$(6x + 9y) - (6x + 9y) = 5 - 2$$

$$6x + 9y - 6x - 9y = 3$$

$$0 = 3 \quad \text{This cannot be true.}$$

Therefore, the system has no solution.

That is, the graph of the system will have parallel and distinct lines. The system is inconsistent and independent.

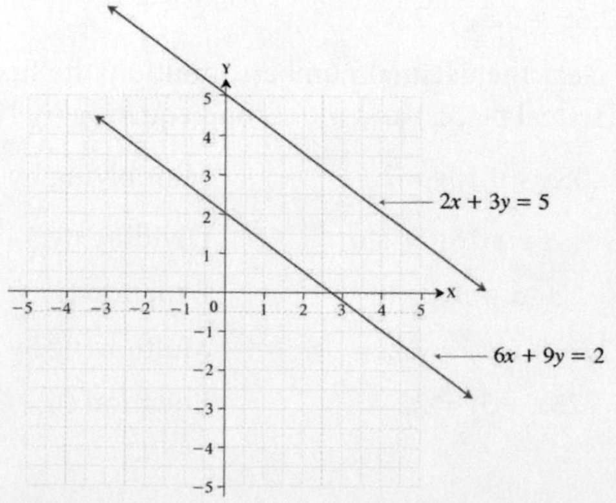

Systems With Many (Infinite) Solutions

If an identity of $0 = 0$ is obtained when solving a system of two linear equations with two variables, then the system has many (infinite) solutions.

Example 9.2-f

Solving a System With Many (Infinite) Solutions

Solve the following system of equations by substitution:

$2x + y - 7 = 0$

$3y = -6x + 21$

Solution

Step 1:

$$2x + y - 7 = 0$$

$$2x + y = 7 \qquad \text{Equation (i)}$$

$$3y = -6x + 21$$

$$6x + 3y = 21 \qquad \text{Equation (ii)}$$

Step 2: The coefficient of y in Equation (i) is 1.

Rearranging, $2x + y = 7$

$$y = -2x + 7$$

Step 3: Substituting this in Equation (ii),

$$6x + 3y = 21$$

$$6x + 3(-2x + 7) = 21$$

$$6x - 6x + 21 = 21$$

$$0 = 0$$

Therefore, the system will have many (infinite) solutions.

The following graph illustrates how the system will have coincident lines. The system is consistent and dependent.

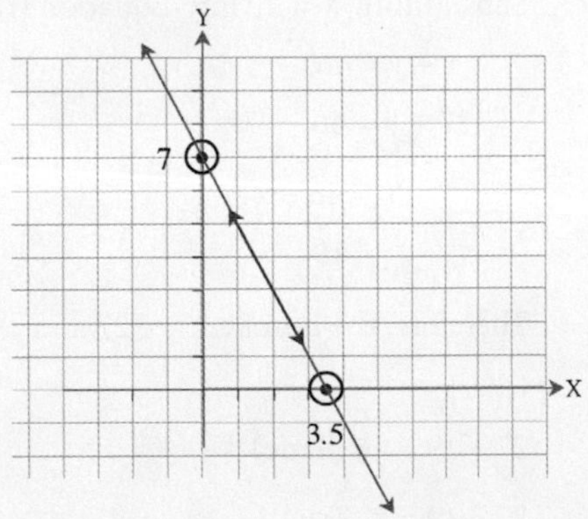

Writing a System of Linear Equations from Word Problems With Two Unknowns

In some problems, there may be two unknowns that need to be determined based on the given information. Although one of the unknowns can be expressed in terms of the other, it is best to write a system of equations in 2 variables and solve for the unknowns using one of the methods learned above.

The following steps will assist in writing the equations:

Step 1: Choose two different variables (x and y) to represent each of the unknown quantities and specify clearly what each variable represents and its unit of measure.

Step 2: Based on the given information, translate the word expressions into mathematical equations.

Step 3: Solve the equations for the unknown variables.

Step 4: Indicate the solutions to the word problem, including units.

Step 5: Check the solutions with the statement in the word problem.

Example 9.2-g **Finding Unknown Numbers**

The sum of two numbers is 46. The difference between the numbers is 8. Find the numbers.

Solution

Step 1: Let the larger number be x and the smaller number be y

Step 2: $x + y = 46$ Equation (i)

$x - y = 8$ Equation (ii)

Step 3: Adding Equations (i) and (ii),

$2x = 54$

$x = 27$

Step 4: Substituting, $x = 27$ into Equation (i),

$x + y = 46$

$27 + y = 46$

$y = 46 - 27$

$= 19$

Step 5: Therefore, the numbers are 27 and 19.

Step 6: Check:

$27 + 19 = 46$ (True)

$27 - 19 = 8$ (True)

Example 9.2-h

Finding an Amount Invested at Different Rates

Steve invested $50,000. He invested part of it in a fixed deposit paying 4% per annum and the remainder in bonds paying 6% per annum. After one year, he received $2,700 as interest from both investments. How much did he invest at each rate?

Solution

Step 1: Let the amount invested at 4% be $\$x$.

Let the amount invested at 6% be $\$y$.

Step 2: $x + y = 50{,}000$ Equation (i)

$4\%x + 6\%y = 2{,}700$

$0.04x + 0.06y = 2{,}700$ Multiplying by 100,

$4x + 6y = 270{,}000$ Dividing by 2,

$2x + 3y = 135{,}000$ Equation (ii)

Step 3: From Equation (i) $x + y = 50{,}000$

$$x = 50{,}000 - y$$

Substituting, $x = 50{,}000 - y$ in Equation (ii),

$$2x + 3y = 135{,}000$$

$$2(50{,}000 - y) + 3y = 135{,}000$$

$$-2y + 3y = 135{,}000 - 100{,}000$$

$$y = 35{,}000$$

Substituting this in Equation(i),

$$x + y = 50{,}000$$

$$x = 50{,}000 - y$$

$$= 50{,}000 - 35{,}000$$

$$x = 15{,}000$$

Step 4: Therefore the amount invested in the fixed deposit at 4% interest rate is $15,000 and the amount deposited in bonds at 6% interest rate is $35,000.

Step 5: Check:

Total interest $= 15{,}000 \times 4\% + 35{,}000 \times 6\%$

$= 600 + 2{,}100$

$= 2{,}700$ (True)

Example 9.2-i

Finding Number of Coins Consisting of Quarters and Dimes

Aran collected 81 coins in quarters (25¢) and dimes (10¢). If all the coins are worth $15.00, find the number of quarters and dimes he collected.

Solution

Step 1: Let the number of quarters be x and the number of dimes be y

Step 2: $x + y = 81$ Equation (i)

Value of x quarters = \$0.25x

Value of y dimes = \$0.10y

$0.25x + 0.10y = 15.00$ Multiplying by 100,

$25x + 10y = 1500$ Dividing by 5,

$5x + 2y = 300$ Equation (ii)

Step 3: Rearranging Equation (i), $x + y = 81$

$y = 81 - x$

Substituting, $y = 81 - x$ in Equation (ii),

$$5x + 2y = 300$$

$$5x + 2(81 - x) = 300$$

$$5x + 162 - 2x = 300$$

$$3x = 300 - 162$$

$$3x = 138$$

$$x = 46$$

Substituting, $x = 46$ in Equation (i),

$$y = 81 - x$$

$$y = 81 - 46$$

$$= 35$$

Step 4: Therefore, the number of quarters is 46 and the number of dimes is 35.

Step 5: Check:

Total coins = 46 + 35 = 81 (True)

Total amount = 0.25 (46) + 0.10 (35)

= 11.50 + 3.50

= 15.00 (True)

9.2 | Exercises

Answers to odd-numbered problems are available online.

Solve the following systems of equations by the Substitution method:

1. $y - 3x + 8 = 0$
   $y - x + 4 = 0$

2. $4x - 7y + 6 = 0$
   $x - 3y + 2 = 0$

3. $3x - 2y = 8$
   $x + 3y = 15$

4. $6x - 9y + 2 = 0$
   $x - 2y - 5 = 0$

5. $x - 3y = 12$

$5x + 2y = 9$

6. $3x + y = -8$

$3x - 4y = -23$

7. $5x + 4y = 14$

$x - 3y = -1$

8. $x - 9y = 6$

$3x - 7y = 16$

9. $3x - 2y = 20$

$y + 4x = 23$

10. $9x - 2y = 12$

$5y + 3x = 21$

11. $7x - 5y + 3 = 0$

$-3x + y + 1 = 0$

12. $6x - 5y + 13 = 0$

$-3x + y - 8 = 0$

Solve the following systems of equations by the Elimination method:

13. $3y + 2x = 24$

$2x - 2y = 14$

14. $7x - 3y = -5$

$5x - 9y = 7$

15. $5x + 3y = 19$

$3x - 5y = -9$

16. $5x - 3y = 2$

$3x - 5y = 7$

17. $5x - 2y + 1 = 0$

$2x - 3y - 4 = 0$

18. $4x + 5y = 11$

$2x + 3y = 5$

19. $5x - 7y = 19$

$2x + 3y = -4$

20. $9x + 8y = 10$

$3x + 2y = 4$

21. $2y + 3x = 14$

$9x - 4y = 2$

22. $3x - 5y = 4$

$5x + 3y = -16$

23. $3y + 7x = 15$

$3x + 5y + 1 = 0$

24. $9y + 4x - 1 = 0$

$4x + 5y + 3 = 0$

Solve the following systems of equations either by the Substitution or the Elimination method:

25. $0.5x - 0.3y = -1.2$

$0.2x - 0.7y = 0.1$

26. $1.2x + 0.6y = 0$

$3.5x + 1.7y = 0.01$

27. $0.7x - 0.4y = 2.9$

$0.6x - 0.3y = 2.4$

28. $1.5x + y = 1$

$0.8x + 0.7y = 1.2$

29. $\frac{x}{5} + \frac{y}{6} = 3$

$\frac{x}{2} - \frac{y}{3} = 3$

30. $\frac{x}{6} - \frac{y}{3} = \frac{2}{3}$

$\frac{x}{4} - \frac{y}{12} = -\frac{3}{2}$

31. $\frac{x}{4} + \frac{y}{2} = 2\frac{1}{4}$

$\frac{2x}{3} + \frac{y}{6} = \frac{3}{2}$

32. $\frac{3x}{10} + \frac{y}{5} = \frac{1}{2}$

$\frac{x}{3} + \frac{y}{3} = \frac{1}{2}$

33. $4(x - 3) + 5(y + 1) = 12$

$(y + 7) - 3(x + 2) = 1$

34. $4(x + 3) - 3(y + 4) = 21$

$2(x + 4) + 5(y - 3) = 10$

35. $2(x-2)-3(y-1)=11$
$5(x+1)+2(y-4)=8$

36. $3(x+1)-6(y+2)=6$
$5(2x-4)+7(y+1)=-17$

37. Two meals for adults and 3 meals for children cost \$48, whereas, 3 meals for adults and 2 meals for children cost \$52. How much is 1 adult meal?

38. Three DVDs and 4 movie tickets cost \$94.00, whereas, 4 DVDs and 3 movie tickets cost \$81. How much is 1 DVD?

39. The sum of a son's age and of his father's age, in years, is 92. The difference in their ages is 28. How old are the son and the father?

40. The sum of 2 numbers is 56 and their difference is 22. What are the numbers?

41. Hanna charges \$20 for the first shirt that you purchase at her store. However, for every additional shirt, she charges \$15. Write an equation that shows the relationship between her total revenue (y) and number of shirts sold (x). If you plot a graph of y vs. x, what are the y-intercept and the slope of the line that would represent the equation?

42. An online music store charges \$2 for the first song that you download. For every additional song that you download, you will be charged only \$1.50. Write an equation that shows the relationship between the total revenue (y) and the number of songs sold (x). If you plot a graph of y vs. x, what are the y-intercept and the slope of the line that would represent the equation?

43. Viktor invested \$25,000, part of it at 5% per annum and the remainder at 4% per annum. If the total interest after one year was \$1,150, how much did he invest at each rate?

44. Two investments were made by Adam, totalling \$22,500. Part of it was invested at 6% per annum and the remainder at 5% per annum. The total interest received after one year was \$1,295. Find the amount invested at each rate.

45. There are 130 coins consisting of quarters (25¢) and dimes (10¢). If the coins are worth \$27.70, how many quarters and dimes are there?

46. There are 175 coins consisting of dimes (10¢) and nickels (5¢). The coins are worth \$15.00. How many dimes and nickels are there?

9 | Review Exercises

Answers to odd-numbered problems are available online.

Without graphing, determine whether each of the following systems of equations has one solution, no solution, or many solutions:

1. $3x-2y+13=0$
$3x+y+7=0$

2. $4x+6y-14=0$
$2x+3y-7=0$

3. $x-3y+2=0$
$3x-9y+11=0$

4. $15x+3y=10$
$5x+y=-3$

5. $2x-4y=6$
$x-2y=3$

6. $3x-y+2=0$
$9x-3y+6=0$

Solve the following systems of equations by using the Graphical method:

7. $y=-2x-1$
$y=3x-11$

8. $y=2x+3$
$y=-2x-1$

9. $2x - 3y - 6 = 0$
   $x + 2y - 10 = 0$

10. $3x + 4y - 5 = 0$
    $2x - y + 4 = 0$

11. $2y = x$ and $y = -x + 3$

12. $3y = 2x$ and $y = -3x + 11$

13. $x + 4y = 8$ and $2x + 5y = 13$

14. $x + y = 3$ and $2x - y = 12$

15. $x + 4y + 12 = 0$ and $9x - 2y - 32 = 0$

16. $x - y - 1 = 0$ and $2x + 3y - 12 = 0$

17. $3x + 2y = 5$ and $y = 2x - 1$

18. $4x + 3y = 12$ and $9 - 3x = y$

Solve the following systems of equations by using the Elimination method:

19. $8x + 7y = 23$
    $7x + 8y = 22$

20. $2x + y = 8$
    $3x + 2y = 7$

21. $9x - 2y = -32$
    $x + 4y = -12$

22. $5x - 2y + 3 = 0$
    $3x - 2y - 1 = 0$

23. $4x + 3y = 12$
    $18 - 6x = 2y$

24. $2x + y + 2 = 0$
    $6x = 2y + 9$

Solve the following systems of equations by either the Substitution method or the Elimination method:

25. $0.4x - 0.5y = -0.8$
    $0.3x - 0.2y = 0.1$

26. $0.2x - 0.3y = -0.6$
    $0.5x + 0.2y = 2.3$

27. $\frac{5x}{3} - \frac{5y}{2} = -5$ and $\frac{x}{3} - \frac{y}{4} = 2$

28. $\frac{x}{4} + \frac{y}{2} = 2$ and $\frac{x}{6} + \frac{2y}{3} = \frac{4}{3}$

29. $(2x + 1) - 2(y + 7) = -1$
    $4(x + 5) + 3(y - 1) = 28$

30. $2(3x + 2) + 5(2y + 7) = 13$
    $3(x + 1) - 4(y - 1) = -15$

31. Find the 2 numbers whose sum is 95 and difference is 35.

32. Find the 2 numbers whose sum is 84 and difference is 48.

33. 300 tickets were sold for a theatrical performance. The tickets cost $28 for adults and $15 for kids. If $7,230 were collected, how many adults and how many children attended this play?

34. 640 tickets were sold for a soccer game between Toronto FC and Liverpool FC. The tickets cost $35 for adults and $20 for students. If $16,250 were collected from sales, how many adults and students attended the game ?

9 | Self-Test Exercises

Answers to all problems are available online.

Without graphing, determine whether each of the following systems of equations has one solution, no solution, or many solutions:

1. $4x + 3y - 16 = 0$
   $2x - y + 2 = 0$

2. $x - 3y + 11 = 0$
   $2x - 6y + 4 = 0$

3. $y = 4x + 8$
   $8x - 2y + 8 = 0$

Solve the following systems of equations by using the Graphical method:

4. $y = 3x + 6$
   $6x - 2y + 12 = 0$

5. $2x + 3y + 4 = 0$
   $3x - y + 7 = 0$

Solve the following systems of equations by using the Substitution method:

6. $2x + 4y + 6 = 0$
   $y - 3x + 9 = 0$

7. $3x + y = -8$
   $2x + 3y = 4$

Solve the following systems of equations by using the Elimination method:

8. $6x - 4y + 3 = 0$
   $4x - 6y - 3 = 0$

9. $3x + 5y - 19 = 0$
   $5x - 2y + 11 = 0$

10. Find the value of two numbers if their sum is 65 and difference is 5.

11. In a coin box, there are 3 times as many quarters (25¢) as dimes (10¢). If the total value of all these coins is $21.25, how many quarters are there?

12. The cost of admission to a concert was $75 for adults and $50 for students. If 400 tickets were sold and $28,125 collected, how many adult tickets were sold?

13. Henry works in a computer store and earns $500 a month plus a commission of 10% on the sales he makes. The relationship between his earnings (y) in a month and the number of computers he sells (x) is given by the equation $y = 500 + 0.10x$.

    a. What would his commission be if his earnings are $14,000 in a month?

    b. What would his earnings be if his sales are $250,000 in a month?

14. The fixed costs (FC) of a factory for the month are $5,000 and the variable costs (VC) to manufacture each product are $5. The total costs ($TC$) for the month are the sum of the fixed costs and the variable costs per unit, multiplied by the number of products produced and sold (x). The relationship between TC, FC, VC, and x is given by the equation $TC = (VC)x + FC$.

    a. What would be the total cost if 90 products were sold this month?

    b. How many products were sold this month if the total cost is $11,375?

Chapter 10
Units of Measurements

Learning Outcomes

- Read, write, and interpret symbols and prefixes used in the metric and US Customary system of units.
- Convert within metric units of length, mass, and capacity.
- Convert within US Customary units of length, mass, and capacity.
- Convert between metric and US Customary units of length, mass, and capacity.
- Convert units of temperature between the Celsius scale and Fahrenheit scale.

Chapter Outline

The primary ways to describe an object are by its length (how long is it?), mass (how heavy is it?), or capacity (how much space/volume does it occupy?). Each of these measurements can be expressed in different units. It is important that these units are well defined so that measurements made in different units may be compared after converting them to an equivalent measurement in another unit. In this chapter, you will learn about the two major systems of measurements - the metric system that is used in most parts of the world and the US Customary system that is mainly used in the USA. You will also learn about the different units of measurements for length, mass, and capacity used within each system, and the conversions of these units between the two systems in order to understand and interpret information such as how 90 km compares to 60 miles, 55 liters compares to 20 gallons, or 70 kg compares to 145 pounds, etc.

10.1 | Metric System of Measurement

Introduction

The units of measurements in the metric system are derived from scientific principles. The **British units** of measurements and the subsequent **US Customary units** of measurements and **Imperial units** of measurements are based on different initial standards, stemming from nature and everyday activities.

Length, weight, capacity (volume), temperature, etc. are measured using several different units of measurements. The two measurement systems generally in use are the **Metric system** and the **US Customary system.**

The metric system is widely used in science, medicine, technology, and engineering. Most of world trade utilizes the metric system of measurements. However, USA and three other countries (Liberia, Yemen, and Myanmar) have not fully adapted to the metric system.

The metric system for measurement is simple to use and can be more easily understood than the US Customary system because in the metric system, all the units are related to one another by multiples of ten.

Converting Within Metric Units of Measurements

The metric system uses meter (m), gram (g), and liter (L) as the base units for the measurements of length, mass, and capacity, respectively. The Celsius (°C) scale is used for temperature.

In this section, you will learn how to convert within the metric units for length, mass, or capacity:

- **Length:** kilometer (km), meter (m), centimeter (cm), and millimeter (mm)
- **Mass:** kilogram (kg), gram (g), and milligram (mg)
- **Capacity:** liter (L) and milliliter (mL)

The conversion factors that relate to the different units in the metric system, including the prefixes used, are as follows:

Table 10.1

Conversion Factors

Prefix	Symbol	Factor	Factor in Word
kilo-	k	1,000	Thousand
hecto-	h	100	Hundred
deca-	da	10	Ten
	Base Unit	1	
deci-	d	1/10 = 0.1	Tenth
centi-	c	1/100 = 0.01	One-hundredth
milli-	m	1/1000 = 0.001	One-thousandth

hecto-, deca-, and deci- units are usually not used as units of measurements for length, mass, and capacity. centi- is used only in the measurement of length, as in centimeter.

The prefix and symbol for units are written in lower case.

Converting from a larger unit to a smaller unit will result in a larger number:

For example, 5 m = 500 cm.

Converting from a smaller unit to a larger unit will result in a smaller number:

For example, 2,000 g = 2 kg.

Converting units within the metric system involves shifting of the decimal point to the right (multiplying by multiples of 10) or to the left (dividing by multiples of 10) by the appropriate number of places.

To convert from a larger unit to a smaller unit, shift the decimal point to the right or multiply by multiples of 10.

For example, to convert from 5 meters (m) to centimeters (cm), shift the decimal point by 2 places to the right (or multiply by 100).

$$5 \text{ m} = (5 \times 100) \text{ cm} = 500 \text{ cm}$$

Length

Converting from larger units to smaller units	Converting from smaller units to larger units
1 km = (1 × 1,000) m = 1,000 m	1 mm = (1 / 10) cm = 0.1 cm
1 m = (1 × 100) cm = 100 cm	1 cm = (1 / 100) m = 0.01 m
1 cm = (1 × 10) = 10 mm	1 m = (1 / 1,000) km = 0.001 km

Mass

Converting from larger units to smaller units	Converting from smaller units to larger units
1 kg = (1 × 1,000) g = 1,000 g	1 mg = (1 / 1,000) g = 0.001 g

Note: 1 metric ton or metric tonne (t) = 1,000 kg

Capacity

The capitalized 'L' is used to represent liter in order to avoid confusion with the number 1.

Converting from larger units to smaller units	Converting from smaller units to larger units
1 L = (1 × 1,000) mL = 1,000 mL	1 mL = (1 / 1,000) L = 0.001 L

Example 10.1-a **Converting Measurements**

Convert the following:

(i) 7.5 cm to millimeters (ii) 1,120 cm to meters

(iii) 2.56 kg to grams (iv) 21,750 mL to liters

Solution

(i) 7.5 cm = 7.5 x 10 mm = 75 mm

(ii) 1,120 cm = 1,120/100 m = 11.2 m

(iii) 2.56 kg = 2.56 x 1,000 g = 2,560 g

(iv) 21,750 mL = 21,750 /1,000 L = 21.75 L

Example 10.1-b **Converting Measurements in Multiple Units**

Convert the following:

(i) 12 m 25 cm to centimeters

(ii) 2 kg 456 g to grams

(iii) 3 L 75 mL to milliliters

Solution

(i) 12 m 25 cm = 12 m + 25 cm

= (12 × 100) cm + 25 cm

= 1,200 cm + 25 cm

= 1,225 cm

(ii) 2 kg 456 g = 2 kg + 456 g

= (2 × 1,000) g + 456 g

= 2,000 g + 456 g

= 2,456 g

(iii) 3 L 75 mL = 3 L + 75 mL

= (3 × 1,000) mL + 75 mL

= 3,000 mL + 75 mL

= 3,075 mL

Example 10.1-c **Converting Measurements and Expressing in Multiple Units**

Convert the following:

(i) 695 cm to meters and then express it in meters and centimeters.

(ii) 2,275 mL to liters and then express it in liters and milliliters.

Solution

(i) $695 \text{ cm} = \left(\frac{695}{100}\right) \text{m} = 6.95 \text{ m}$

= 6 m + 0.95 m

= 6 m + (0.95 × 100) cm

= 6 m + 95 cm

= 6 m 95 cm

(ii) $2{,}275 \text{ mL} = \left(\frac{2{,}275}{1{,}000}\right) \text{L} = 2.275 \text{ L}$

= 2 L + 0.275 L

= 2 L + (0.275 × 1,000) mL

= 2 L + 275 mL

= 2 L 275 mL

Example 10.1-d

Converting Measurements Involving Two Steps

Convert the following:

(i) 5 km 20 m to centimeters

(ii) 3,125,000 mg to kilograms and grams

Solution

(i) 5 km 20 m to centimeters

Step 1: Convert 5 km 20 m to meters

$$5 \text{ km } 20 \text{ m} = 5 \text{ km} + 20 \text{ m}$$
$$= (5 \times 1{,}000) \text{ m} + 20 \text{ m}$$
$$= 5{,}000 \text{ m} + 20 \text{ m}$$
$$= 5{,}020 \text{ m}$$

Step 2: Convert 5,020 m to centimeters

$$5{,}020 \text{ m} = (5{,}020 \times 100) \text{ cm}$$
$$= (5 \times 1{,}000) \text{ m} + 20 \text{ m}$$
$$= 502{,}000 \text{ cm}$$

(ii) 3,125,000 mg to kilograms and grams

Step 1: Convert 3,125,000 mg to grams

$$3{,}125{,}000 \text{ mg} = \left(\frac{3{,}125{,}000}{1{,}000}\right) \text{g}$$
$$= 3{,}125 \text{ g}$$

Step 2: Convert 3,125 g to kilograms and grams

$$3{,}125 \text{ g} = \left(\frac{3{,}125}{1{,}000}\right) \text{kg}$$
$$= 3.125 \text{ kg}$$
$$= 3 \text{ kg} + 0.125 \text{ kg}$$
$$= 3 \text{ kg} + (0.125 \times 1{,}000) \text{ g}$$
$$= 3 \text{ kg} + 125 \text{ g}$$
$$= 3 \text{ kg } 125 \text{ g}$$

10.1 | Exercises

Answers to odd-numbered problems are available online.

Calculate the missing values in Problems 1 to 8.

		meters (m)	centimeters (cm)	millimeters (mm)
1.	a.	2.40	?	?
	b.	?	860	?
	c.	?	?	34,420

		meters (m)	centimeters (cm)	millimeters (mm)
2.	a.	1.20	?	?
	b.	?	975	?
	c.	?	?	23,170
3.	a.	0.25	?	?
	b.	?	58	?
	c.	?	?	8,470
4.	a.	0.67	?	?
	b.	?	95	?
	c.	?	?	5,200

		kilometers (km)	meters (m)	centimeters (cm)
5.	a.	1.62	?	?
	b.	?	2,390	?
	c.	?	?	2,320
6.	a.	1.25	?	?
	b.	?	1,454	?
	c.	?	?	1,190
7.	a.	0.65	?	?
	b.	?	154	?
	c.	?	?	1,770
8.	a.	0.17	?	?
	b.	?	230	?
	c.	?	?	9,400

For Problems 9 to 12, convert the following measurements to the units indicated.

9. a. 23 m 21 cm = ___ cm
   b. 16 cm 7 mm = ___ mm
   c. 5 km 252 m = ___ m

10. a. 335 cm = ___ m ___ cm
    b. 603 mm = ___ cm ___ mm
    c. 1,487 m = ___ km ___ m

11. a. 7 m 49 cm = ___ cm
    b. 45 cm 8 mm = ___ mm
    c. 2 km 725 m = ___ m

12. a. 793 cm = ___ m ___ cm
    b. 379 mm = ___ cm ___ mm
    c. 6,745 m = ___ km ___ m

13. Arrange the following measurements in order from smallest to largest:
    0.15 km, 150,800 mm, 155 m, 15,200 cm
14. Arrange the following measurements in order from largest to smallest:
    19,750 cm, 1.97 km, 1,950 m, 195,700 mm
15. The distance between my house and the park is 1.7 km. I walked 925 m. How many more meters would I have to walk to reach the park?

16. In a 2.5 km race, there is a checkpoint at 875 m from the finish line. Calculate the distance, in meters, that I would have to run to reach the checkpoint.
17. Ali is 1.75 m tall. Eric is 30 mm taller than Ali. Calculate Eric's height, in centimeters.
18. Five-year-old Aran's height is 1.2 m. His sister Girija is 40 mm taller than him. Calculate Girija's height, in centimeters.

Calculate the missing values in Problems 19 to 26.

		kilograms (kg)	grams (g)	milligrams (mg)
19.	a.	1.65	?	?
	b.	?	4,950	?
	c.	?	?	6,440
20.	a.	2.45	?	?
	b.	?	8,700	?
	c.	?	?	3,890
21.	a.	0.76	?	?
	b.	?	35,760	?
	c.	?	?	50,300
22.	a.	0.45	?	?
	b.	?	25,090	?
	c.	?	?	20,080

		kilograms (kg)	grams (g)
23.	a.	2.62	?
	b.	?	6,750
24.	a.	3.79	?
	b.	?	8,620
25.	a.	0.84	?
	b.	?	580
26.	a.	0.32	?
	b.	?	930

For Problems 27 to 30, convert the following measurements to the units indicated.

27. a. 18 kg 79 g = ___ g

    b. 2 kg 116 mg = ___ mg

    c. 3 t 74 kg = ___ kg

28. a. 7 kg 89 g = ___ g

    b. 14 kg 547 mg = ___ mg

    c. 15 t 90 kg = ___ kg

29. a. 5,903 g = ___ kg ___ g

    b. 2,884 mg = ___ g ___ mg

    c. 9,704 kg = ___ t ___ kg

30. a. 5,014 g = ___ kg ___ g

    b. 6,629 mg = ___ g ___ mg

    c. 3,075 kg = ___ t ___ kg

31. Arrange the following measurements in order from smallest to largest:
    0.075 t, 123,200 g, 850,250 mg, 125 kg

32. Arrange the following measurements in order from largest to smallest:
    0.025 t, 50,750 mg, 125,700 g, 27 kg

33. If one tablespoon of salt weighs 5.5 g, how many tablespoons of salt are there in a box containing 1.1 kg of salt?

34. If a bowl can hold 40 g of cereal, how many bowls of cereal will you obtain from a box that has 1.35 kg of cereal?

35. Linda is baking a cake. She bought 0.75 kg of sugar and used 575 g. Calculate the quantity of sugar left, in grams.

36. Megan bought 1.5 kg of flour and used 925 g of it. Calculate the quantity of flour left, in grams.

37. 450 g of butter cost $3.25. At this price, how much will it cost to buy 2.25 kg of butter?

38. 250 g of cheese cost $2.75. At this price, how much will it cost to buy 2 kg of cheese?

Calculate the missing values in Problems 39 to 42.

		liter (L)	milliliter (mL)
39.	a.	3.25	?
	b.	?	5,060
40.	a.	1.75	?
	b.	?	1,975
41.	a.	0.045	?
	b.	?	220
42.	a.	0.015	?
	b.	?	5,730

For Problems 43 to 46, convert the following measurements to the units indicated:

43. a. 5 L 85 mL = ___ L

    b. 2 L 5 mL = ___ L

44. a. 9 L 25 mL = ___ L

    b. 1 L 205 mL = ___ L

45. a. 2,708 mL = ___ L ___ mL

    b. 12,080 mL = ___ L ___ mL

46. a. 6,503 mL = ___ L ___ mL

    b. 32,096 mL = ___ L ___ mL

47. A bottle can hold 900 mL of orange juice. Calculate the total volume of orange juice from 5 such bottles. Express your answer in liters.

48. Andy drinks 250 mL of milk every day. Calculate the quantity of milk he will require for 7 days. Express your answer in liters.
49. A milk packet contains 1.75 L of milk. If three glasses with a volume of 320 mL each are filled with milk from the packet, how much milk will be left in the packet? Express your answer in milliliters.
50. A bottle can hold 1.5 L of wine. If four glasses with a volume of 280 mL each are filled with wine from the bottle, how much wine will be left in the bottle? Express your answer in milliliters.

10.2 | US Customary System of Measurement

In the United States, units in the **US Customary system** are primarily used for the purposes of measurements. **Imperial units** of measurement were historically used in the British Commonwealth countries.

While the imperial and US Customary systems are very similar, they are not identical. There are a number of differences between them.

For example,

- The imperial ton is 2,240 pounds, whereas the US ton is 2,000 pounds. (1 U.S. ton = 0.893 Imperial ton)
- The imperial gallon is the volume of 10 pounds of water, whereas the US gallon is the volume of 81/3 pounds of water. (1 U.S. gallon = 0.833 Imperial gallons)

The US Customary system uses the yard (yd), the pound (lb), and the gallon (gal) as the base units for the measurements of length, mass, and capacity, respectively. The Fahrenheit (°F) scale is used for temperature.

In the United States, many items are measured using US Customary units. For example, road distance is measured in miles, butter is measured in pounds, and gasoline is measured in gallons.

In this section, you will learn how to convert within the commonly used units of length, mass, and capacity within the following US Customary units:

- **Length:** inch (in.), foot (ft), yard (yd), and mile (mi)
- **Mass:** ounce (oz), pound (lb), and ton (ton)
- **Capacity:** fluid ounce (fl oz), cups (c), pint (pt), quart (qt), and gallon (gal)

Converting Within US Customary Units of Measurements

Length

- 1 foot is 12 inches — 1 ft = 12 in.
- 1 yard is 3 feet — 1 yd = 3 ft
- 1 mile is 5,280 feet — 1 mi = 5,280 ft

Mass

- 1 pound is 16 ounces — 1 lb = 16 oz
- 1 ton is 2,000 pounds — 1 ton = 2,000 lb

The US Customary unit for ton is called 'short ton' and is represented by the word 'ton'. This is to distinguish it from the metric ton that has the symbol 't', where t = 1,000 kg.

Capacity

- 1 cup is 8 fluid ounces — 1 c = 8 fl oz
- 1 pint is 2 cups — 1 pt = 2 c
- 1 quart is 2 pints — 1 qt = 2 pt
- 1 gallon is 4 quarts — 1 gal = 4 qt

There are a number of methods or ways for converting measurements from one unit to the other. In Section 10.1, in converting units within the metric system, we multiplied or divided by multiples of 10 because factors that relate to the different units in the metric system are in the order of 10, 100, 1000, 1/10, 1/10, 1/1000, etc.

Converting units within the US Customary system can be done using various methods. Sometimes, conversions can be performed easily using simple direct multiplication or division. For example, if we know the relationship 1 foot = 12 inches and want to convert 5 feet into inches, then we can convert it by using simple multiplication: 5 feet = 5 × 12 inches = 60 inches.

There are times when we need to apply a method to convert between units. In this section, you will learn about two of the commonly used methods - the conversion factor (ratio) method and the proportion method - to perform conversions of units within the US Customary system.

Example 10.2-a

Converting a Measurement with Multiple Units to One with Single Unit Using Direct Multiplication

Convert the following:

(i) 2 ft 10 in. to inches

(ii) 5 lb 9 oz to ounces

(iii) 2 gal 3 qt to quarts

Solution

(i) 2 ft 10 in. = 2 ft + 10 in.

= (2 × 12) in. + 10 in. [using 1 ft = 12 in., 2 feet = 2 × 12 inches]

= 24 in. + 10 in.

= 34 in.

(ii) 5 lb 9 oz = 5 lb + 9 oz

= (5 × 16) oz + 9 oz [using 1 lb = 16 oz, 5 lb = 5 × 16 oz]

= 80 oz + 9 oz

= 89 oz

(iii) 2 gal 3 qt = 2 gal + 3 qt

= (2 × 4) qt + 3 qt [using 1 gal = 4 qt, 2 gal = 2 × 4 qt]

= 8 qt + 3 qt

= 11 qt

Example 10.2-b

Converting a Measurement with Single Unit to one with Multiple Units Using Direct Division

Convert the following:

(i) 6,730 ft to miles and feet

(ii) 73 oz to pounds and ounces

(iii) 95 qt to gallons and quarts

Solution

Divide the given smaller unit by the known conversion factor using the method of long division. The quotient will be the larger unit and the remainder will be the smaller unit.

(i) $6{,}730 \text{ ft} = \left(\frac{6{,}730}{5{,}280}\right) \text{ mi}$ [using 1 mile = 5,280 ft]

$$\begin{array}{r} 1 \\ 5{,}280 \overline{)\ 6{,}730} \\ \underline{5{,}280} \\ 1{,}450 \end{array}$$

= 1 mi 1,450 ft

Solution
continued

(ii) $73 \text{ oz} = \left(\frac{73}{16}\right) \text{lb}$ [using 1 lb = 16 oz]

$$\begin{array}{r} 4 \\ 16\overline{)73} \\ \underline{64} \\ 9 \end{array}$$

= 4 lb 9 oz

(iii) $95 \text{ qt} = \left(\frac{95}{4}\right) \text{gal}$ [using 1 gal = 4 qt]

$$\begin{array}{r} 23 \\ 4\overline{)95} \\ \underline{8} \\ 15 \\ \underline{12} \\ 3 \end{array}$$

= 23 gal 3 qt

Conversion Factor (Ratio) Method

Changing a measurement from one unit to another can be achieved using the conversion factor (ratio) method.

For a known relationship between the two units, we can find two conversion factors to use in converting units.

For example, consider the relationship 1 foot = 12 inches.

Dividing both sides by 12 inches, we get,

$$\frac{1 \text{ foot}}{12 \text{ inches}} = \frac{\cancel{12 \text{ inches}}}{\cancel{12 \text{ inches}}} = 1$$

Similarly, dividing both sides by 1 foot, we get,

$$\frac{\cancel{1 \text{ foot}}}{\cancel{1 \text{ foot}}} = \frac{12 \text{ inches}}{1 \text{ foot}}$$

$$= \frac{12 \text{ inches}}{1 \text{ foot}}$$

Therefore, the relationship between two units can be written as two conversion factors or ratios of $\frac{1 \text{ foot}}{12 \text{ inches}}$ or $\frac{12 \text{ inches}}{1 \text{ foot}}$, both equaling 1.

Since the conversion factor is equal to 1, this can be used to multiply the given measurement to convert it from one unit to the other unit.

Example 10.2-c

Finding Conversion Factors for a Given Relationship

Find the two conversion factors for the known relationship, 1 yard = 3 feet.

Solution

1 yard = 3 feet

Dividing both sides by 3 feet: $\frac{1 \text{ yard}}{3 \text{ feet}} = \frac{3 \cancel{\text{feet}}}{3 \cancel{\text{feet}}} = 1$

Similarly, dividing both sides by 1 yard: $\frac{1 \cancel{\text{yard}}}{1 \cancel{\text{yard}}} = \frac{3 \text{ feet}}{1 \text{ yard}} = 1$

Therefore, the two conversion factors are $\frac{1 \text{ yard}}{3 \text{ feet}}$ and $\frac{3 \text{ feet}}{1 \text{ yard}}$.

Example 10.2-d

Using a Conversion Factor to Convert Units of Measurements

Convert 90 in. to feet. Use 1 foot = 12 inches.

Solution

90 in. to feet

Step 1: Write the two conversion factors: $\frac{1 \text{ foot}}{12 \text{ inches}}$ and $\frac{12 \text{ inches}}{1 \text{ foot}}$

Step 2: Write the measurement to be converted: 90 inches

Step 3: Identify the correct conversion factor that will cancel the unit to be converted: (In this case, the conversion factor that has the unit 'inches' in its denominator) $\frac{1 \text{ foot}}{12 \text{ inches}}$

Step 4: Multiply the measurement to be converted by this conversion factor: 90 inches × $\frac{1 \text{ foot}}{12 \text{ inches}}$

Step 5: Cross-cancel the units that appear in both the numerator and denominator and simplify the fraction to get the answer:

$$90 \text{ inches} = 90 \cancel{\text{inches}} \times \frac{1 \text{ foot}}{12 \cancel{\text{inches}}}$$

$$= \left(\frac{90}{12}\right) \text{ feet}$$

$$= 7.5 \text{ feet}$$

Therefore, 90 inches is equal to 7.5 feet.

Since the conversion factor has a value equal to 1, this conversion factor method can be expanded to perform conversions in a single step.

For example, knowing that 1 foot = 12 inches and 1 yard = 3 feet, the conversion factor can be expanded as follows:

$$\frac{1 \text{ foot}}{12 \text{ inches}} \times \frac{1 \text{ yard}}{3 \text{ feet}}$$

When simplified: $\frac{1 \text{ }\cancel{\text{foot}}}{12 \text{ inches}} \times \frac{1 \text{ yard}}{3 \text{ }\cancel{\text{feet}}} = \frac{1 \text{ yard}}{36 \text{ inches}}$

Therefore, this results in a new conversion factor of $\frac{1 \text{ yard}}{36 \text{ inches}}$; i.e., 1 yard = 36 inches.

Example 10.2-e

Using Expanded Conversion Factor Method to Convert the Units of Measurements

Convert the following measurements:

(i) 5.9 yd to inches (ii) 4.5 gal to cups

Solution

(i) 5.9 yd to inches

Multiply with the conversion factor $\left(\frac{3 \text{ feet}}{1 \text{ yard}}\right)$ and $\left(\frac{12 \text{ inches}}{1 \text{ feet}}\right)$

to cross-cancel the units 'yards' and 'feet'.

$$5.9 \text{ yards} = 5.9 \text{ }\cancel{\text{yards}} \times \left(\frac{3 \text{ }\cancel{\text{feet}}}{1 \text{ }\cancel{\text{yard}}}\right) \times \left(\frac{12 \text{ inches}}{1 \text{ }\cancel{\text{feet}}}\right)$$

$$= 5.9 \times 3 \times 12 \text{ in.}$$

$$= 212.4 \text{ in.}$$

Therefore, 5.9 yd is equal to 212.4 in.

(ii) 4.5 gallons to cups

Multiply with the conversion factor $\left(\frac{4 \text{ quarts}}{1 \text{ gallon}}\right)$, $\left(\frac{2 \text{ pints}}{1 \text{ quart}}\right)$, and $\left(\frac{2 \text{ cups}}{1 \text{ pint}}\right)$

to cross-cancel the units 'gal', 'qt', and 'pt'.

$$4.5 \text{ gallons} = 4.5 \text{ }\cancel{\text{gallons}} \times \left(\frac{4 \text{ }\cancel{\text{quarts}}}{1 \text{ }\cancel{\text{gallon}}}\right) \times \left(\frac{2 \text{ }\cancel{\text{pints}}}{1 \text{ }\cancel{\text{quart}}}\right) \times \left(\frac{2 \text{ cups}}{1 \text{ }\cancel{\text{pint}}}\right)$$

$$= 4.5 \times 4 \times 2 \times 2 \text{ cups}$$

$$= 72 \text{ cups}$$

Therefore, 4.5 gal is equal to 72 c.

Proportion Method

This is similar to the method learned in Chapter 4.

In this method, we equate two sets of ratios, where one of the ratios is formed from a given or known relationship. The second ratio is formed from the question asked, using the value for the unit to be converted and the unit required. These two ratios are equated to form the proportion equation and the unknown unit is solved for by using cross-multiplication and simplification.

When forming the proportion equation, the order in which the units of the terms in the ratio are written should be consistent on either side of the equation;

i.e., km : m = km : m

Example 10.2-f **Using Proportion Method to Convert Units of Measurements**

Convert the following measurements:

(i) 8.5 miles to feet (ii) 25 pints to gallons

Solution

(i) 8.5 miles to feet

$$\text{mi} : \text{ft} = \text{mi} : \text{ft}$$

$$8.5 : x = 1 : 5{,}280 \qquad \text{[Using 1 mile = 5,280 feet]}$$

In fractional form, $\frac{8.5}{x} = \frac{1}{5{,}280}$

Cross-multiplying, $x = 8.5 \times 5{,}280 = 44{,}880$ ft.

Therefore, 8.5 mi is 44,880 ft.

(ii) 25 pints to gallons

First, converting from pints to quarts,

$$\text{qt} : \text{pt} = \text{qt} : \text{pt}$$

$$x : 25 = 1 : 2 \qquad \text{[Using 1 qt = 2 pt]}$$

In fractional form, $\frac{x}{25} = \frac{1}{2}$

Cross-multiplying, $2x = 25$

$$x = \frac{25}{2} = 12.5$$

i.e., 25 pt = 12.5 qt

Converting from quarts to gallons,

$$\text{gal} : \text{qt} = \text{gal} : \text{qt}$$

$$x : 12.5 = 1 : 4 \qquad \text{[Using 1 gal = 4 qt]}$$

In fractional form, $\frac{x}{1} = \frac{12.5}{4}$

Cross-multiplying, $4x = 12.5$

$$x = \frac{12.5}{4} = 3.125$$

i.e., 25 pt = 12.5 qt = 3.125 gal

Therefore, 25 pt is equal to 3.125 gal.

Note: The conversion factor method is preferable over the proportion method when two or more steps are involved in the conversion.

For example, converting 25 pt to gallons in Example 10.2-f can be performed using the conversion factor method, as follows:

Convert 25 pt to gallons,

1st conversion factor from 1 qt = 2 pt
2nd conversion factor from 1 gal = 4 qt

$$25 \text{ pt} = 25 \cancel{\text{pt}} \times \left(\frac{1 \cancel{\text{qt}}}{2 \cancel{\text{pt}}}\right) \times \left(\frac{1 \text{ gal}}{4 \cancel{\text{qt}}}\right)$$

$$= \left(\frac{25}{2 \times 4}\right) \text{gal} = 3.125 \text{ gal}$$

Therefore, 25 pt is equal to 3.125 gal.

10.2 | Exercises

Answers to odd-numbered problems are available online.

Calculate the missing values in Problems 1 to 8.

		yard (yd)	feet (ft)	inch (in.)
1.	a.	42	?	?
	b.	?	48	?
	c.	?	?	648
2.	a.	84	?	?
	b.	?	72	?
	c.	?	?	540
3.	a.	46.5	?	?
	b.	?	22.5	?
	c.	?	?	2,880
4.	a.	67.5	?	?
	b.	?	37.5	?
	c.	?	?	3,960

		miles (mi)	yard (yd)	feet (ft)
5.	a.	3	?	?
	b.	?	6,160	?
	c.	?	?	10,560
6.	a.	2	?	?
	b.	?	9,680	?
	c.	?	?	18,480
7.	a.	2.25	?	?
	b.	?	2,200	?
	c.	?	?	6,192

		miles (mi)	yard (yd)	feet (ft)
8.	a.	42.5	?	?
	b.	?	3,080	?
	c.	?	?	25,080

In Problems 9 to 12, convert the measurements to the units indicated.

9. a. 12 yd 1.5 ft = ___ ft
   b. 11 ft 10 in. = ___ in.
   c. 1 mi 121 yd = ___ yd

10. a. 78 ft = ___ yd ___ ft
    b. 570 in. = ___ ft ___ in.
    c. 5,705 yd = ___ mi ___ yd

11. a. 15 yd 7.5 ft = ___ ft
    b. 12 ft 11 in. = ___ in.
    c. 2 mi 45 yd = ___ yd

12. a. 56 ft = ___ yd ___ ft
    b. 420 in. = ___ ft ___ in.
    c. 7,350 yd = ___ mi ___ yd

13. A sheet of paper is 7 ft long. A piece that is 5 ft 9 in. long is cut from it. Calculate the length of the paper left, in inches.
14. An iron rod is 7 ft in length. One piece of 5 ft 3 in. is cut from it. Calculate the length of the remaing portion of the rod, in inches.
15. A wire of length 10.5 yd is cut into 7 equal parts. Calculate the length of each piece, in feet.
16. A wooden fence of length 32 yd is made up of 12 equal panels. Calculate the length of each panel, in feet.
17. The length of a river is 39,600 ft. Calculate the length of the river, in miles.
18. The height of a mountain is 81,840 ft. Calculate the height of the mountain, in miles.

Calculate the missing values in Problems 19 to 26.

		pound (lb)	ounce (oz)
19.	a.	?	288
	b.	8	?
20.	a.	?	384
	b.	12	?
21.	a.	?	232
	b.	25.25	?
22.	a.	?	296
	b.	19.75	?

		ton (ton)	pound (lb)
23.	a.	35	?
	b.	?	14,500
24.	a.	37	?
	b.	?	23,500

	ton (ton)	pound (lb)
25. a.	12.75	?
b.	?	65,000
26. a.	17.25	?
b.	?	47,000

In Problems 27 to 30, convert the measurements to the units indicated.

27. a. 11 lb 10 oz = ___ oz

    b. 2 ton 1,250 lb = ___ lb

28. a. 55,825 lb = ___ ton ___ lb

    b. 150 oz = ___ lb ___ oz

29. a. 9 lb 3 oz = ___ oz

    b. 5 ton 1,175 lb = ___ lb

30. a. 79,125 lb = ___ ton ___ lb

    b. 200 oz = ___ lb ___ oz

31. Arrange the following measurements in order from largest to smallest:

    34,400 oz, 1.2 ton, 2,250 lb

32. Arrange the following measurements in order from smallest to largest:

    0.95 ton, 1,920 lb, 29,760 oz

33. A cake weighing 2 lb 8 oz is cut into 8 equal portions. Calculate the weight of each piece, in ounces.

34. The weight of 12 cans of softdrink is 5 lb 4 oz. Calculate the weight of each can of soft drink, in ounces.

35. A wholesaler bought 1.25 tons of cashews. He wanted to sell them in packages of 2.5 pounds each. Calculate the number of packages that can be made.

36. A bookstore received a shipment of 1,600 mathematics textbooks. The total weight of the shipment is 2.2 tons. Calculate the weight of each book, in pounds.

Calculate the missing values in Problems 37 to 44.

	quart (qt)	pint (pt)	cup (c)
37. a.	22	?	?
b.	?	38	?
c.	?	?	68
38. a.	28	?	?
b.	?	26	?
c.	?	?	74
39. a.	32.5	?	?
b.	?	45	?
c.	?	?	94
40. a.	47.5	?	?
b.	?	51	?
c.	?	?	102

	gallon (gal)	quart (qt)	pint (pt)
41. a.	12	?	?
b.	?	18	?
c.	?	?	56
42. a.	15	?	?
b.	?	24	?
c.	?	?	64
43. a.	7.5	?	?
b.	?	14	?
c.	?	?	50
44. a.	9.5	?	?
b.	?	22	?
c.	?	?	30

In Problems 45 to 48, convert the measurements to the units indicated.

45. a. 19 qt 1 pt = ___ pt
b. 15 pt 3 c = ___ c
c. 12 gal 1 qt = ___ qt

46. a. 19 pt = ___ qt ___ pt
b. 39 c = ___ pt ___ c
c. 63 qt = ___ gal ___ qt

47. a. 14 qt 1 pt = ___ pt
b. 27 pt 1 c = ___ c
c. 17 gal 1 qt = ___ qt

48. a. 23 pt = ___ qt ___ pt
b. 55 c = ___ pt ___ c
c. 75 qt = ___ gal ___ qt

49. Arrange the following measurements in order from smallest to largest:
29 c, 6 qt, 14 pt, 2 gal

50. Arrange the following measurements in order from largest to smallest:
45 c, 23 pt, 10 qt, 3 gal

51. Mythili drinks 2 c of milk every day. How many gallons of milk will she require for a month of 30 days?

52. If a family uses an average of 8 c of milk everyday, how many gallons of milk will be required for a week?

53. A juice container had 12 pt of juice. If 15 c of juice was used from the container, how many cups of juice is left in the container?

54. A water-bottle contained 8 qt of springwater. If 25 c of water was used from the bottle, how many cups of water are left in the bottle?

10.3 | Conversion Between Metric and US Customary Units

Converting units between the metric and US Customary systems is achieved by using conversion tables. Conversion tables for the conversion of commonly used metric and US Customary units of measurement are provided below:

Length

- **Metric units:** kilometer (km), meter (m), centimeter (cm), and millimeter (mm)
- **US Customary units:** inch (in.), foot (ft), yard (yd), and mile (mi)

Conversion Table

US Customary Units	Metric Units
1 in.	2.54 cm
1 ft	30.48 cm
1 yd	0.9144 m
1 mi	1.609 km

Example 10.3-a

Converting Metric Units of Length to US Customary Units

Convert the following measurements:

(i) 250 km to miles (ii) 45 m to feet

Solution

(i) 250 km to miles

Use $\left(\frac{1 \text{ mi}}{1.609 \text{ km}}\right)$ as the conversion factor to cross-cancel the unit 'km' to convert to miles.

$$= 250 \text{ km} \times \left(\frac{1 \text{ mi}}{1.609 \text{ km}}\right)$$

$$= 250 \times \frac{1}{1.609} \text{ mi}$$

$$= 155.376009\ldots \text{ mi}$$

$$= 155.38 \text{ mi}$$

Therefore, 250 km is equal to 155.38 mi.

(ii) 45 m to feet

Use $\left(\frac{100 \text{ cm}}{1 \text{ m}}\right)$ as the first conversion factor to cross-cancel the unit 'm'

Solution *continued*

and $\left(\frac{1 \text{ ft}}{30.48 \text{ cm}}\right)$ as the second conversion factor to cross-cancel the unit 'cm' to convert to feet.

$$= 45 \cancel{\text{m}} \times \left(\frac{100 \cancel{\text{cm}}}{1 \cancel{\text{m}}}\right) \times \left(\frac{1 \text{ ft}}{30.48 \cancel{\text{cm}}}\right)$$

$$= 45 \times \frac{100}{30.48} \text{ ft}$$

$$= 147.637795... \text{ ft}$$

$$= 147.64 \text{ ft}$$

Therefore, 45 m is equal to147.64 ft.

Example 10.3-b

Converting US Customary Units of Length to Metric Units

Convert the following measurements:

(i) 8.75 yd to centimeters (ii) 2.5 mi to meters

Solution

(i) 8.75 yd to centimeters

Use $\left(\frac{0.9144 \text{ m}}{1 \text{ yd}}\right)$ as the first conversion factor to cross-cancel the unit 'yd'

and $\left(\frac{100 \text{ cm}}{1 \text{ m}}\right)$ as the second conversion factor to cross-cancel the unit 'm' to convert to centimeters.

$$= 8.75 \cancel{\text{yd}} \times \left(\frac{0.9144 \cancel{\text{m}}}{1 \cancel{\text{yd}}}\right) \times \left(\frac{100 \text{ cm}}{1 \cancel{\text{m}}}\right)$$

$$= 8.75 \times 0.9144 \times 100 \text{ cm}$$

$$= 800.1 \text{ cm}$$

Therefore, 8.75 yd is equal to 800.1 cm.

(ii) 2.5 mi to meters

Use $\left(\frac{1.609 \text{ km}}{1 \text{ mi}}\right)$ as the first conversion factor to cross-cancel the unit 'mi'

and $\left(\frac{1{,}000 \text{ m}}{1 \text{ km}}\right)$ as the second conversion factor to cross-cancel the unit 'km' to convert to meters.

$$= 2.5 \cancel{\text{mi}} \times \left(\frac{1.609 \cancel{\text{km}}}{1 \cancel{\text{mi}}}\right) \times \left(\frac{1{,}000 \text{ m}}{1 \cancel{\text{km}}}\right)$$

$$= 2.5 \times 1.609 \times 1{,}000 \text{ m}$$

$$= 4{,}022.5 \text{ m}$$

Therefore, 2.5 mi is equal to 4,022.5 m.

Mass

- **Metric units:** kilogram (kg) and gram (g)
- **US Customary units:** ounce (oz), pound (lb), and ton (ton)

Conversion Table

US Customary Units	Metric Units
1 oz	28.35 g
1 lb	0.454 kg
1 ton	907.2 kg

Example 10.3-c

Converting Metric Units of Mass to US Customary Units

Convert the following measurements:

(i) 2.5 kg to pounds (ii) 400 g to ounce

Solution

(i) 2.5 kg to pounds

Use $\left(\frac{1 \text{ lb}}{0.454 \text{ kg}}\right)$ as the conversion factor to cross-cancel the unit 'kg' to convert to pounds.

$$= 2.5\,\cancel{\text{kg}} \times \left(\frac{1 \text{ lb}}{0.454\,\cancel{\text{kg}}}\right)$$

$$= 2.5 \times \frac{1}{0.454} \text{ lb}$$

$$= 5.506607... \text{ lb}$$

$$= 5.51 \text{ lb}$$

Therefore, 2.5 kg is equal to 5.51 lb.

(ii) 400 g to ounce

Use $\left(\frac{1 \text{ oz}}{28.35 \text{ g}}\right)$ as the conversion factor to cross cancel the unit 'g' to convert to ounces.

$$= 400\,\cancel{\text{g}} \times \left(\frac{1 \text{ oz}}{28.35\,\cancel{\text{g}}}\right)$$

$$= 400 \times \frac{1}{28.35} \text{ oz}$$

$$= 14.109347... \text{ oz}$$

$$= 14.11 \text{ oz}$$

Therefore, 400 g is equal to 14.11 oz.

Example 10.3-d **Converting US Customary Units of Mass to Metric Units**

Convert the following measurements:

(i) 1.75 lb to grams (ii) 225 oz to kilograms

Solution

(i) 1.75 lb to grams

Use $\frac{0.454 \text{ kg}}{1 \text{ lb}}$ as the first conversion factor to cross-cancel the unit 'lb' and $\left(\frac{1{,}000 \text{ g}}{1 \text{ kg}}\right)$ as the second conversion factor to cross-cancel the unit 'kg' to convert to grams.

$$= 1.75 \cancel{\text{lb}} \times \frac{0.454 \cancel{\text{kg}}}{1 \cancel{\text{lb}}} \times \left(\frac{1{,}000 \text{ g}}{1 \cancel{\text{kg}}}\right)$$

$$= 1.75 \times 0.454 \times 1{,}000 \text{ grams}$$

$$= 794.5 \text{ grams}$$

Therefore, 1.75 lb is equal to 794.5 g.

(ii) 225 oz to kilograms

Use $\left(\frac{28.35 \text{ g}}{1 \text{ oz}}\right)$ as the first conversion factor to cross-cancel the unit 'oz' and $\left(\frac{1 \text{ kg}}{1{,}000 \text{ g}}\right)$ as the second conversion factor to cross-cancel the unit 'g' to convert to kilograms.

$$= 225 \cancel{\text{oz}} \times \left(\frac{28.35 \cancel{\text{g}}}{1 \cancel{\text{oz}}}\right) \times \left(\frac{1 \text{ kg}}{1{,}000 \cancel{\text{g}}}\right)$$

$$= 225 \times \frac{28.35}{1{,}000} \text{ kg}$$

$$= 6.37875 \text{ kg}$$

$$= 6.38 \text{ kg}$$

Therefore, 225 oz is equal to 6.38 kg.

Capacity

Metric units: liter (L), and milliliter (mL)

US Customary units: fluid ounce (fl oz), cups (c), pint (pt), quart (qt), and gallon (gal)

Conversion Table

US Customary Units	Metric Units
1 fl oz	29.57 mL
1 c	236.6 mL
1 pt	473.2 mL
1 qt	0.946 L
1 gal	3.785 L

Example 10.3-e

Converting Metric Units of Capacity to US Customary Units

Convert the following measurements:

(i) 60 L to gallons (ii) 425 mL to fluid ounces

Solution

(i) 60 L to gallons

Use $\left(\frac{1 \text{ gal}}{3.785 \text{ L}}\right)$ as the conversion factor to cross-cancel the unit 'L' to convert to gallons.

$$= 60 \cancel{\text{L}} \times \left(\frac{1 \text{ gal}}{3.785 \cancel{\text{L}}}\right)$$

$$= 60 \times \frac{1}{3.785} \text{ gal}$$

$$= 15.852047\ldots \text{ gal}$$

$$= 15.85 \text{ gal}$$

Therefore, 60 L is 15.85 gal.

(ii) 425 mL to fluid ounces

Use $\left(\frac{1 \text{ fl oz}}{29.57 \text{ mL}}\right)$ as the conversion factor to cross-cancel the unit 'mL' to convert to fluid ounces.

$$= 425 \cancel{\text{mL}} \times \left(\frac{1 \text{ fl oz}}{29.57 \cancel{\text{mL}}}\right)$$

$$= 425 \times \frac{1}{29.57} \text{ fl oz}$$

$$= 14.372675\ldots \text{ fl oz}$$

$$= 14.\ 37 \text{ fl oz}$$

Therefore, 425 mL is equal to14.37 fl oz.

Example 10.3-f

Converting US Customary Units of Capacity to Metric Units

Convert the following measurements:

(i) 2.5 gal to liters (ii) 30 fl oz to liters

Solution

(i) 2.5 gal to liters

Use $\left(\frac{3.785 \text{ L}}{1 \text{ gal}}\right)$ as the conversion factor to cross-cancel the unit 'gal' to convert to liters.

$$= 2.5 \text{ gal} \times \left(\frac{3.785 \text{ L}}{1 \text{ gal}}\right)$$

$$= 2.5 \times 3.785 \text{ L}$$

$$= 9.4625 \text{ L}$$

$$= 9.46 \text{ L}$$

Therefore, 2.5 gal is equal to 9.46 L

(ii) 30 fl oz to liters

Use $\left(\frac{29.57 \text{ mL}}{1 \text{ fl oz}}\right)$ as the first conversion factor to cross-cancel the unit 'fl oz' and $\left(\frac{1 \text{ L}}{1{,}000 \text{ mL}}\right)$ as the second conversion factor to cross-cancel the unit 'mL' to convert to liters.

$$= 30 \text{ fl oz} \times \left(\frac{29.57 \text{ mL}}{1 \text{ fl oz}}\right) \times \left(\frac{1 \text{ L}}{1{,}000 \text{ mL}}\right)$$

$$= 30 \times \frac{29.57}{1{,}000} \text{ L}$$

$$= 0.8871 \text{ L}$$

$$= 0.89 \text{ L}$$

Therefore, 30 fl oz is equal to 0.89 L.

Useful Comparisons

- 1 kg is a little more than 2 pounds.
- 1 L is a little more than a quart.
- 1 km is a little more than half a mile.
- 1 m is a little more than a yard.
- 1 cm is a little less than half an inch.

Conversion of Temperature Scales

There are two main temperature scales in use:

(1) °C, the Celsius scale

(2) °F, the Fahrenheit scale

The Celsius scale (°C) is part of the metric system, used in most countries. The Fahrenheit scale (°F) is primarily used in the USA.

The Celsius scale (°C) has a basis in which water freezes at 0°C and boils at 100°C. The Fahrenheit scale (°F) has a basis in which water freezes at 32°F and boils at 212°F.

Therefore, the difference between the freezing and boiling points of water is 100° in the Celsius scale (100°C – 0°C) and 180° in the Fahrenheit scale (212°F – 32°F).

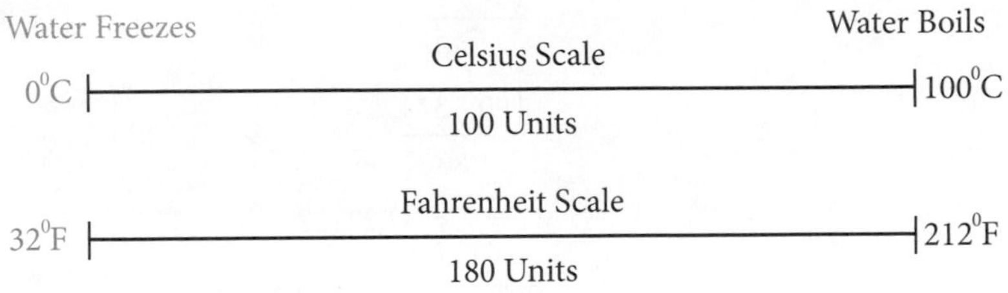

100 units in the Celsius scale, starting from 0°C, is equivalent to 180 units in the Fahrenheit scale, starting from 32°F.

Therefore, to convert from °C to °F, multiply °C by a factor of 1.80 $\left(=\frac{180}{100}\right)$ and add 32°.

$$°F = 1.80(°C) + 32°$$

Similarly, to convert from °F to °C, subtract 32°F and divide by 1.80.

$$°C = \frac{(°F - 32)}{1.80}$$

Conversion Table

On a hot day, a temperature of 38°C is about 100°F and a room temperature of 73°F is about 23°C.

°C to °F	$°F = 1.80(°C) + 32$
°F to °C	$°C = \frac{(°F - 32)}{1.80}$

Example 10.3-g

Converting Between the Celsius (C) Scale and Fahrenheit (F) Scale

Convert the following:

(i) 25°C to °F (ii) 90°F to °C

Solution

(i) 25°C to °F

$$°F = 1.80(°C) + 32$$
$$°F = 1.80(25) + 32$$
$$= 77°F$$

Therefore, 25°C is equal to 77°F.

Solution
continued

(ii) 90°F to °C

$$= \frac{(°F - 32)}{1.80}$$

$$= \frac{(90 - 32)}{1.80}$$

$$= \frac{58}{1.80} = 32.222222...°C = 32.22°C$$

Therefore, 90°F is equal to 32.22°C.

Example 10.3-h **Comparing Temperatures Measured Using Different Scales**

Which is the higher temperature: 80°C or 175°F?

Solution

Convert 80°C to °F and compare with 175°F

= 1.80(°C) + 32

= 1.80(80) + 32

= 176°F

i.e., 80°C = 176°F > 175°F

i.e., 80°C > 175°F

or,

Convert 175°F to °C and compare with 80°C

$$= \frac{(°F - 32)}{1.80} = \frac{(175 - 32)}{1.80}$$

= 79.44°C

i.e., 175°F = 79.44°C < 80°C

Therefore 80°C is a higher temperature than 175°F.

10.3 | Exercises

Answers to odd-numbered problems are available online.

Calculate the missing values in Problems 1 to 12.

		Metric Units		US Customary Units
1.	a.	250 km	=	? mi
	b.	? km	=	120 mi
2.	a.	175 km	=	? mi
	b.	? km	=	80 mi
3.	a.	17.5 m	=	? yd
	b.	? m	=	22 yd
4.	a.	11 m	=	? yd
	b.	? m	=	12.5 yd
5.	a.	250 m	=	? ft
	b.	? m	=	75 ft

		Metric Units		US Customary Units
6..	a.	12 m	=	? ft
	b.	? m	=	45.5 ft
7.	a.	100 cm	=	? in.
	b.	? cm	=	3.5 in.
8.	a.	80 cm	=	? in.
	b.	? cm	=	7.5 in.
9.	a.	250 km	=	? mi
	b.	? km	=	120 mi
10.	a.	175 km	=	? mi
	b.	? km	=	80 mi
11.	a.	17.5 m	=	? yd
	b.	? m	=	22 yd
12.	a.	11 m	=	? yd
	b.	? m	=	12.5 yd

13. Arrange the following measurements in order from largest to smallest:
    82.5 ft, 900 in., 4,250 cm, 28 yd, 24 m
14. Arrange the following measurements in order from smallest to largest:
    1280 cm, 44 ft, 15 yd, 450 in., 12 m
15. June bought 5.5 meters of fabric and used 10 feet of it to make a curtain. Calculate the remaining quantity of fabric, in meters.
16. A swimming pool is 12.5 meters wide. It is divided into 5 lanes of equal width. Calculate the width of each lane, in feet.
17. The distance from Toronto to Niagara Falls is 320 km. After driving 100 miles from Toronto, calculate the distance left to reach Niagara Falls, in kilometers.
18. The distance from Niagara Falls to New York is 410 miles. After driving 550 kilometers from Niagara Falls, what is the distance to be travelled, in kilometers, to reach New York?

In Problems 19 to 26, convert the measurements that are in metric units to US Customary units, and vice versa. Round your answers to two decimal places.

		Metric Units		US Customary Units
19.	a.	3,500 km	=	? tons
	b.	? km	=	2.5 tons
20.	a.	4,250 km	=	? tons
	b.	? km	=	4 tons
21.	a.	15.5 km	=	? lb
	b.	? km	=	45 lb
22.	a.	70 km	=	? lb
	b.	? km	=	135.5 lb

		Metric Units		US Customary Units
23.	a.	1,200 g	=	? lb
	b.	? g	=	6.5 lb
24.	a.	750 g	=	? lb
	b.	? g	=	4.5 lb
25.	a.	200 g	=	? oz
	b.	? g	=	4 oz
26.	a.	175 g	=	? oz
	b.	? g	=	2.5 oz

27. Arrange the following measurements in order from largest to smallest :

    2.5 kg, 2,450 g, 5.7 lb, 80 oz

28. Arrange the following measurements in order from smallest to largest:

    4.5 kg, 4,560 g, 9.5 lb, 155 oz

29. Carol bought 2 pounds of butter and used 750 grams of it to make a cake. Calculate the remaining quantity of butter, in grams.

30. A recipe requires 600 grams of butter. I bought 1.5 pounds of butter and used 600 grams of it. Calculate the remaining quantity of butter, in grams.

31. William weighs 80 kg. His brother weighs 25 pounds less than him. Calculate his brother's weight, in kg.

32. A travel bag weighs 2.25 kg. The total weight of the travel bag with its contents is 50 pounds. Calculate the weight of the contents in the bag, in kg.

In Problems 33 to 42, convert the measurements of capacity that are in metric units to US Customary units, and vice versa. Round your answers to two decimal places.

		Metric Units		US Customary Units
33.	a.	50 L	=	? gal
	b.	? L	=	10.5 gal
34.	a.	25.5 L	=	? gal
	b.	? L	=	30 gal
35.	a.	15 L	=	? qt
	b.	? L	=	14 qt
36.	a.	22 L	=	? qt
	b.	? L	=	12 qt
37.	a.	7.5 L	=	? pt
	b.	? L	=	14 pt
38.	a.	6 L	=	? pt
	b.	? L	=	10.5 pt
39.	a.	4.5 L	=	? c
	b.	? L	=	14 c

		Metric Units		US Customary Units
40.	a.	5 L	=	? c
	b.	? L	=	18 c
41.	a.	8 mL	=	? fl. oz
	b.	? mL	=	20.5 fl. oz
42.	a.	3.5 mL	=	? fl. oz
	b.	? mL	=	15 fl. oz

43. Arrange the following measurements in order from largest to smallest:
    3.5 L, 4.8 qt, 10.5 pt, 1 gal
44. Arrange the following measurements in order from smallest to largest.
    7.5 L, 8.5 qt, 15 pt, 1.7 gal
45. The capacity of a fuel tank of a car is 54 liters. The tank is 1/3 empty. Calculate the capacity of fuel in the tank, in gallons.
46. The fuel tank of a van can hold 18 gallons. It is 2/3 empty. Calculate the capacity of the fuel in the tank, in liters.
47. A container had 3.5 liters of milk. Ten cups of milk were used from this container. Calculate the quantity of milk, in liters, that remains in the container.
48. A bottle contained 1.2 liters of juice. Someone drinks 3 cups of juice from this bottle. Calculate the remaining quantity, in liters.

In Problems 49 to 58, convert the temperatures that are in Celsius (°C) to Fahrenheit (°F), and vice versa. Round your answers to the nearest one decimal place, where necessary.

49. 21 °C = ___°F
50. 10 °C = ___ °F
51. 98.6 °F = ___°C
52. 85 °F = ___ °C
53. 140 °C = ___°F
54. 180 °C = ___°F
55. 112 °F = ___°C
56. 400 °F = ___ °C
57. −40 °C = ___°F
58. −40 °F = ___ °C

10 | Review Exercises

Answers to odd-numbered problems are available online.

Calculate the missing values in Problems 1 to 12.

1. a. 7 m 5 cm = ___cm
   b. 15 km 50 m =___m
   c. 75 mm =___cm __mm
   d. 905 cm =___m ___cm
2. a. 37 m 2 cm =___cm
   b. 6 km 59 m = ___m
   c. 1,026 mm = ___cm __mm
   d. 405 cm = ___m ___cm
3. a. 39 yd 1 ft = ___ft
   b. 4 ft 7 in. = ___in.
   c. 115 in. = ___ft___in.
   d. 5,290 yd = ___mi___yd
4. a. 43 yd 2 ft = ___ft
   b. 15 ft 1 in. = ___in.
   c. 102 in. = ___ft___in.
   d. 3,085 yd = ___mi___yd
5. a. 10 kg 32 g = ___g
   b. 45 g 52 mg = ___mg
   c. 3.62 kg = ___kg___g
   d. 42,007 mg = ___g___mg
6. a. 3 kg 753 g = ___g
   b. 7 g 87 mg = ___mg
   c. 2.783 kg = ___kg___g
   d. 29,005 mg = ___g___mg
7. a. 6 lb 7 oz = ___oz
   b. 29,005 mg = ___g___mg
   c. 32,000 lb = ___ton___lb
   d. 120 oz = ___lb___oz
8. a. 26 lb 2 oz = ___oz
   b. 1 ton 249 lb = ___lb
   c. 23,000 lb = ___ton___lb
   d. 245 oz = ___lb___oz
9. a. 6 L 49 mL = ___mL
   b. 9,006 mL = ___L___mL
   c. 9 gal 2 qt = ___qt
   d. 75 pt = ___qt___pt
10. a. 86 L 630 mL = ___mL
    b. 2,092 mL = ___L___mL
    c. 15 gal 3 qt = ___qt
    d. 32 pt = ___qt___pt
11. a. 410°F =___°C
    b. 80°C =___°F
    c. 125°F = ___°C
    d. 30°C =___°F
12. a. 82°F =___°C
    b. 25°C =___°F
    c. 300°F =___°C
    d. 5°C =___°F
13. Convert the following:
    a. 65 km to miles
    b. 9 m to feet
    c. 2.5 yd to centimeters
    d. 3.2 mi to meters
14. Convert the following:
    a. 89 km to miles
    b. 4 m to feet
    c. 6.5 yd to centimeters
    d. 0.5 mi to meters

15. Convert the following:
    a. 5 kg to pounds
    b. 1,250 g to ounces
    c. 0.25 lb to grams
    d. 320 oz to kilograms
16. Convert the following:
    a. 4.4 kg to pounds
    b. 750 g to ounces
    c. 1.25 lb to grams
    d. 150 oz to kilograms
17. Convert the following:
    a. 35 L to gallons
    b. 26 mL to fluid ounces
    c. 17 gal to liters
    d. 42 fl oz to liters
18. Convert the following:
    a. 115 L to gallons
    b. 12 mL to fluid ounces
    c. 45 gal to liters
    d. 75 fl oz to liters
19. Arrange the following measurements in order from largest to smallest:

    7.5 km, 9,200 yd, 5.25 mi
20. Arrange the following measurements in order from smallest to largest:

    3.75 mi, 7,000 yd, 6 km
21. Arrange the following measurements in order from largest to smallest:

    7 lb, 3 kg, 115 oz
22. Arrange the following measurements in order from smallest to largest:

    4.5 kg, 9 lb, 150 oz
23. Arrange the following measurements in order from largest to smallest:

    70 L, 18 gal, 75 qt
24. Arrange the following measurements in order from smallest to largest:

    11 gal, 40 L, 45 qt
25. Paul travelled 23 km by car to the train station in Toronto. From there, he travelled another 125 mi to Cleveland, USA, by train. Calculate the total distance travelled, in (a) kilometers and (b) miles.
26. The total distance a marathon runner needs to run to complete the race is 26 miles and 385 yards. If after completing 32 km 200 m of the distance the runner pauses for a short break, how much further would he have to run to complete the race, in (a) miles and (b) kilometers?
27. Diana went on a diet and lost 26 pounds. Her weight at the end of the dieting period was 79 kg. What was her original weight, in (a) pounds and (b) kilograms?
28. The maximum weight an elevator can carry is 340 kg. Three people with an average weight of 65 kg and 2 people with an average weight of 155 pounds are waiting to get into the elevator. Determine if the elevator will be able to carry all 5 of them at the same time.
29. Tracy rented a car with a full tank and used up 8.5 gallons of fuel. If the total capacity of the fuel tank is 42.5 L and she needs to return the car with a full tank, how much fuel would she need to purchase, in (a) gallons and (b) liters?
30. Jerry brought in a 31 gal fruit punch for an anniversary party. If at the end of the party, 32 L of fruit punch remained in the barrel, calculate the quantity of fruit punch consumed, in (a) gallons and (b) liters.

10 | Self-Test Exercises Answers to all problems are available online.

Calculate the missing values in Problems 1 to 6.

1. a. 27 cm 3 mm = ___cm
   b. 12 m 50 cm = ___m
   c. 8,105 m = ___km___m
   d. 1,065 mm = ___cm___mm
2. a. 15 yd 2 ft = ___ft
   b. 5 ft 2 in. = ___in.
   c. 430 in. = ___ft___in.
   d. 5,700 yd = ___mi___yd
3. a. 53 kg 107 g = ___g
   b. 6 g 223 mg = ___mg
   c. 5,519 mg = ___g___mg
   d. 84,176 g = ___kg___g
4. a. 7 lb 15 oz = ___oz
   b. 4 ton 30 lb = ___lb
   c. 40,000 lb = ___ton___lb
   d. 149 oz = ___lb___oz
5. a. 5 L 7 mL = ___mL
   b. 9,060 mL = ___L___mL
   c. 26 gal 1 qt = ___qt
   d. 83 pt = ___qt___pt
6. a. 15°F = ___°C
   b. – 10°C = ___°F
   c. 90°F = ___°C
   d. 30°C = ___°F
7. Convert the following:
   a. 250 km to miles
   b. 45 m to feet
   c. 8.75 yd to centimeters
   d. 2.5 mi to meters
8. Convert the following:
   a. 2.5 kg to pounds
   b. 400 g to ounces
   c. 1.75 lb to grams
   d. 225 oz to kilograms
9. Convert the following:
   a. 60 L to gallons
   b. 425 mL to fluid ounces
   c. 2.5 gal to liters
   d. 30 fl oz to liters
10. Arrange the following measurements in order from largest to smallest:

    65 m, 215 ft, 2,500 in.
11. Arrange the following measurements in order from smallest to largest:

    2.5 lb, 1,200 g, 45 oz
12. Arrange the following measurements in order from largest to smallest:

    84 L, 22 gal, 175 pt
13. Helicopter A is flying at an altitude of 8,250 ft above ground and Helicopter B is at 2,208 m above ground. What is the difference in altitude between the two helicopters, in (a) feet and (b) meters?
14. A baby weighed 7.3 pounds at birth and another baby weighed 2.8 kg. Calculate the difference in weight of the two babies, in (a) ounces and (b) grams.
15. A carton contains 0.75 gal of milk. After pouring 5 glasses of milk, each holding 250 mL, calculate the amount of milk left in the carton, in (a) gallons and (b) milliliters.

Glossary

Absolute value of a number is its distance from the origin '0' on the number line. Since it is a distance, it is always positive and the direction does not matter.

Addition refers to combining (finding the total or sum of) numbers.

Algebra is a branch of mathematics that is used to analyze and solve day-to-day business and finance problems. It deals with different relations and operations by using letters and symbols to represent numbers, values, etc.

Annual salary is the amount that an employee will be paid for service over a period of one year.

Base (B) refers to the whole quantity or value (100%). It is usually followed by the word 'of', or 'percent of'.

Billions group is the fourth group of three digits starting from the right of a whole number.

Binomial is a polynomial with 2 terms.

Bi-weekly pay period refers to payment received once in two weeks. An employee will receive 26 bi-weekly payments through the year.

Celsius scale (°C) is part of the metric system. It has a basis in which water freezes at 0°C and boils at 100°C.

Coefficient is the numerical factor in front of the variable in a term.

Commission payment that an employee receives for selling a product or service.

Commission rate rate used to calculate the commission payment that an employee receives for selling a product or sevice.

Common factor is a factor that is common to two or more numbers.

Common logarithm is a logarithm to the base 10.

Complex fraction is a fraction in which one or more fractions are found in the numerator or denominator.

Complex number is a number that consists of real numbers and imaginary numbers.

Composite number is a whole number that has at least one factor other than 1 and the number itself.

Consistent linear system is a linear system of two equations that has one or many solutions.

Constant is a term that has only a number, without any variables.

Consumer Price Index (CPI) is an indicator of changes in consumer prices experienced by Canadians.

Currency cross-rate table is used to display the currency exchange rates for quick reference.

Denominator represents the total number of equal parts into which the whole unit is divided.

Dependent system of equations is a system of equations that has an infinite number of solutions.

Division can be thought of as repeated subtractions.

Elimination method is a method of solving systems of linear equations, when none of the equations in the system has a variable with a coefficient of 1 or −1.

Equivalent ratio is obtained when all the terms of the ratio are multiplied by the same number or divided by the same number.

Exchange rates also called the foreign exchange rate or forex rate, is used for converting currencies between countries.

Exponent represents the number of times the base of an exponential notation is multiplied.

Exponential notation is used to represent a number that is multiplied by itself repeatedly.

Expression is a combination of terms. It usually refers to a statement of relations among variables.

Factor refers to each of the combinations of variables and/or numbers multiplied together in a term.

Factor of a number is a whole number that can divide the number with no remainder.

Fahrenheit scale (°F) is primarily used in the USA. It has a basis in which water freezes at 32°F and boils at 212°F.

Formula is similar to an equation. In a formula, the relationship among many variables is written as a rule for performing calculations.

Fraction is a method of representing numbers, where one integer is divided by another non-zero integer.

Fraction bar represents the division sign.

Fraction in its lowest terms is a fraction in which the numerator and denominator have no factors in common (other than 1).

Fractional exponent is when the exponent of a number or variable is a fraction.

Highest Common Factor (HCF) of two or more numbers is the largest common number that divides the numbers with no remainder. HCF is also known as the Greatest Common Divisor (GCD).

Hourly rate of pay refers to payments received per hour for service provided.

Imaginary Number is a number, which when raised to the power of 2, results in a negative real number.

Improper fraction is a fraction in which the numerator is greater than the denominator; i.e., the value of the entire fraction is more than 1.

Inconsistent linear system is a linear system of two equations that has no solutions.

Independent system of equations is a system of equations that has one or no solutions.

Index number is used to express the relative value of an item compared to a base value.

Inflation is a rise on the general level of prices of goods and services in an economy over time.

Interest is a fee that borrowers pay to lenders for using their money temporarily for a period of time.

Interest percentage (%) is the product of the interest rate (r) and the time.

Irrational number is a number that cannot be expressed as a fraction.

Like terms are terms that have the same variables and exponents.

Linear equation is an algebraic equation with one or two variables (each to the power of one), which produces a straight line when plotted on a graph.

Logarithm is a faster method of solving for an unknown exponent. It is the exponent to which the base is raised to get the number.

Lowest Common Denominator (LCD) of a set of two or more fractions is the smallest whole number that is divisible by each of the denominators.

Lowest Common Multiple (LCM) of two or more numbers is the smallest multiple that is common to those numbers.

Markdown is the amount by which the selling price of a product is reduced in determining the sale price.

Markup is the amount that a business adds to the cost of the product to arrive at the selling price of the product.

Maturity value (S) is the sum of the accumulated value of interest over time and the principal amount of the loan or investment.

Metric system of measurement uses meter (m), gram (g), and liter (L) as the base units for the measurements of length, mass, and capacity, respectively. Celsius (°C) scale is used for temperature.

Millions group is the third group of three digits starting from the right of a whole number.

Mixed number consists of both a whole number and a proper fraction, written side-by-side, which implies that the whole number and proper fraction are added.

Monomial is an algebraic expression that has only one term.

Monthly pay period refers to payment received once a month. An employee will receive 12 monthly payments through the year.

Multiple of a number is a whole number that can be divided by the number with no remainder.

Multiplication can be thought of as repeated additions.

Natural logarithm is a logarithm to the base 'e', where the constant $e = 2.718282\ldots$.

Number line is used to represent numbers graphically as points on a horizontal line.

Numerator represents the number of equal parts in a fractional number.

Order of a ratio is the order in which a ratio is presented.

Order of operations is the order in which arithmetic operations are carried out in an equation. The order that is followed is: Brackets, Exponents, Division, Multiplication, Addition, and Subtraction (BEDMAS).

Ordered pair is used to locate a point in the coordinate system. The ordered pair (x, y) describes a point in the plane by its x- and y-coordinates.

Overtime payment refers to additional payment eligible to be received for working more than the specified number of hours in a week.

Overtime rate of pay refers to the rate used to calculate the overtime payment for working more than the specified number of hours in a week.

Parallel lines are lines that have the same slope. All vertical lines are parallel to each other and all horizontal lines are parallel to each other.

Pay period refers to the frequency of payments (how often payments are being made).

Payroll is a record of the payment made to every employee of an organization.

Percent (per cent or per hundred in the literal meaning) is used to express a quantity out of 100 units and is represented by the symbol '%'.

Percent change is often used to express the amount of change to the initial (original) value; i.e., the amount of change (increase or decrease) is calculated as a percent change ($\%C$) of its initial value.

Perfect root is a whole number whoose root is also a whole number.

Perfect square is any whole number base with an exponent of 2; i.e., a whole number multiplied by itself results in a perfect square.

Perpendicular lines are lines that have a slope of -1. The lines are also perpendicular if one of them is vertical and the other is horizontal.

Place value is the position of each digit in a number.

Polynomial is an algebraic expression that has two or more terms.

Portion ($\underline{P}$) refers to the portion of the whole quantity or value (portion of the base).

Prime number is a whole number that has only two factors: 1 and the number itself.

Principal (P) is the initial amount of money invested or borrowed.

Principal root is the positive root of a number.

Proper fraction is a fraction in which the numerator is less than the denominator.

Proportion is used to describe two sets of ratios that are equal.

Pro-ration is defined as sharing or allocating the quantities, usually the amounts, on a proportionate basis.

Purchasing power of money is the number of goods/services that can be purchased with a unit of currency.

Quadrant is one of the 4 regions that is formed by the X- and Y-axes in the rectangular coordinate system. They are numbered counter-clockwise from one (I) to four (IV).

Rate is a special ratio that is used to compare two quantities or amounts having different units of measure.

Rate (R) refers to the percent relationship between the base and portion. It usually carries the percent sign (%) or the word 'percent'.

Ratio is a comparison or relationship between two or more quantities with the same unit.

Rational number is a fraction where one integer is divided by another non-zero integer.

Real number includes rational and non-rational numbers.

Reciprocal is the fraction that is obtained by inverting the original fraction.

Repeating decimal is a decimal that does not end but shows a repeating pattern.

Root is the inverse of exponents.

Rounding numbers makes them easier to work with and easier to remember. Rounding changes some of the digits in a number but keeps its value close to the original.

Rules or Laws of Exponents are used to simplify expressions that involve exponents.

S&P/TSX is an index of stock prices of the largest companies on the Toronto Stock Exchange.

Sale price (S_{Red}) of an item refers to the reduced (or discounted) selling price; i.e., the price after markdown (D).

Selling price (S) of an item refers to the regular (or normal) selling price; i.e., the price before markdown (D).

Sharing quantities refers to the allocation or distribution of a quantity into two or more portions (or units) based on a given ratio.

Short ton is the US customary unit for ton and is represented by 'ton'.

Simplifying fractions is when you divide both the numerator and denominator of a fraction by the same number, which results in an equivalent fraction.

Slope (m) is the steepness of the line relative to the X-axis. It is the ratio of the change in the value of y (called 'rise') to the corresponding change in the value of x (called 'run').

Stock index is an application of index numbers and is used to measure the performance of stock markets.

Substitution method is a method of solving systems of linear equations, when one of the equations in the system has a variable with a coefficient of 1 or −1.

Subtraction refers to finding the difference between numbers.

Term is a number, variable, or a combination of numbers and variables that are multiplied and/or divided together.

Terminating decimal is a decimal that ends.

Term of a ratio is the quantity in a ratio.

Thousands group is the second group of three digits starting from the right of a whole number.

Time period (t) is the time taken to settle a loan or an investment.

Trillions group is the fifth group of three digits starting from the right of a whole number.

Trinomial is a polynomial with 3 terms.

Unit price is the unit rate when it is expressed in unit currency (dollars, cents, etc.).

Unit rate represents the number of units of the first quantity (or measurement) that corresponds to one unit of the second quantity.

Units group is the first group of three digits starting from the right of a whole number.

Unlike terms are terms that have different variables or the same variables with different exponents.

US customary system of measurement uses the yard (yd), the pound (lb), the gallon (gal) as the base units for the measurements of length, mass, and capacity, respectively. Fahrenheit (°F) scale is used for temperature.

Variable is a letter that represents one or more numbers.

Weekly pay periodw refers to payment received once a week. An employee will receive 52 weekly payments through the year.

Whole number is any counting number (0, 1, 2, 3, 4…), including zero (0) and any natural number or positive integer (1, 2, 3, 4...).

Workweek is the standard working hours per week specified by the organization.

x-intercept is the point at which the line crosses the X-axis and where the *y*-coordinate is zero.

y-intercept is the point at which the line crosses the Y-axis and where the *x*-coordinate is zero.

Zero is the smallest whole number.

Index

T

U

V

W